MW01077769

SUNBURST AND LUMINARY

SUNBURST AND LUMINARY

AN APOLLO MEMOIR

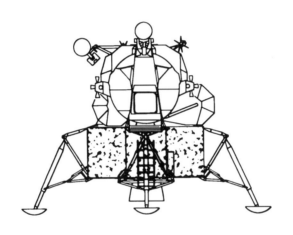

DON EYLES

FORT POINT PRESS
BOSTON
2018

Copyright © 2017 by Don Eyles

All rights reserved. No part of this book may be reproduced without written permission except for brief quotations in critical articles and reviews.

Designed by the author. The book is set in Apollo, a type designed by Adrian Frutiger and released in 1962, supplemented by Minion italics and Frutiger capitals. Printed in the United States of America.

Library of Congress Control Number: 2017948571

ISBN 978-0-9863859-0-2

Includes glossary, bibliography, notes and index.

Publisher's Cataloging-in-Publication data:

> Name: Eyles, Don Edgar, author.
>
> Title: Sunburst and luminary: an Apollo memoir / Don Eyles.
>
> Description: Includes bibliographical references and index. | Boston, MA: Fort Point Press, 2018.
>
> Identifiers: ISBN 978-0-9863859-0-2 | LCCN 2017948571
>
> Subjects: LCSH Eyles, Don Edgar. | Project Apollo (U.S.) | United States. National Aeronautics and Space Administration--History--20th century. | Astronautics--Social aspects--History--20th century. | Space flight to the moon. | Computer software developers--United States--Biography. | Nineteen sixties. | BISAC BIOGRAPHY & AUTOBIOGRAPHY / Science & Technology | BIOGRAPHY & AUTOBIOGRAPHY / Personal Memoirs
>
> Classification: LCC TL789.8.U6 .E95 2018 | DDC 629.45/4092-dc23

This volume is the first publication of Fort Point Press, founded by the author in the Fort Point neighborhood of Boston with the ambition to publish books of literary and historical excellence that do not underestimate the technical literacy of the 21st century audience.

Fort Point Press
249 A Street
Suite 42
Boston, MA 02210

WWW.FORTPOINTPRESS.COM

WWW.SUNBURSTANDLUMINARY.COM

to the great men
who allowed me to participate in their dream,
so many of whom departed this Earth while I was writing this book

AND FOR DENISE

CONTENTS

FOREWORD

I have often been asked, "What is the most dangerous part of walking on the Moon?"

My answer is, without hesitation, "Landing on the Moon."

The Lunar Module must slow from about 3,800 miles per hour to a level hover at 100 feet above an unknown surface and descend through thick dust to a soft touchdown amongst craters, boulders and rocks that have never been seen on any photograph. The margin for error is essentially nil. There is no assistance from Mission Control; there is no back-up computer; and only 30 seconds of propellant reserve is available when the decision must be made to either land and shut down the engine, or command an abort back to lunar orbit. There will never be another chance to try again or to return to the Moon.

During the most critical phase of the landing, the LM must be controlled internally from 50,000 feet to touchdown through a single, very small, and very slow, computer, using software programs that were written, by hand, by a single engineer. That software must be absolutely infallible. When the guidance software for the lunar landing was to be developed, this daunting task was assigned to an engineer who had no formal computer training (none available) and who was only 23 years old! That engineer was Don Eyles, and the software he wrote was part of a program called Luminary.

Eyles was a member of an extended family of 400,000 dedicated engineers, pilots, scientists, managers and other essential members of a remarkable team that repeatedly relied on a single individual to invent, conceive, or imagine one of the vast number of essential elements of the mission that had to work. This amazing feat of the Apollo family was achieved during the 1960s, a period of national and international conflict, confusion, turbulence, and disappointment. And during this difficult period, and during Apollo, a contrast of cultures was blended into this remarkable family with no (or very little) conflict, confusion, or turbulence. As history will show, time and time again, members of this diverse and often culturally-opposed family stepped up to a challenge that seemed impossible — but theirs was success after success, nearly beyond imagination.

In this book, Don Eyles has described his life and times among this family during this remarkable period. His descriptions are concise, coherent, and complete — the book is both entertaining and educational. We learn about the technology — computers, simulators, procedures and techniques. We learn about the people — throughout the book, Eyles relates his interactions with notable astronauts and NASA managers, and his impressions of their characters and capabilities. And we learn about the cultures — how he was assigned his tasks, how he worked night after night, and even how he might otherwise have gone to Woodstock.

Eyles highlights another unique aspect of the Apollo culture, a management style that facilitated open communication among astronauts, engineers, and scientists. He spent many hours in simulators with astronauts. He obtained an understanding of the demands and challenges of spaceflight and learned how to formulate complex computer instructions for the crews to use during normal and emergency flight operations. Concurrently, astronauts became familiar with the challenges of writing effective software for our small, slow computer. This teamwork was typical of Apollo and it marks Apollo as a major milestone in productive human relationships among culturally and intellectually diverse individuals.

Among his other achievements, Apollo 14 brought Eyles a special notoriety — including an invitation to the White House. Less than four hours prior to the planned descent from lunar orbit, the bright red Abort button on the LM's instrument panel illuminated and began sending a spurious signal to the computer that would have aborted Alan Shepard and Edgar Mitchell's landing at the moment the descent engine was ignited. Eyles had written the code that monitored that signal. At 1:00 in the morning he was called on to attempt to write a workaround for the problem, with no allowance for error. In less than two hours, not only did he write the workaround, but it was verified in simulators at both MIT and Houston, and then read up to the crew.

That clever workaround simply changed a few registers, first to fool the abort monitor into thinking that an abort was already in progress, and then to clean up afterward so that the landing could continue unaffected. The procedure required inserting 61 precise and sequential keystrokes on the computer keyboard (the DSKY) under severe time pressure. Mitchell executed the procedure flawlessly and it worked perfectly. Apollo 14 landed at its target point on time, and the Apollo program once again proceeded without a major setback.

An Apollo 14 failure, coming after the near-tragic failure of Apollo 13, would very likely have doomed my mission, Apollo 15, to a paper exercise. (Apollos 16 and 17 were already facing cancellation.) Eyles solved that problem—and thank goodness he did. He gave all 400,000 members of the Apollo family an opportunity to finish the Apollo program successfully and with pride and satisfaction—an opportunity to complete the history of the first humans on the Moon without another failure. In this remarkable book, Don Eyles gives the rest of us an opportunity to share and learn about a major part of this history. Read and enjoy.

David R. Scott
Commander, Apollo 15
Los Angeles
March 2015

AUTHOR'S NOTE

This book began in the mid-1980s as a sixty-page outline. From that point, if not before, I accepted responsibility for telling the story of the LM flight software as I experienced it. David Chandler and Paul Larson read the outline and encouraged the project. However I did not return to it until well past the millennium.

As, rather suddenly, the story began to seem complete, readership exploded. First came my amore, Denise Bosco, with her sharp eye for errata. Peter Adler, David Mindell, John Tylko, Paul Fjeld and Marjorie Shepatin read early versions and made valuable comments.

Norm Sears, a key participant in the events, gave me his point of view. For many years we regularly played tennis and ate Chinese food—at the Royal East Restaurant on Main Street when it was still the domain of Otto Chang—in a group that also included Hal Laning and Dick Battin. I have benefited tremendously from their friendship and from the remembrances and insights they provided me.

Allan Klumpp and George Cherry, whose friendship proved more durable than their rivalry, shared details of their earlier lives with me. Klumpp and Charley Muntz have allowed me to quote from material they wrote. Steve Copps, George Kalan and Malcolm Johnston were generous with their memories of specific events. For the problems on LM-1 and Apollo 11, George Silver was an indispensable source and, regarding the causality of the latter, Hugh Blair-Smith an acute interlocutor.

Drew Crete and Kathleen Grantchelli at the Charles Stark Draper Laboratory have let me reproduce historic photographs from the Lab's archives. Librarians at several other archives and historical collections were helpful—but ultimately disappointing, because certain key documents that I know once existed have continued to elude me.

Charles Slack, Kristen Crosby and Bernard Burdick were tasked to find problems and succeeded. At a late stage the historians Andrew Chaikin and Roger Launius reviewed the manuscript. Their praise gave me a welcome lift at a time, although summer, when my feet were feeling a little chilly. Chaikin's notes cured my naive reliance on the official voice transcripts of the Apollo missions and saved me from significant errors.

In a category by herself is Dana Densmore, who figures in the story both as colleague and lover, and in the creation of this book both as a very careful reader of the manuscript and as an advisor on bringing the volume to print. She excelled in, and kept in balance, all those roles.

Others who have helped during the long incubation of this project, by reading, discussing, or in some other way, include my friends Bob Draper, George Fifield, Matthew Day Jackson, Joanne Kaliontzis, Steve and Jaynee Lipman, Ariane Mahmud-Ghazi, Doug Matthews, Dallas Mayr, Larry McGlynn, Amy Meltzer, Laird Nolan, Anne Salemme, Helen Schulman, Paula Shepatin, Jeff Smith, Clif Stoltze, Lenore Tenenblatt, Raber Umphenour, Emily White and Tim White.

The inquisitive MIT students in Dick Battin's Apollo-themed freshman seminar during 2002–2005, and in the course titled "Engineering Apollo," currently offered at MIT every two years by professors Larry Young and David Mindell, helped me understand some of the questions I needed to address in this book.

I flew a few lunar landings with Dave Scott in the simulator at Cape Canaveral in 1971 when he was training for his mission to Hadley Rille. Years later we became better acquainted as perennial guest lecturers at MIT. In 2013 I gave Scott an electronic copy of the manuscript. He read it on the airplane back to California, and he has been a pillar of support ever since. His foreword for this book overstates, but places in context, my contributions.

After the four troubled missions that came before, Dave Scott on Apollo 15 inaugurated a string of three nearly perfect missions of genuine exploration. He is a great astronaut and a great-hearted friend.

Several editors and literary agents declined to publish or represent this book because "the subject matter is too technical." I have profited from that reaction by seeking to improve my explanations, but it has also made me stubborn. An essential part of my story is the joy of working in the rigorous but responsive medium of computer code — and seeing it fly in space — so I am obliged to touch on the intricacies of the act itself, even to the extent of exhibiting a few lines of code.

The young readers whom I want most to excite will be more comfortable with the vocabulary of computers and spaceflight than the average literary agent. Those readers may reasonably see in my story a part of the foundation myth of the contemporary digital culture. I hope in fact to help turn that culture toward more ambitious goals than the next internet start-up or the next social medium — even towards idealistic, planetary goals. Exploring others. Sustaining this one.

Just as I trace the vertical connection between coding details and historical events, I expand the story horizontally by including scenes from my eclectic personal life — intending to add to the collective portrait of the era a few brush strokes placed in the area that separates the counterculture from the space program, where the painting's unpigmented ground still shows through. I was typical only in my atypicality and I represent no one but myself, but I was there and my eyes were open.

Any account of my personal life would be deceptive without touching on my amours, which were those of a young man from the South, far less experienced than would be possible today at his age, who was preoccupied, in greater proportion than represented here, by his efforts to find love. I value very high the spirit and generosity of the women who were liberated enough, and confident enough in their egos and bodies, to enter into the relationships I describe.

I believe it is the duty of a memoirist who has been a participant in or close witness to significant events, to say what he believes to be true even when he cannot document it. If I have left clues that help historians learn more, then I thank them now in advance.

For the errors that must inevitably be present in this book, despite the help of those I have thanked by name, and others, only I am responsible. I apologize for any insufficiency of tact or failure of good taste.

SUNBURST AND LUMINARY

FIRST MISSION OF THE LUNAR MODULE

Apollo 5
January, 1968
Unmanned
LM-1 — SUNBURST 120
Earth Orbit

PROLOGUE

January 22, 1968. It's a cold night in Cambridge.

The Lunar Module is spaceborne, launched four hours ago from temperate Cape Canaveral on a Saturn 1B booster. This is LM-1, later designated Apollo 5. It is the LM's first flight, a six-hour solo performance in low Earth orbit.

The Lunar Module is designed to carry two astronauts from lunar orbit to the surface of the Moon, support them while they explore, carry them back to orbit, and rendezvous with the Command Module that will return them to Earth. The LM is the first pure space craft, the first to disregard the requirements of atmospheric flight. There is no heat shield—no possibility of surviving reentry. That is why tonight the LM is flying without a crew. Commands will be sent remotely from Mission Control at the Manned Spacecraft Center in Houston.

Ungainly to some, distrusted by others because of the problems that bedeviled her construction, to us the LM is beautiful. We imagine her movements in orbit. An invisible puff from the maneuvering jets, she spins smoothly. Sunlight catches her delicate skin. Another quick puff and she stops on her mark. She is the prima ballerina and we know her intimately because we built her brain, the onboard guidance computer, and wrote the computer program, called SUNBURST, that is transforming her tin and transistors into an almost-living being.

Twenty men and women have crowded into a small room on the third floor of one of the nondescript buildings that house the MIT Instrumentation Laboratory. A squawk box connects us to mission control in Houston.

Next to me stands Allan Klumpp, who worked out the guidance equations that I programmed in the onboard guidance computer. It is our first flight too, our first chance to see our work in action. When

I joined the Laboratory, 18 months ago, fresh out of college, this day seemed unimaginably far in the future. Now it is upon us.

It is also our first chance to screw up.

The LM will fire its descent engine twice. The guidance programs that Allan and I wrote will control the second burn. The same equation that is intended to guide the LM to a soft landing at a preselected spot on the Moon will be used tonight to satisfy target conditions just as stringently specified — but they represent a spot in empty space. After that the descent stage will be jettisoned and the ascent engine will fire to simulate the return to orbit from the lunar surface.

But before any of that comes a 38-second firing of the descent engine to simulate the burn that will place the LM in the right orbit for the start of the landing. The guidance computer is in Mission Phase 9. The LM is in the correct orientation for the burn. The countdown begins. If there were astronauts onboard, they would see the dwindling number of seconds until the time of ignition — TIG, pronounced "tig" — in the computer's display.

At TIG minus 30 seconds, powered-flight navigation begins. When in orbit or coasting between the Earth and the Moon navigation is leisurely, relying on computations and the occasional star sighting. For powered flight the accelerometers have to be read every two seconds, velocity updated, position recalculated — and that is just the beginning of it.

At TIG minus 7.5 seconds, attitude thrusters fire downwards. This is the *ullage* burn. It pushes fuel and oxidizer to the bottoms of their tanks to eliminate the bubbles that form in zero-G. The word is a brewer's term for the open space at the top of a keg of beer.

At zero, the Descent Propulsion System — DPS, pronounced "dips" — will come to life. We lean closer to the squawk box.

From Houston we hear "DPS on."

Several seconds pass, far too few.

"DPS off."

Huh? But soon we begin to understand what happened. The Delta-V Monitor — a small part of the computer program, written by me, whose purpose was to monitor the velocity change imparted by the engine — had sent an off command because it thought the engine had failed. To give the engine time to come up to thrust the monitor checked three times at two-second intervals. But this time, on the third check, the engine still had not registered enough velocity change. The burn was over before it started.

Unknown to us, leak tests on the control valves between the fuel manifold and the descent engine had caused concern. Premature entry of fuel would have been dangerous. The decision was made just before launch, on the recommendation of the engine manufacturer TRW, to delay the pressurization of the propellant tanks. In fact, the signal to activate the explosive valves that released the helium that propelled the propellant was not sent until about 1.3 seconds *after* our software issued the engine-on command. The engine was slow to start because the fuel pump was activated late. We could have adjusted how long the monitor waited before it concluded that something was wrong with the engine — if we had known.

If NASA had tried again it would have worked because the manifolds were now charged, but the software was less flexible than it would be for the manned missions, and perhaps mission control was still honing the art and tenacity it later exhibited. In the NASA film about the mission you can hear flight director Gene Kranz tuning up his famous voice of command.

Houston turned off the onboard computer. The engine firings were performed under ground control. The LM passed her audition. Such a beautiful dancer, even with her brain turned off.

The mission was called a success but that was no consolation. We hung our heads in disappointment, and endured a public reaction that blamed the computer software, because, after all, the computer had issued the engine-off command. The mission report blamed the "slower than normal thrust buildup" and concluded that "the guidance system and the descent engine functioned as designed," but the movie NASA made about the mission contained the statement:

> The inability of an onboard computer to cope with a programming error was overcome by the infinitely more flexible mind of man.

With that perception hanging over us, Allan and I would have to wait 18 months more, less two days, before our programs would get another chance to guide the Lunar Module.

PART ONE ⚜ LEARNING

TERMS OF REFERENCE

SPACECRAFT

CM	Command Module, carries crew during boost and entry
SM	Service Module, attached to CM during most of mission
CSM	Refers to combined CM and SM when attached to each other
LM	Lunar Module, lands on Moon and returns to lunar orbit

PROPULSION SYSTEMS

APS	Ascent Propulsion System, LM engine for return to orbit
DPS	Descent Propulsion System, LM engine for powered descent
RCS	Reaction Control. System, maneuvering jets on CM or LM
SPS	Service Propulsion System, engine in the SM

GUIDANCE SYSTEM COMPONENTS

AGC	Apollo Guidance Computer
DSKY	Display and keyboard connected to AGC
IMU	Inertial Measurement Unit, the spacecraft's compass
LGC	LM Guidance Computer, refers to the AGC in the LM

LM POWERED FLIGHT MODES

P40s	Orbital or midcourse burns on DPS, RCS, APS
P63	Lunar landing braking phase, starts at altitude of 50,000 feet
P64	Lunar landing visibility phase, starts at altitude of 7600 feet
P66	Final landing phase, typically entered at about 400 feet
P70	Lunar landing abort on DPS
P71	Lunar landing abort on APS after staging
P12	Normal ascent from lunar surface to lunar orbit

I was a cute kid. My parents thought I looked like General Eisenhower, who was much in the news when I was an infant. On my first birthday, the month after D-Day, they took my picture in a garrison cap with four paper stars pinned to it. My mother wanted real stars but my father, a commissioned officer in the US Public Health Service with a rank equivalent to major, was reluctant to walk into a military outfitter and ask for the insignia of a full general.

My earliest authentic memory (since no one else remembers it) is of a machine with gears that sat in a field near our house in Milledgeville, Georgia. I could turn one wheel and another wheel would move but more slowly. After that we lived in Baltimore for two years while my father went to Johns Hopkins for his doctorate in parasitology. I was fascinated by the old shot tower where buckshot had been manufactured by dropping dollops of lead that hardened into spheres during their moment of weightlessness on the way down. The Battleship *Missouri* ran hard aground in fourteen-foot water in Chesapeake Bay. "The Mighty Mo got stuck in the mud," I sang. When her captain was court-martialed it was a lesson in responsibility. After Baltimore we moved to Memphis, where my father set up a laboratory to study malaria.

The spaceships I designed were cute too, stubby things with fins that needed an exceptionally energetic propellant because there was not much space left for fuel and oxidizer after arrangements were made for the comfort of the voyagers and their pets.

I pored over the spreads in Collier's Magazine that depicted, in gorgeous renderings by Chesley Bonestell, Wernher von Braun's conception of a ring-shaped space station that created artificial gravity by rotating, a sinuous blue-skinned "ferry rocket" quite different in appearance but about the same size as the future Saturn V, and a skeletal lander kicking up dust as it touched down on the Moon. I learned that in space velocity is more important than position. You needed almost 18,000 miles per hour to get there at all—but when I calculated that as only 300 times our speed on Highway 51 in a 1954 Chevrolet, and a few years later attacked the ratio in a 1956 Pontiac that would hit 100 without even trying, it did not seem impossible.

One summer, movies featuring the cowboy hero Hopalong Cassidy were screened at school on Saturdays, along with short films that showed A-bombs and H-bombs lighting up the sky, followed seconds later by great winds that seemed to sweep everything away.

My first major engineering project was a fort in the back yard, near the mimosa tree, that started with four large wooden crates and grew to have two stories, a tower from which you could see the traffic out on the highway, and a cannon with a square barrel that could lob the sawn off end of a two-by-four into the next yard using a cherry bomb from the fireworks shack just south of the Mississippi border.

In eighth grade I went to bop parties. A song like "The Great Pretender" takes me back to those days—I am in a white sport coat, dancing awkwardly in someone's garage—but music was changing, and nearby. My sister and I, both sleep evaders, went to bed with our colorblind AM radios and had a system for alerting each other when a DJ on WHBQ or WDIA put on a hot record. I don't know if I was listening to Dewey Phillips the night near my eleventh birthday when he played "Elton Preston's" debut single "That's All Right Mama" six times in a row, the night of the day it was recorded at Sun Studios on Poplar Avenue, but I could have been. Later we watched Phillips's subversive after-school show on WHBQ-TV—Dewey in a studio sitting behind two sixteen-inch Rek-O-Kut turntables while his sidekick Harry Fritsius horsed around and frequent guests played live or lip-synced, most memorably Jerry Lee Lewis. One day Fritsius got too frisky with a life-size cutout of a Hollywood blonde and the show was taken off the air.

In these same years, before I was old enough to drive, I took a summer shop class with a man who I remember only by his ham-radio call sign, W4LRO ("lonesome radio operator"). I got my own license (K4ZHF) and operated for a while on the 40-meter and 6-meter bands.

I read with excitement about the Vanguard project to launch the first artificial satellite, and in ninth grade felt cheated when the first satellite was Russian instead. In 1952 I had posted "I like Ike" signs around the house—while my parents quietly voted for Adlai Stevenson—but by 1960 I was for Stevenson myself. I watched his last hurrah, at the 1960 Democratic convention, on a black and white TV at the home of my French teacher, Mrs. Matthews. I was there to pick up her daughter for a meeting of the "great books" group that met at Southwestern University. We read *Brave New World, Darkness at Noon, Heart of Darkness*. I read *Time* magazine cover to cover every week. I heard and understood President Eisenhower's warning, in his farewell address, against the "economic, political, even spiritual" influence of the "military-industrial complex." Soon enough, I loved Jack Kennedy.

At Whitehaven High School I worked on theatre. Every year we did a play in the fall, and in the spring a musical in a full-scale production with orchestra. I did the lighting and special effects. Hydrogen and oxygen in thick Coke bottles—pull out the stopper and ignite—simulated the fireworks in *Our Town*. For *South Pacific* I rewired our antique lighting board. At home I experimented with electrical arcs using surplus carbon rods from the projection room.

We fancied ourselves the intellectual set, believing in Black civil rights and not necessarily in God. We resented it when our theatre was taken over for an overtly racist community meeting having to do with the dividing line between white and black neighborhoods. My classmate Kurt Harris, always full of hot air, became not just a blowhard but a very brave blowhard, in that time and place, when he strode on stage and took the microphone from the startled speaker, beginning, "Two thousand years ago there lived a man named Jesus Christ..." only to be set upon and pulled away, while we shouted outrage from the balcony. The commotion that followed broke up the meeting.

We were threatened, called communists, queers, nigger-lovers (which were synonyms), but we also heard the N-word used with paternalistic pride. Our seventh-grade teacher, Miss Anna Leigh McCorkle, who was from the oldest family in Whitehaven, was proud that the "McCorkle niggers" in Mississippi had qualified to vote despite a state law that disenfranchised black people whose grandparents had not been literate. Bessie, the dear black lady who came to baby sit, lived on McCorkle land in Whitehaven with her much older husband, Spencer Knowles, in a little house guarded by geese and surrounded by cotton fields. Knowles's older sister, whom we glimpsed in her rocking chair on the side porch, had been born a slave.

I had visited the Civil War battlefields in Virginia and Pennsylvania with my father when we lived in Baltimore. My ancestors fought on both sides, but like every white lad growing up in the South I was stirred by stories of the Confederate generals, who battled so resourcefully against superior odds. I wrestled with the paradox of the admirable Southern military brilliance, and the hateful crime it defended; and with the contemporary riddle of "states' rights," personified by another kinsman, Senator Richard Russell of Georgia (my mother's second cousin), and the injustice that principle perpetuated. I could not bring myself to disrespect Robert E. Lee, or my august cousin, but I saw clearly that they were in the wrong.

We had older friends in downtown Memphis, beatniks, hard drinkers, homosexuals although that was scarcely acknowledged. I joined a youth group that met Sunday evenings at the Unitarian Church to hear talks by alternative believers and free thinkers. We frequented a coffee house, ate Italian food that to us was exotic, heard the blues wafting down from upstairs rooms on Beale Street, and stopped to listen to an *a cappella* quartet practicing under a bridge late at night. We climbed the tower of an abandoned Victorian mansion on East Adams Street to sit under the stars. When the Mississippi River was low we picnicked on a sandbar on the Arkansas side. I had my first sloppy experience with alcohol intoxication.

For making out I liked a spot under the bridges, where the dark water swirled away like liquid marble toward distant Arkansas and the powerful spotlight of a southbound towboat might transfix us for an instant as the river pilot checked his marks for the big right bend just below downtown. Sometimes we went to the Bellevue Drive-In on Highway 51, or drove south to find a dark spot among the cotton fields. Laurie, Lisa, Merle Glenda. Fearful of ruining our lives, as we had been schooled to think, by an unwanted pregnancy—and as unschooled in how to avoid that as in the act itself—we held back.

For a few years I took piano lessons with Mildred Allen, who had studied with Nadia Boulanger, from whom the line extended to Liszt, Beethoven and Haydn. We worked on Beethoven's *Appassionata* and the etudes of Frédéric Chopin. A friend named Rodney Gates, who had a superior hi-fi, introduced me to the operas of Mozart, Verdi, and Richard Strauss.

Driving to my piano lessons I listened to the Saturday broadcasts from the Metropolitan Opera in New York, but opera really clicked for me when the Met came to Memphis in 1959 and I saw live performances for the first time. Opera seemed an art form of a higher order, built atop a huge edifice of tradition and learning, with its mix of media, theatrical machinery on the grandest scale, and endless melodies and tonalities rendered by the most expressive instrument of all — by singing actors so exposed and challenged on the stage that their own heroism seemed to parallel that of the characters they were playing. More than that, the theatre, when the house lights went down and the overture began, was for me the nearest thing to a sacred space that I had ever experienced.

When the Met came to town the next year I carried a spear across the stage in *Il Trovatore*, earning two dollars. "Pull up your tights," was the incessant admonition backstage. When we were not needed we visited the nearby King Cotton Carnival in costume (pulling up our tights) or watched the performance from a catwalk above the stage. I got to know the Municipal Auditorium from top to bottom, including secret entry points. After that I saw everything that came through.

I took a job as assistant manager at the Guild Art Theatre on Poplar Avenue. The Guild was Memphis's art house, managed by a southern gentleman named Bill Kendall with a quiet disregard for the prevailing hypocrisies. The *Carry On* films and the Ealing Studios comedies were our bread and butter, but we also screened the new wave: *Breathless*, *La Notte*, *L'Eclisse* and *L'Avventura*, and *The Crucible* in French with Yves Montand, Simone Signoret, and as the troublemaker Abigail Williams my special object of desire, Mylène Demongeot. I prized a movie still from another film in which she posed provocatively in a bikini. When Bob Draper's girlfriend showed up at the pool in a much more modest two-piece it caused a mild scandal.

One week we screened an art film that included a brief shot of a woman's breast as it escaped from the bodice of her ball gown during a moment of passion. It packed the house. One night four dudes in black suits showed up just after the second show started. The one who did the talking had a squeaky voice. They all wore white shirts and thin black ties except Elvis Presley himself, whose shirt was open at the collar and ruffled. Naturally I waived the admission charge. They sat at the very back and were gone in a flash when the show broke.

HIRED

I was in high school at Whitehaven during the years when fiery launch failure followed fiery launch failure at Cape Canaveral, while Sputnik passed overhead. I was about to graduate, in 1961, when in quick succession Yuri Gagarin orbited the globe, Alan Shepard followed suborbitally, and John Kennedy made his galvanizing call for a manned landing on the Moon within the decade. I was starting my sophomore year at Boston University when Kennedy explained why:

> We choose to go to the Moon in this decade and do the other things, not because they are easy, but because they are hard, because that goal will serve to organize and measure the best of our energies and skills...

I came back from class on a November Friday during my junior year to hear the news from Dallas — and watched the scene at the graveside with a special empathy. We had buried my father in the same cemetery just a few weeks before. He had died suddenly, in Malaysia, after completing an assignment that stemmed from one of science's accidental discoveries.

At his laboratory in Memphis he was running an experiment that required dissecting, in a short period of time, a great many mosquitoes infected with malaria. His technique was to stun the insect with a puff from his ever-present cigar and then go to work on it under a binocular microscope. It did not matter if a few mosquitoes got away because the malaria they carried, *Plasmodium cynomolgi* (subspecies *bastianelli*), only infected monkeys and apes, not humans.

My father came down with malaria anyway. Bob Coatney, his boss in Washington, reports the following telephone conversation:

"Bob, I have monkey malaria."

"If you have monkey malaria don't take any drugs."

"I thought you would say that so I took chloroquin before I placed this call to you."

Coatney wanted the infection identified before it was treated. My father, with the same thought, had drawn blood and injected it in a clean rhesus macaque before starting the chloroquin. The monkey came down with the same subspecies of *Plasmodium cynomolgi* eight days later. When a lab worker also got sick her blood was injected into another monkey, and for good measure into two prison-inmate volunteers, with the same result in all cases. (Treatment quickly cleared the parasite in all the human participants.)

It was big news for malariologists. Coatney sent my father to Malaya (as it was then) to find out if the infection was a laboratory fluke or if transmission between apes and humans regularly occurred in the field. If it did, that would make it harder to target the mosquitoes that carried the human *Plasmodia*. The work involved testing a large number of people, apes, monkeys and mosquitoes to see what parasites they carried. Mosquitoes were trapped using caged monkeys as bait. When the technician climbed the ladder to vacuum up the mosquitoes he kept his parong handy because he might encounter a python with its own ideas about the monkey. My father traveled to Cambodia to buy more monkeys, met Prince Sihanouk, and came back with slides of a strange overgrown temple called Angkor Wat.

I joined my family in Kuala Lumpur during the summer of 1962 — visiting Europe for the first time along the way. I was met by my father's anger about the car (an Isetta not a DeSoto) that I had ceremonially consigned to the Mississippi River when no one would give me fifteen dollars for it. The car had rolled backward into the river and the single headlight that still burned colored the water yellow as it went down. But the Big Muddy is unpredictable. The car washed up downstream, was traced to me, and became the subject of an article in the *Memphis Commercial Appeal*, which someone had helpfully forwarded to my parents in the Far East. The newspaper would dredge the incident up again ten years later when it ran a story about my activities in (or near) another sphere.

In Kuala Lumpur we had a pleasant, government-allocated residence near Ampang Road. Our pet gibbon Watu lived in a tree in the back yard, where I sometimes joined him for a banana. Watu's worst habit was pulling Benny's tail. Benny was a big brown dog who came with the house, the sort of dog who seemed to follow the bidding when we played bridge. He may have out-learned the ape during their interactions because he finally got his jaws around Watu's waist and gave him a terrible scare. Downtown in the afternoon you heard the rattle of mah-jongg tiles from the second story windows. Durian stunk by the road — but tasted delicious. Umbrellas were one dollar Malay when it was dry, three Malay (about a dollar) during the afternoon downpour. At night Sikh guards slept in front of the shop entrances. I believe K.L. is quite different now.

I went along on an expedition to take blood smears from a group of aboriginal people (called Orang Asli) who lived on the far side of a large rubber plantation near Kuantan on the east coast. We were escorted by the government doctor who made regular rounds. When we arrived the village chief, in a white lab coat, brought out the medical record book, and in the same spirit of dress-up the women scurried to don bras. The people lived on comfortable looking roofed platforms.

Malaria didn't kill my father but the cigar may have. He died of a heart attack, in Penang harbor, after boarding the ship that was to bring my parents and siblings back to the United States. I learned of the event in Boston when my uncle came looking for me carrying a garbled but undeniable telegram. My father's group in Malaya identified several new malarias. After he died one of them, a malaria of gibbons, was given the name *Plasmodium eylesi*.

I had come to Boston University for college against the expectation that I would follow my parents to Emory University in Atlanta, where they had met (in the office of biology professor Woolford Baker) and where my grandfather, John Gordon "Graveyard" Stipe, had been Vice President. Truth was, I wanted to escape the bigotry and willful ignorance I had seen so much of in the 1950s South.

I had pictured college as a big tasting menu but it turned out I was required to concentrate. Philosophy was a possibility — I had relished an introductory course with Charles Bigger at Southwestern College in Memphis — but when I tried to sign up for metaphysics with Peter Bertocci I found that to have a second-semester freshman in his class was beneath his dignity. I settled on a mathematics major almost by default, but the courses I remember best were a medieval art class that had me designing gothic facades for a while, philosophy of science with Marx Wartofsky, and a challenging, eclectic physics lab where I first heard the word *byte*.

There were no such highlights in my love life, even including my long-looked-for sexual initiation. I had finally "lost" something I wanted to lose, but I had not gained the satisfaction or the confidence I hoped for from it, or even learned very much. At some point I memorized the opening soliloquy of *Richard III*. It was fun to quote Shakespeare and fun to play the villain, but, underneath, perhaps I began to wonder if in some way I was not shaped to "caper nimbly in a lady's chamber / to the lascivious pleasing of a lute" — whose music I heard all around me. At least, I was off to a late start with my capering.

In my senior year, bored with German and differential equations, I fell into the habit of playing bridge all day instead of going to class. I flunked out and lived in Atlanta for half a year with my mother — now a much-loved science teacher at Druid Hills High School — and my siblings, before the university let me back in. Stuck with a dismal academic record, and partly to reassure myself, I joined Mensa before I went back to Boston (and dropped out soon after). I completed my major with courses in number theory and symbolic logic, and so I graduated, one year late, and skipped the ceremony.

It was 1966. I lived alone in an apartment of two-hundred square feet in the threadbare Fenway neighborhood, carless, nearly broke. B-52s were bombing North Vietnam and the US commitment on the ground in South Vietnam was approaching 400,000 men. I tramped around town to interviews. I would have taken anything. I thought I wanted to program computers because I liked puzzles, but I had never written a line of code. When an interviewer asked me how I would write a program to alphabetize a list of names I pulled a blank.

On a hot day in June, walking home sweaty from another dispiriting interview in the business world, I noticed a sign saying "MIT Instrumentation Laboratory" on an old brick building across the railroad tracks from the main campus of the Massachusetts Institute of Technology. I had heard a few things about the Instrumentation Lab, enough to be daunted by the prospect of walking in and asking for a job. On the other hand, what did I have to lose? If my self-esteem had been higher I might have hesitated longer. The receptionist handed me a long application to fill out; then, barely glancing at it, she asked if I would like to talk to personnel officer John McCarthy then and there.

It was disorienting! McCarthy seemed to be trying to convince *me*—and he had my number from the start. He drew a contrast between the culture at "the Lab" and the more regimented conditions in private industry. At the Lab "making it work" was the only thing that mattered.

The Instrumentation Lab had been founded by the ultimate make-it-work guy, an MIT Professor called Doc Draper, sometimes called the Father of Inertial Guidance. He did not invent it but he made it work, in time to help win the Second World War by developing a gunsight that made it easier for ack-ack gunners to lead their targets. Later the Lab designed inertial guidance systems for nuclear submarines that needed to navigate for months at a time without surfacing, and for the new ballistic missiles they carried. Then, seventy-six days after Kennedy's electrifying speech, the Laboratory had received the first contract awarded on Project Apollo: to build the primary guidance and navigation system for going to the Moon.

Five years later major parts of the job still had to be done.

My references were checked; I was described as bright and well-liked and likely to do well, provided it was a job that excited me. Interviews were arranged. I met first with Bob White, who needed someone for the "analysis" group, and then with George Cherry, who led the team programming the computer on the Lunar Module. (Both groups were part of a "mission development" division led by Dick Battin.) Cherry did not care that I had no computer experience. He said he had even hired literature majors. No one at the time knew much about programming spacecraft guidance computers, just as no one knew how to land on the Moon. We would be the ones to figure out both. I thought White's offer was the safer choice but it was Cherry's challenge that excited me. MIT offered $640 a month and I didn't quibble. There was one other benefit. The job provided deferment from the draft.

THE MISSION

I sat at a borrowed desk reading about something called the "pings." It was spelled PGNCS and it meant the Primary Guidance, Navigation and Control System. That was the Lab's contractual part of the Apollo puzzle: the sensors and electronics that provided the brain and nervous system for the Apollo spacecraft. There was one version for the Command Module, and another, with similar hardware but quite different software, for the Lunar Module.

I learned that guidance, navigation and control were three distinct disciplines. *Control* stabilized the spacecraft in a given orientation (called *attitude*), or rotated it as commanded. *Guidance* made it go somewhere in particular such as a given orbit or a spot on the Moon, usually by firing a rocket engine. *Navigation* underlay both: where are we now, how fast and in what direction are we moving, and which way are we pointed?

Other manuals covered the Apollo Guidance Computer, known as the AGC, and the two languages used to program it, each documented by its creator. The language called *Basic* was described in "Memo #9," fifty loosely stapled pages by Hugh Blair-Smith, whose office was a few doors down. Basic (no relation to other computer languages of that name) was made up of simple instructions that the computer's circuits could understand directly. Blair-Smith had provided an *assembler* that made it possible to write these instructions using names and symbols instead of ones and zeros.

The manual for the language called *Interpretive* was a slicker production in blue vinyl covers by Charley Muntz (around the corner). Interpretive gave us the ability to work efficiently with vectors and matrices, the mathematical tools of three-dimensional navigation. Interpretive was more compact than Basic, but it ran much slower.

This was purgatory! It is notoriously difficult to learn a computer language without the motivation of a specific assignment. I did not yet know that with one it is easy. It was high summer and the banks of the Charles River were visible out the window to my left. This lasted until the man whose desk I was using was due back from vacation — something his office mates seemed to be looking forward to.

The antidote to the melancholy of having to work for a living was a document that described the steps by which an Apollo mission would reach the surface of the Moon. It was exciting enough in itself but there was a special tang. I did not yet know what part of the mission I would be assigned to, but it was in there somewhere. It was as if I was looking out over a roomful of people knowing that with one of them I would soon be intimate....

To be honest the metaphor would not have occurred to me at the time. So far I had no idea how, much less where, I was supposed to fit in, or when I would find out. I was not so familiar with intimacy either. Nevertheless, if only as a dream seen through a daze, I was reading my future.

A Moon mission begins in fire and thunder. The three-stage Saturn V, the most powerful locomotive ever built, will lift off from Launch Complex 39 near Cape Canaveral and head east. Twelve minutes and five million pounds of fuel and oxidizer later, 16,500 miles per hour have been gained — added to the thousand contributed by the Earth's eastward spin — and the Command Module, the Service Module, the delicate Lunar Module in her protective shroud, and the partially depleted third stage (the S-IVB) are in orbit around the Earth. The combined spacecraft will be by far the largest object ever lifted into space, 114 feet in length, over 300,000 earth-pounds in mass. They circle the Earth while the astronauts check out the Command Module's systems to make sure they survived the launch in working order.

Then the Saturn third stage will be lit up again to propel the stack out of Earth orbit on a path that leads to the Moon. In the lingo of three-letter acronyms that mark the milestones in an Apollo mission, this is TLI, trans-lunar injection. Right after the engine firing, or *burn*, the spacecraft will be moving away from Earth at about 25,000 miles per hour and fully committed to going to the vicinity of the Moon.

Next, the Command Module and the Service Module, known as the CSM when they are connected, separate from the S–IVB, to which the LM is still attached. For a moment two independent spacecraft, with relative motions of less than a foot per second, hurtle through cislunar space in formation. Then the CSM turns around and noses back in. The pointed end of the Command Module engages with a hatch in the ceiling of the LM's crew compartment and the CSM draws the LM away from the spent third stage. The hatch is opened and the astronauts can move between the two spacecraft.

The LM itself is in two parts, the wide-hipped, four-legged descent stage, which will be left behind on the Moon, and the ascent stage, which will return to lunar orbit after surface operations are finished. The lower segment contains the descent propulsion system (DPS, pronounced "dips"), a very unusual rocket engine that can be throttled through a range of thrusts. The upper part contains the crew compartment, where two astronauts will stand facing large (for a spacecraft) triangular windows; and the ascent propulsion system (APS, pronounced "apps"), a simple engine designed to lift the LM off the surface and back into a safe lunar orbit. The LM was designed by the Grumman Aircraft Engineering Company in Bethpage, Long Island, a corporation that got its start manufacturing pontoons for amphibious airplanes.

It's a three day coast to the Moon. At first the road is uphill as the spacecraft is tugged from behind by the Earth's gravity. Gradually it slows, until, finally, at the top of the hill, lunar gravity becomes dominant and the spacecraft speeds up as it coasts towards the Moon. That happens at a point almost nine-tenths of the way between Earth and Moon. Along the way there may be a few mid-course corrections, small rocket firings designed to tweak the trajectory. During the coast to the Moon the combined spacecraft weigh almost 100,000 pounds.

Three days out, our companion orb fills the spacecraft's windows. The spacecraft shaves her leading edge—the left edge as we view the Moon from a northern-hemisphere perspective—and passes behind her. Three astronauts become the loneliest humans that ever were and see landscapes never before beheld.

While behind the Moon, the CSM fires the Service Module engine (the SPS) to place the combined spacecraft in a lunar orbit at an altitude of sixty nautical miles above the cratered surface. That is called LOI, lunar orbit insertion. LOI is a critical juncture and it must take place out of sight and out of communication with Earth. There is a tense wait for the spacecraft to emerge and report the result of the engine firing. A bad LOI burn could put the spacecraft on a path from which there could be no return.

That was all very well—but George Cherry had hired me to be a LM guy and now, in lunar orbit, our diva takes center stage. She weighs about 34,000 pounds, most of it fuel and oxidizer for her engines.

The LM separates from the CSM and performs a pirouette so the astronaut left behind in the Command Module can confirm that her legs have extended properly. Then she fires the descent engine for less than a minute to lower her orbital low point to nine miles, an orbit dipping to airliner altitude that would be impossible on a planet with a significant atmosphere. This is DOI, descent orbit insertion. (It was the simulated DOI burn that went wrong on the LM-1 Mission.)

About an hour after DOI the LM reaches the nine-mile orbital low point. The descent engine is lit up again for about twelve minutes to descend to the surface. The moment the engine is lit is called PDI, powered descent initiation. The landing is controlled by a guidance equation that starts with the LM flying feet-first and ends with the spacecraft standing upright on the surface. If all goes well, the first part of President Kennedy's challenge will have been accomplished.

After a stay of some length—no concern of ours—the LM rises from the surface on its ascent stage, leaving the spent descent stage behind. At this point the spacecraft is a bug-like thing that left its legs and abdomen behind on the Moon. Back in orbit, tanks almost empty, the LM is down to 5500 pounds.

Meanwhile, the CSM circles and circles in its sixty-mile orbit, one go-around every two hours. Passive it remains as the LM arranges the rendezvous—a complicated procedure involving several small burns that ends with the two spacecraft in close proximity, and finally linked together. The surface party, grimy with moon dust, returns to the Command Module.

That ends the mission for the Lunar Module. Kissed goodbye, she will return to the lunar surface, this time, like Offenbach's seductive automaton Olympia, who sings and dances herself to smithereens, as junk strewn across the craters and rills and mares.

Oh yes, the CSM burns out of lunar orbit ib the SPS, coasts for three days, jettisons the Service Module, hits the Earth's atmosphere just right, pops chutes, and drops into the ocean.

THE LUNAR LANDING

My most recent automotive debacle, a Mercedes 220 from a used car lot in Atlanta, was unlamented history. Now I bought a small motor-cycle, a Yamaha with a high-revving two-cylinder 180cc engine and a five-speed gearbox. To my surprise bicycle-riding had given me most of the skills that were required and I drove the Yamaha confi-dently from the beginning. I remember, not more than a week later, the sunny late-summer day, how the road undulated through the countryside west of Boston, and the pressure on my hips of the legs, in white jeans, of the girl on the back.

I hung out with a former roommate. We played tennis almost every evening on clay courts in Brookline. After a stop at the Beacon Supermarket to get something to cook for dinner we would go back to the ramshackle house populated by his irascible father, kindly mother, four siblings, and, most interestingly, the girlfriends of his older sister. On the first of September I played the Boston game of musical apart-ments and moved into a former front parlor on Marlborough Street, with high ceilings, a working fireplace and the comfortable, old-wood smell of a Back Bay mansion.

One day during my second week I was talking to George Cherry when a gangling, crew-cut person wandered by, stopped, scratched his back on the door jamb, and gave me a quizzical look. George made the intro-ductions and I met the man who would be my mentor and teammate for the next six years. Allan Klumpp was working on the guidance algorithm that would control the LM during the maneuver at the apex of the whole mission, the descent from lunar orbit to the lunar surface.

How do you land on the Moon? Klumpp! But it was a big job and Allan needed help. I moved to a new office near his hideout on the third floor.

Allan gave me two papers to read, one by Cherry and the other his own. Cherry's paper proposed a guidance equation that was capable of satisfying the complicated end conditions required to land safely. Allan's paper described a practical system incorporating George's equation.

The lunar landing was the most complex phase of the Apollo mission and also the most dangerous. Almost from the beginning the LM would be on a trajectory that will intersect the surface, one way or another — barring an ignominious abort. The burn would be timed to begin just as the LM reached the lowest point in its orbit, about 50,000 feet above the lunar landscape. Our use of units was a hodgepodge of metric and English, but from that point down to the surface, following the lead of the astronauts and the flight controllers in mission control, we always spoke of altitude in feet.

The start of the landing, the moment when the engine would be lit and the guidance equation engaged, was called powered descent initiation, or PDI. (That three-letter combination would raise the hairs on your neck too if it were the moment your software was going to take control of the spacecraft, two lives, a national goal, and, if you like, human destiny.)

Guidance would be processed every two seconds, repeatedly correcting and refining the trajectory based on new data from navigation. Into the guidance equation, with each turn of the crank, went the LM's position and velocity, known together as the *state vector*. Out came a pointing command for the autopilot and a thrust command for the descent engine. Between the in and the out was an equation that compared the current state of the spacecraft to target conditions that were specified not only in terms of position and velocity but also of acceleration, jerk (rate of change of acceleration), and one dimension of *snap* — as Allan was pleased to dub the rate of change of jerk, pointing to *crackle* and *pop* for the next two derivatives.

If the guidance equation did its job right, the LM would touch down on the lunar surface before it ran out of fuel, right-side up, at the right spot, at a steady throttle setting, and moving very slowly at the moment of contact.

But it was not quite that simple. There were uncertainties. How accurate will the navigation be, given the Moon's lumpy gravitational field? How will the descent engine perform? What is the nature of the lunar terrain at the target spot? Lunar surface mapping was not precise. Boulders the size of cars were said to be too small to show up in photographs taken from orbit. Even if the targeted spot was perfect, how close could an automatic system get to it anyway, given the other uncertainties?

Unmanned spacecraft like the Surveyors that NASA sent to the Moon between 1966 and 1968 accepted the uncertainties, played the probabilities. At worst an expensive machine would be destroyed—as happened in two out of seven tries.

This time it was a given that we had human beings on board. We could not accept the same level of risk. But how would we deal with the uncertainties? By using the skills of the human beings on board. We needed people in the spacecraft because we had people in the spacecraft. The profit was in the exploration that was possible after reaching the destination.

Astronauts may have begun as "spam in a can"—Chuck Yeager's derisive phrase for the original astronauts, as reported by Tom Wolfe—but that was not going to be the case on an Apollo Moon mission. Human input was essential and the guidance system had to be designed for it.

Uppermost among the expected uncertainties were the surprises sure to be lurking in the lunar terrain. The crew needed to see the landing site they were heading towards, and they needed a way to bend the trajectory if they did not like where they were going. With that in mind, Allan had broken the landing up into three main phases.

The braking phase, designated P63, begins some minutes before braking actually begins. First it computes the time of ignition, and the attitude the spacecraft must be in at that time, then maneuvers the spacecraft to that orientation. The countdown starts. Powered flight navigation begins. Maneuvering jets fire briefly to settle the fuel, the crew pushes the PROCEED key on the computer keyboard.

The descent engine is lit. Twenty-six seconds after ignition the engine is throttled up to its maximum thrust and the guidance equation is engaged.

The braking phase is all about shedding forward velocity. The burn begins with the spacecraft flying horizontally, feet first, thrusting directly against its orbital velocity.

The braking phase is punctuated by two important events. First, the landing radar must lock onto the surface and start to measure its distance (the LM's altitude) and relative speed. It is unsafe to land without this double-check on the inertial navigation.

The other event has to do with how we operate the LM's descent engine (the DPS) and is called *throttle down*.

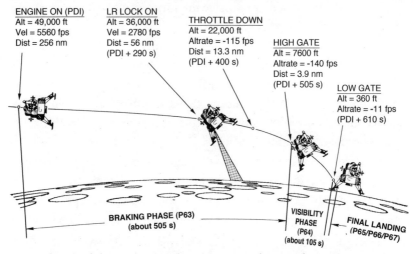

Phases of the Lunar Landing. Not to scale. Numbers are approximate. Low Gate as shown represents the approximate point at which we expect the crew to take over partial control from the fully-automatic system.

At the start of the braking phase, the guidance equation calls for about 16,000 pounds of thrust, whereas the engine can provide only about 10,000 pounds. The shortfall occurs during the first part of the braking phase when the LM is at its heaviest. We can compensate by adjusting the target conditions. So far so good.

But another limitation is more troublesome. We have been advised not to operate the DPS at thrusts between 63 percent and maximum because in that range the nozzle may erode excessively. That means that we must wait until the thrust requested by guidance falls below that percentage (with a margin) before we can start following the guidance command precisely. That transition, when in one swoop we throttle the engine from maximum down to about 57 percent, is called throttle down. Throttle down is a psychologically charged event. If it happens when expected it will give the astronauts, Houston, and everyone else, the warm feeling that guidance is doing its job right. A plot showing the thrust "desired" by guidance versus the thrust that the engine will actually deliver was almost the first thing Allan showed me after I was assigned to work with him.

The braking phase ends when the guidance equation has satisfied a set of target conditions called High Gate, which lie at an imaginary point about 7600 feet above and four nautical miles short of the landing site. At High Gate we switch automatically from P63 to P64, from braking phase to visibility phase.

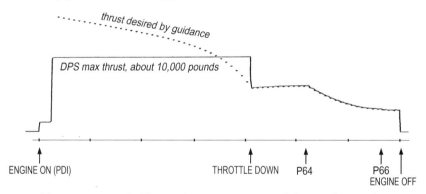

Thrust commanded by guidance, versus actual thrust, during the powered lunar descent. Time from descent engine ignition (PDI) to engine cut-off after lunar touchdown is about 700 seconds.

Now we aim for a new set of targets called Low Gate, which lie just above the landing site. The targets for the braking and visibility phases shape the trajectory so that the forward velocity that is shed during the former now allows the spacecraft to take a more upright posture. The LM pitches sharply forward and the alien landscape, thrown into hard relief by the oblique, unfiltered sunlight from behind the spacecraft, fills the triangular windows.

Astronauts will train for this moment above all others. Will they recognize the intended landing spot in the jumble of craters toward which they are rapidly descending? Will they see any spot at all where a landing will be safe? Where exactly down there is the computer taking them anyway?

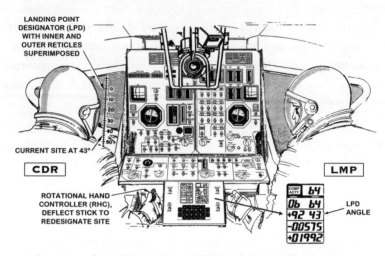

The LM cockpit during the visibility phase (P64): The commander, on the left, positions his eye so that the inner and outer reticles coincide. The current landing site then lies along the reticle at the point indicated by the LPD angle that is displayed on the DSKY and read aloud by the LM pilot.

The guidance system can try to answer the last question. During the visibility phase we will continuously compute and display an angle that indicates where the LM will land. It is called the LPD angle, which stands for *landing point designator*. The angle is referenced to a scale painted in photo-luminescent paint on the inner and outer panes of the left-hand window. The LM pilot, on the right side, will read out the angle aloud. The mission commander, on the left, will align his eye with the scales on the window and peer at the indicated spot. If he doesn't like what he sees he can flick his joystick (the RHC, not then needed for maneuvering) to signal the computer to shift the site — short, long, left, or right. For the computer this will be the busiest part of the landing and the most intense period in an Apollo mission for either spacecraft.

How the visibility phase ends depends on who, or what, is flying the spacecraft. There is a completely automatic option called P65 that will take over at about 100 feet. It simply nulls out any remaining horizontal velocity and descends at three feet per second. P65 is only useful in simulations with no man in the loop and the surface assumed to be smooth.

On a real mission we expect the astronauts to take control at around 400 feet. The takeover is as simple as switching the autopilot mode switch from AUTO, the mode in which the autopilot accepts commands from the guidance equation, to ATT HOLD, short for *rate-command attitude-hold*, a mode in which deflecting the joystick commands a rotation rate in the corresponding axis, and returning the stick to detent stops the rotation.

It is by controlling the LM's attitude, thus regulating the horizontal component of the LM's thrust, that the astronaut is able to maneuver horizontally. He will enter the phase pitched back perhaps fifteen degrees from vertical. By holding or increasing pitch he can pull up short, or, by leveling off, extend the trajectory downrange. At the same time, if he leans the joystick left or right to create roll, he can bend his path left or right. The goal is to bring the spacecraft to a stop over a safe spot to touch down, and then descend vertically.

After that there are two ways to go about it. P67 is seat-of-the-pants. The commander operates the joystick for attitude control with his right hand, and operates the throttle with his left hand to control altitude. Flying in P67 is a "formidable" piloting task.

The other option is slick. In P66 as in P67 the astronaut jockeys the LM across the surface with the joystick, but in P66 our software will control the throttle to maintain a constant rate of descent. The commander can change that rate using a spring-detent toggle switch near his left hand, called the ROD switch. One click up or down will decrease or increase the LM's rate of descent by one foot per second. The goal is to come down easy with very low horizontal velocity. It would turn out that in the fixed-base LM simulator at Cape Canaveral, with the help of P66, even a software engineer like me could make a respectable landing.

———

So that is how you land on the Moon, I thought. Each step seemed plausible. I did not understand all the details but it seemed to hang together.

But in July 1966 the landing guidance had only just been designed and the only place it was actually running was in an Earth-based computer program named after Allan Klumpp's wife Susan. In flight, the guidance equation would be processed every two seconds in real time. Downstairs in the computer room, SUSANK processed the equation every two seconds in imaginary time and chirped out the results on a mechanical printer — but the printout was a mess.

Here suddenly was my first assignment. Would I construct a format for the data printed out every pass by SUSANK — arrange the required data, a collection of about twenty numbers, and triads of numbers called vectors, in a pleasing and logical pattern?

Allan showed me the section of code where the data was printed out and gave me the clue that began to illuminate the workings of the computer. A computer variable is not a number, it is a location, a register, simply a cubbyhole where a number (or other data) can be stored. A computer program can contain a statement like this:

```
X = X + 1
```

That's crazy math. But it is not an equation, it is an instruction. It means, take the number from location X, add one, and put the result back in location X.

SUSANK

SUSANK was written in MAC, which stood for MIT Algebraic Compiler — already the third computer language swimming in my head after two weeks on the job.

MAC was the brainchild of J. Halcombe Laning Jr. (downstairs near Charley Muntz). I could see that Hal Laning was greatly respected and I began to learn why. Among other things, in the summer of 1952 he had created the first *compiler* in computer history for MIT's Whirlwind.

Whirlwind was a digital computer with a memory of 2048 sixteen-bit words, and it occupied space in a two-story building at 211 Massachusetts Avenue that still stands. After that legend muddies the water. Whirlwind occupied between 2500 square feet and the whole building plus basement. It used between 3300 and 18,000 vacuum tubes and maybe the electric company had to be notified when it was powered up. Perhaps all those things were true at some point.

It was the summer of 1952 and Hal Laning was using Whirlwind to develop guidance equations for ballistic missiles, when he got tired of writing code in Whirlwind's "native" or machine language. What if he could type in ordinary algebra instead? So Laning created a program that could translate what he typed into strings of finer-grained instructions that the computer could understand directly. It was called a *compiler*. It *compiled* a program in machine language that performed exactly the operations described by the algebraic *source code*. It was an idea that instantly exploded the power of the computer. For the first time the machine could be programmed in something resembling natural mathematical language.

MAC was a highly evolved version of Laning's original compiler language for Whirlwind. It appealed to scientists and engineers, among other reasons, because it looked like real math on the page. Each statement could occupy three lines, so a barbaric statement like this in Fortran:

```
V(I) = X**2
```

Could be written more readably in MAC as

```
E            2
M     V = X
S     I
```

Either way it means take the number in location X, square it, and store the result in the component of the vector V that is designated by the number in location I. The bar over the V indicates it is a vector. The MAC compiler knew which line was which by the letter in the first column of the punch card — E for exponent, M for main, S for subscript. Laning credited Dick Battin for the idea of using three lines.

I said I wanted to program computers and now they had called my bluff. I had everything I needed, a MAC language manual, my own copy of SUSANK in the form of a box containing a deck of IBM punch cards — and the printout of a successful compilation and run corresponding to the deck. That was important. I knew I was starting with a good deck. Any problems that arose were ones I created.

The deck began with a few cards that told the Honeywell 1800s downstairs in the computer room what to do with it — in this case to invoke the MAC compiler to operate on the deck. Then came the program itself, the source code. That was most of the deck. Finally, there were cards that told the mainframe, if the compilation was successful, to run the machine code that resulted[*].

I handed in the deck at the window of the computer room. Some hours later on a nearby table I would find the same deck along with a sheaf of printout. If all went well, the printout contained a listing of the program along with the printout that resulted from running it. If the compilation failed, or the run crashed, the printout was much thinner.

My assignment was to clean up SUSANK'S presentation of information about the landing it was simulating. Each block of printout corresponded to two seconds of simulated time. Every block began with the Mission Elapsed Time (MET). Then came position, velocity and acceleration vectors. Angles in sets of three expressed the attitude and angular rate of the spacecraft. Single numbers represented the thrust level commanded by guidance, the mass of the spacecraft, and so on.

I had to get used to a new way of expressing numbers on paper. When MAC printed the number 12345, for example, it looked like:

1.234500000E+04

E meant exponent so this meant the number 1.2345 multiplied by ten raised to the fourth power.

---

[*] We used the word "code" in a sense that was equivalent to the word "prose." One wrote a quantity of code, not a code or a number of codes. A hunk of code shaped to accomplish some function was called a routine or subroutine or program, just as a quantity of prose might be a note, blurb, article, essay, play, novel, and so on — none of these being very precise terms in either domain.

This was called scientific notation but it was not that MAC was doing the scientists a big favor because that was also how numbers were stored in the computer. MAC divided numbers into two parts, one expressing an exponent, the other the abscissa—the number to be multiplied by ten raised to the exponent power. The exponent could be positive or negative, so both very large and very small values could be accommodated. This way of storing numbers was called *floating point* because the decimal point moved around.

Floating point made it easy for the programmer because you did not have to worry very much about the magnitude of the numbers you were manipulating. The opposite of floating point was *fixed point*. If you were programming a fixed-point computer you definitely did have to worry about the magnitude of the numbers involved in your arithmetic. The Apollo Guidance Computer was a fixed point machine. That will come up later.

At the moment I was functioning as a sort of graphic designer as I tried to arrange a collection of simulation data on a page in a way that was logical and more or less pleasing to the eye. Was it logical and easy to take in because it was pleasing to the eye, or pleasing to the eye because it was logical, I wondered.

I saw that sculpting computer code was like modeling clay—not like chipping marble. It was a sensitive medium, malleable, responsive, but demanding. I would make a few changes in the program, then attempt to compile it. MAC was an easy language but at first even my most trivial modification seemed to provoke an error message. Sometimes a single tiny change would create a dismaying cascade of error messages. If the program compiled successfully, it would be executed. Then I would see the results of my latest changes, which were seldom quite as I expected—and so I wore a path from my office on the third floor to the computer room on the first.

I heard people referring to computer code as elegant, or otherwise, and I began to grasp the concept. It meant straightforward, economical, clever but not obscure. It was something to aspire to. Within a couple of weeks I got the printout organized.

DOC DRAPER AND INERTIAL NAVIGATION

Days grew shorter and work-days longer. My social life was sparse and my love life Saharan. I had lost touch with my Memphis-music roots. I knew there was a big rock-and-roll club called the Boston Tea Party on Berkeley Street but I had never ventured there. At least there was opera, a predilection I tested by attending the first American performance of Arnold Schoenberg's difficult but spectacular *Moses und Aron*, staged and conducted by Sarah Caldwell, in November.

I was too busy to understand yet that I had been inducted, through no virtue of my own except availability and lucky timing, into a fraternity not so much secret as opaque, with a brilliant history that traced back to the youth of a man somewhat younger than my grandparents.

Doc Draper hitchhiked across the country in 1922 with an undergraduate degree in psychology from Stanford University and a background that included a stint as the municipal electrician in his home town of Windsor, Missouri. He came with friends to investigate Harvard University for graduate school but he stopped at MIT on his way up Massachusetts Avenue and never made it to Harvard Square.

MIT's philosophy of *mens et manus*—mind and hand—fit Draper like a glove. Between 1922 and 1938 he created the longest transcript that MIT had ever seen and earned several degrees. He inserted chits redeemable for a bottle of good whiskey between the pages of his doctoral thesis. His reviewers were chagrined when he revealed the trick. They were already so familiar with his work that none of them had bothered to read the write-up. Draper became a professor and taught aircraft instrumentation. Later he headed the Department of Aeronautics, itself established in 1914. Under his leadership, two years after Sputnik, it was renamed the Department of Aeronautics and Astronautics.

At MIT Draper found the sort of environment that he later tried to establish at the Instrumentation Lab, an "Athenian democracy where talent ruled." He aimed to pioneer "technology leading to the realization of means for satisfying the needs and desires of society."

The formulation is too tortuous not to have been intentional and is repeated in similar words elsewhere. Technology is erotic. It is about satisfying human desires, but it only provides the means and the rest depends on good will, or otherwise. The dark side of Doc's formulation was his insistence on the neutrality of the technology itself. He would say, "I'm going to develop it and it's up to others to decide how to use it." In that he differed with Jerome Wiesner, famous as JFK's science advisor and later MIT President. Conscious of the destabilizing potential of accurate missiles, Wiesner was disappointed, time after time, when Doc dashed his hope that the precision of ballistic missile guidance had at last reached an inherent limit.

Doc Draper was a swashbuckler. He was almost flip when in October 1961 (although the actual date is in doubt) he was summoned to Washington to be grilled by the Administrator, the Deputy Administrator and the Technical Director of NASA. But if you are picturing stern officials sitting in a row at a government-issue table you have got it wrong. Ralph Ragan, under Doc my ultimate boss, tells it this way:

> Along in October Mr. Webb invited Doc and a lot of his people to have dinner with him in his Georgetown mansion, and Bob Seamans was there, and Jerry Wiesner.... We had a great dinner, and after dinner Webb said, "Let's have some after-dinner drinks in the living room." So we all marched into the living room in front of this large fire on this cool October night. Jim Webb sat down by the fireplace and said, "Sit here, Doc." Doc grabbed me and plunked me into the chair, and Doc sat on the floor. I think he knew what was coming and I think he wanted to be in a subservient position for what was going to happen.

> After everything was settled, Jim Webb said, "Doc, can you design a guidance system that will take men to the moon and back safely?" Doc said, "Yes." Quiet. Jim said, "Well, when will it be ready?" Doc said, "It'll be ready when you need it, Mr. Webb." Another silence. Jim said, "Well, how will I know that it'll work?" Doc said, "I'll go along with it."

Doc followed up with a letter detailing his advantages as an astronaut. He was sixty and wore spectacles. As a youth he had failed to get into the Army Air Corps because of motion sickness....

But I am unfair. Doc had learned to fly anyway, acquired his own airplane, and was a good enough pilot to terrorize, without killing, everyone who flew with him. Whatever he said to the NASA managers, sitting on a fine carpet in Jim Webb's parlor with a brandy balloon in his hands, it must have been convincing. We got the job. As Ragan added, "Procurement was a little different in those days."

Doc's laboratory had come into existence as a group of students under his influence. "It was not really much of a laboratory. It was Doc Draper designing flight instruments and having some students wire stuff together, and he'd put it in his own little airplane and go out and try them out," as Dick Battin put it.

In the 1930s the Lab became independent of the academic faculty. During the Second World War it was called the Confidential Instruments Development Lab. Later it was renamed the Instrumentation Laboratory (IL) because CID, as embroidered on the back of a lab coat, looked too much like CIO. During the span of this book we were again renamed — as The Charles Stark Draper Laboratory.

That was Doc's full name. To his friends he was Stark. In the press he was Dr. Gyro. He called himself a "greasy thumb mechanic." For the three thousand people who worked at the Instrumentation Laboratory he was just Doc, a silver-haired, bespectacled, broken-nosed (from boxing), five-and-a-half foot bon vivant who wore a beret and drove to work in a dark green Morgan roadster with the license plate MIT-IL. Doc's office was in another building and I never entered it. (He would visit mine once.) I certainly was not present on those legendary afternoons (during my infancy) when engineering was argued over gin disguised as "nonlinear damping fluid" — but stories like that gave Doc a raffish image that only increased our loyalty.

In the late 1920s Doc turned his attention to the internal combustion engine and found that no good way existed to measure even the most fundamental parameters of the engine, such as cylinder pressure, temperature, and gas mixture. Doc put quartz windows in cylinder heads and used a spectroscope to analyze the flame. Later he explored methods for measuring linear and torsional movement in engines, which led to the invention of a "knock" indicator for aircraft. A piston engine burns a mixture of fuel and air. If the mixture is perfect and the spark occurs at the right moment it burns cool and smooth. Too rich, fuel is wasted. Too lean, the mixture detonates quick and hot, damaging the engine. It makes a pinging or knocking sound but that is an unreliable indicator. Doc put sensors on the engine heads to detect the characteristic vibrations and indicator lights in the cockpit. It gave pilots the means to adjust the fuel mixture and the spark timing. Not many years later pilots flying combat missions over the Pacific used the device to maximize their range.

As a pilot, Doc understood "the potentially disastrous consequences of a failure in adequate geometrical information," as he primly put it. "You need to have instruments for geometry the same way you have a watch for time." The accurate accelerometers and gyroscopes that would be required were already being developed, and Doc and Professor Walter Wrigley began to formulate the principles of inertial navigation. The work languished for lack of support. But as war broke out Doc saw a way to apply his gyroscopes to a problem of acute concern to the US Navy—the defense of surface ships from air attack.

It was not so much Pearl Harbor, where the Navy hardly returned fire at all. It was what happened east of the Malay Peninsula three days later when the British battleship *Prince of Wales* (survivor of her encounter with the German battleship *Bismarck* six months before), and the battle cruiser *Repulse*, were attacked by Japanese torpedo bombers flying from bases near Saigon. The ships were steaming in open water, escorted by destroyers, and the crews were at battle stations. Eleven torpedoes struck the capital ships and both sank. Apparently three attacking aircraft were shot down.

Doc's group quickly developed a gunsight for light antiaircraft guns. In early tests they mounted the device on a .22 rifle and fired at a towel pulled along a clothesline. The gunsight used gyroscopes to measure the angular rate as the gun tracked the target and deflected a mirror in the optical path so that all the gunlayer had to do was place the sight on the enemy aircraft. The device corrected for the motion of the target and the motion of the vessel carrying the gun.

The gunsight was called the Mark 14. The number 14 was deceptive, chosen to confer respectability on what was truly a Mark 1. Doc said he chose the number to commemorate his infamous practice of standing on 14 at blackjack. "If the gunsight could overcome the handicap of being named Mark 14, it would do well in any job to which it might be assigned."

The newly launched battlewagon *South Dakota*, identified in the press for secrecy as Battleship X, went to sea with Mark 14s on its 20-mm and 40-mm antiaircraft guns and in October 1942 took part in the battle of Santa Cruz, near Guadalcanal. The ship bagged 32 attacking aircraft. Maybe it was 26, but the main thing was that the ship, and the aircraft carrier it was protecting, survived the attack. The Navy ordered 85,000 units during the war. Adding a radar to measure range made the gunsight even more deadly. A version for aircraft helped account for the Sabre Jet's superiority over the MIG-15 during the Korean War.

In the case of the gunsight, Doc Draper's laboratory brought a complex design to the prototype stage, then worked with an industrial partner (the Sperry Gyroscope Company) to produce service units. The pattern was repeated when the Lab tackled the guidance systems for the Thor and Polaris missiles. It was the success of this business model, as much as the technology that was inside the units, that later gave Doc and his Lab the credibility to win and hold the Apollo contract. Doc's friendship with Jim Webb, dating back to the war years when Webb was at Sperry, was also an advantage.

Technology advances when the solution to a particular problem finds a more general application. By about 1950 the tools were there. Accelerometers and gyroscopes were steadily becoming smaller and more accurate. A cadre of theorists and technicians was in place and poised for the next steps. Whirlwind pointed the way to the real-time computers that would be required. Now Doc Draper and his team finally got to apply their tools to the general problem of navigating in three-dimensional space—and the result was breathtaking.

It sounds like magic. A black box with no connection to the outside world can know where it is, always, provided it knows at the start.

You are a spy, seized in a strange city, blindfolded, thrown in a car. The car makes frequent turns to shake off pursuers. All you have to go on are the sensations of acceleration and side force as the car speeds up and turns and brakes. Can you keep track of where you are? If you can, you are an inertial navigation system. The concept is simple. Doc Draper and the group he led, while I was in kindergarten and elementary school, figured out how to put it together and make it work. The impetus was the Cold War. The Navy was building submarines that would cruise for months at a time isolated from the outside world. The Air Force was starting to realize that guiding missiles to their targets with radio beams was not practical, or at least not accurate.

In 1953 Doc's team installed their first entirely self-contained inertial navigation system in MIT's B-29 bomber and tested it by flying automatically from Hanscom Field near Boston to Los Angeles. Eleven men were onboard. Pilot Chip Collins would have preferred otherwise; it was a test flight with an unproven machine controlling the aircraft. "When you run a house of ill repute you have to take on all comers," was Doc's retort.

Air traffic control allocated airspace at 10,000 feet to Denver and on to Los Angeles at 20,000. The crew's only job was to operate the engines and control altitude. During the first part of the flight the system was tweaked based on ground sightings but after Denver the airplane entered clouds. Then Collins reported that for some unknown reason the rudder was commanding a heading change of almost 35 degrees to the right. In back, Doc, and Roger Woodbury, who managed the project, were only aware that the gyros had moved with respect to the aircraft. Was the system malfunctioning? Should Collins take over? Doc said, "Don't touch it." When they broke out into clear air, 75 miles from their destination, they were dead on course. The automatic system had been correcting for an unexpected wind shift caused by a developing front over the Rocky Mountains. After a 2232 nautical mile, 12 hour and 38 minute flight, the system's position error was about nine miles.

It was a set-up. Although Collins did not know it until the bomber was in the air, he was flying Doc's team to Los Angeles to attend a hush-hush symposium at the University of California on self-contained navigation systems.

At the meeting, Doc listened quietly as several speakers proved that an inertial system could not navigate an aircraft accurately over a long distance. Then Doc sprang to his feet and strode to the front of the room. From the foot of the stage, in front of the podium, Doc Draper announced that he had just done precisely that. "There were audible gasps in the audience," Collins recalled.

The system was called SPIRE, for Space Inertial Reference Equipment. The prototype on the B-29 weighted about 3000 pounds. The next version was down to 1400 pounds and the error on the same route was reduced to 2 miles. In a 1958 photograph Draper is seen explaining the device to the CBS reporter Eric Sevareid. The two men are stooping next to a spherical assembly about 3 feet in diameter set into the deck of the airplane.

The spherical case is the hallmark of an inertial navigation system. By the time of Apollo its diameter was down to about one foot. Inside the case was the inertial sensor itself. On Apollo we called it the *inertial measurement unit* or IMU. At its core, literally, were accelerometers and gyroscopes.

If you removed the cover of the IMU's spherical case (as has been done in the photograph provided elsewhere) you would see another, partial sphere, attached at two opposite points to the enclosing structure so it is free to rotate. Peel back that sphere and see... another partial sphere, this one attached in the same way to the first moveable sphere. Look inside of that and behold a lumpy assembly, roughly a six-inch cube, attached in the same way to the inner sphere.

In other words there are three sets of swivels or pivot points between the outer case and what is called the *inertial platform* at the core. The pivots are called *gimbals* because they resemble the mechanisms that cradle a ship's binnacle compass. In this case the purpose of the arrangement is to allow the core platform to move freely to any orientation within the case or — more to the point — vice versa.

Mounted on the inertial platform at the core are three gyroscopes, oriented so that their spin axes are mutually perpendicular, and three accelerometers oriented along the same axes.

Accelerometers measure acceleration. You need them to measure the effects of engine firings and of atmospheric drag, which, unlike gravitational influences, cannot be computed with precision but can be measured. Think of an accelerometer as a set of fuzzy dice dangling from your rearview mirror. It will tilt back as you accelerate, return to vertical when your speed is constant, and tilt forward when you brake. The motion of the pendulum can be turned into an electrical signal. In Apollo the accelerometers, called PIPAs, sent pulses to the computer where they were tallied by a counter and made available to the software. In the LM each increment represented a change in velocity of one centimeter per second. (PIPA meant pulse integrating pendulous accelerometer.)

A gyroscope wants to keep its orientation because the momentum of its spinning wheel resists the tilting of the axle. The orientation it "wants" to keep has nothing to do with the surface of the Earth or any other local phenomenon. It is fixed to *inertial* space. Point the spin axis of a perfect gyroscope at a particular star in the sky and it will forever point to that star. As a matter of fact stars do very slowly shift—but that perfect gyroscope that you could hold in your hand might as well be bolted to the cast iron framework of the universe itself.

The gyroscopes in an IMU like the one on Apollo took advantage of another characteristic of gyroscopes, that if you disturb one by rotating it around an axis perpendicular to the spin axis, it will try to rotate around the third axis. The output force can be turned into an electrical signal proportional to the angular rate of the disturbance. In other words, a gyroscope can provide a direct readout of angular rate.

The function of the gyroscopes in the Apollo IMU was to maintain the alignment of the inertial platform. The wheel in each gyroscope, consisting of a beryllium hub and a steel rim, was about 4 cm in diameter, weighed 84 grams, and spun at 24,000 rpm. By itself such a gyro was too feeble to hold its orientation against a serious disturbance, but these gyros were not effectors but sensors—sensors of sublime sensitivity—linked to motors in each of the gimbals. When the gyros sensed a disturbance the motors would react. As a result the inertial platform never moved. Hence its second name: the *stable member*.

So it was that deep inside an Apollo spacecraft, surrounded by electronic assemblies, suspended inside a spherical case, was an object that never budged from its fixed relationship to the stars, no matter how the spacecraft maneuvered. That was the equivalent of a compass. A compass does not tell you where you are on the ocean, it tells you a single angle—and that is enough. The inertial sensor goes beyond that. It gives you three angles that together define your orientation in three dimensions, and it works anywhere—even in space away from Earth's magnetic field.

Add optics for sighting on stars, and a table of star vectors, and you can align the inertial platform to any orientation you like—and correct for the drift of gyroscopes that, after all, are not quite perfect. Add precise information on the motion of nearby bodies like the Earth and Moon, and you can use the same optics to determine your position and velocity from scratch by sighting on horizons and landmarks. And if you add a pilot, engines, and a radar, you can attempt complex maneuvers like landing on another planet.

But you must also add a digital computer—to collect data from the IMU and other sensors, from ground transmissions, from the switches and controls that the crew operate; to run the software that navigates, guides and controls; to display information to the crew and send telemetry data to the ground; and to command the engines, maneuvering jets, antennas, and the other effectors that animate the spacecraft. Most of all, the computer will write the plot, apply the higher-level logic that pulls the strings to accomplish the mission. The IMU has the star role, spare like Garbo; the guidance computer plays Svengali.

By 1966 the context had been set: the guidance system hardware had been designed, the operating system and software development tools were in place, the LM itself was being built. Many of the programs that the LM had in common with the Command Module were already written and tested. But with the end of the decade not so far away it was up to me and perhaps a score of others, many of us new hires, to add the LM mission software that would provide the "means for the realization" of the big dreams of the little man in the beret.

Probably my fate was in the balance as I completed the SUSANK task. I had written some MAC code and perused the manuals for the two languages used to program the onboard computer, I knew a bit about vectors, matrices and coordinate systems—but was I really expected to program a part of the Moon mission itself? Or would I be shunted off to be a technical writer, or a tester of other people's software?

Allan must have given the thumbs up. My next assignments took me straight into the heart of lunar landing guidance.

Or rather, the reasonable facsimile of it that Allan had devised for the LM-1 mission, the Lunar Module's first, unmanned flight in Earth orbit. Our guidance programs would control the LM during the second firing of the descent engine. The burn would be guided by the same equation as a real lunar landing, but this time it would only modify the LM's orbit. After that, the descent stage would be jettisoned, the ascent engine would be tested, and then the LM, an intricate and unprecedented machine fussed over for years in Grumman's clean rooms, would burn up in the atmosphere. If in one mission the LM could prove itself safe for men to rely on it would be worth every gray hair and silver dollar.

The computer program for the first LM mission was called SUNBURST. For flight it would be encoded in a very reliable form of memory that resembled a rope woven from thin copper wire, but we knew it best on paper. It was the 1960s. We had no terminals of any kind, no DECs, no VAXes, no PCs, no Macs—much less the menagerie of devices that exist as I write this. What we gazed at when we wanted to think about the mission and the computer program was paper.

On paper, SUNBURST was a book or "listing" of 11x15 inch fanfold computer printout about five inches thick and growing thicker by the day as new code was added. The final version of SUNBURST

43

would have 1284 pages. Each page contained up to 50 lines of code following a header at the top of every page that read

YUL SYSTEM FOR AGC: REVISION 20 OF PROGRAM SUNBURST BY NASA

and then a contract number, the date that the listing was printed, and the page number. The number 20 is my guess at the revision number when I first encountered SUNBURST. The revision number increased as development proceeded and the program was modified. SUNBURST 120 would fly the LM-1 mission.

Not that SUNBURST 1 was the true beginning. SUNBURST came into the world as a version of AURORA, and AURORA sprang by way of RETREAD from the Ur-rope, ECLIPSE. Out of SUNBURST would come SUNDANCE (for Apollo 9), and finally LUMINARY.

On the Command Module side ECLIPSE begat SUNRISE, SUNRISE begat CORONA, and CORONA begat SUNSPOT (for the ill-fated Apollo 1) and SOLARIUM (which flew two unmanned missions). Meanwhile from RETREAD sprang SUNDISK (for Apollo 7), and from SUNDISK would come COLOSSUS, which first flew on the Command Module that went to lunar orbit on Apollo 8, and COMANCHE.

These programs were living bodies of information that acquired more and more juju as labor and logic were poured into them. The Sun-related names acknowledged an oddity: that the Moon landing program bore the name of the ancient Greek God of the Sun — and harked back to a system Doc Draper had flight tested in 1948 that was dubbed FEBE in honor of Phoebus Apollo. NASA manager Bill Tindall called it "MIT's weird preoccupation with the Sun."

SUNBURST, in each of its iterations, was created by something formally called the Yul Assembler, Hugh Blair-Smith's creation, itself a program that ran on our Honeywell 1800s and later our IBM 360s. Blair-Smith named it Yul ("Yule" unfinished) to commemorate an earlier project that had been dubbed the "Christmas Computer" but had failed to meet its schedule.

Blair-Smith was a tall, lanky guy who had already improved on the bare chin visible in his badge photo with the mariner's beard he still sports. He had worked in the computer labs at Harvard University before being lured to MIT to work on guidance computers.

He complained that his first assignment at was to create an "assembler for an unknown number of machines with unknown characteristics." What did he expect? He was hired to help shape those characteristics.

An assembler is different from a compiler. When I wrote a statement in the MAC language, the compiler translated that statement into a string of machine-language instructions. The Yul Assembler simply made it easier to write your *own* machine-language code. It let you program the AGC using instructions with somewhat meaningful names — CA meant clear and add (fetch), AD meant add, TS meant transfer to storage, TC meant transfer control (jump), BZF meant branch on zero to an address in fixed memory. The names were thought up by machine designers, not users, and many of them harked back to the instruction set of the legendary Whirlwind.

The assembler also made it possible to assign names (limited to eight characters) to locations in memory. For example, the variable ALTRATE in *erasable* (read-write) memory contained altitude rate, the speed at which the LM was descending during the lunar landing. The constant POSMAX in *fixed* (read-only) memory was the largest positive number that a single word of memory could accommodate (all 1's except the sign bit). P63LM marked the spot in fixed memory to which control was transferred if the astronaut selected the landing programs on the DSKY.

The assembler kept a copy of the current version of each program and gave you the ability to modify and add to it. It enforced the language rules and when it detected an error it issued a *cuss* — Blair-Smith's whimsical term for an error message. When we picked up the results of an assembly the first thing we looked at was the number of cusses. That did not necessarily correspond to the number of actual errors. Sometimes a single error could unleash an obscene tirade.

When an assembly succeeded the assembler could spit out data tapes for use by the simulators and, ultimately, to guide the manufacture of the memory that would be inserted in the flight computer — and for each assembly it created a paper listing.

SUNBURST was a big book but you could open it on a table and thumb through easily, or put your feet up on the desk and cradle it in your lap. A symbol table at the back made it possible to follow all the references to any named variable, tag, or constant. You could mark the sections you were interested in using colored markers on the edges of the paper. If you also wrote the revision number on the edge it was easier to pull the version you wanted out of a stack. You wanted a copy printed one at a time on the 11 x 15 inch green-bar paper. The computer room had multi-part carbon paper for printing two or three copies at the same time—there was a machine to divide the carbon copies into separate listings, which usually spilled paper all over the floor in the process—but listings printed that way were nasty things, smelly, ugly, and certain to blacken your hands. You wanted the green-bar, preferably warm from the printer.

We joked that if we really wanted to defeat our Russian rivals in the Moon race we would drop listings on them—not to crush but to confound. One night in my apartment with a few friends (and no fire in the fireplace) we hilariously ripped apart and crumpled up an entire listing. It filled the former front parlor of a Back Bay brownstone to a depth of about three feet.

But a listing was truly not made of paper and to open it was to enter a deep new world.

Our universe seems to obey certain rules. It needs rules, you could say, to exist at all. In the same way the characteristics of the Apollo computer and its languages, as enforced by the Yul Assembler, created a world that might not be qualified for flight, that might be full of bugs, but a world that was guaranteed to have a logical coherence—and it was all there in one book. You knew that for every riddle the listing posed, it contained an answer, if you could only follow the maze that connected them.

The first time I looked at a listing of SUNBURST I was surprised how much plain English was there. That was another way the assembler tried to help us. Besides keeping track of the binary data—the only thing the machine needed to know—the assembler allowed room for descriptive comments. There were whole blocks of it—explanations of what the next section of code was trying to do, instructions for the use of a subroutine, occasional attempts at wit. Near the start of the listing was a section called ASSEMBLY AND OPERATION INFORMATION made up entirely of descriptions and lists.

That was not all, because throughout, on the right hand side of the page, on the same lines as the code itself, space for 40 characters was available for explanatory comments. Every programmer (although I have known exceptions) understands his own code. The trick was to help someone else understand it. That depended on how well you picked your words, how honestly you anticipated the reader's questions, and how much trouble you were willing to go to to answer those questions in advance. There were whole pages with no annotations at all, but at least, if you had the will, Blair-Smith's assembler gave you the means. On the receiving end, until you began to see the meaning in the code itself the comments were something to cling to.

SUNBURST was organized in chapters that were called *log sections*. For example, names were assigned to locations in read-write memory in a log section called ERASABLE ASSIGNMENTS. Erasable memory was so limited that often several variables time-shared the same location. Making sure they did not interfere with each other was a major headache.

The section titled EXECUTIVE contained code, conceived by the same Hal Laning who created the MAC compiler, that made it possible to schedule blocks of software called *jobs* that were executed in order of priority. The code in the WAITLIST section was for scheduling smaller units of software called *tasks* that had to execute at a precise time. Together, EXECUTIVE and WAITLIST provided the Apollo computer's operating system. INTERPRETER contained the code that implemented the language we called Interpretive. PINBALL GAME BUTTONS AND LIGHTS operated the DSKY (rhymes with "whiskey"), the display and keyboard unit that was the main means of communication between the computer and the crew. If something went wrong, ALARM AND ABORT would come into play.

Other mysterious sections contained the control system, also known as the *digital autopilot* or DAP. The autopilot controlled the spacecraft's attitude using the maneuvering jets — the *reaction control system*, or RCS — or by swivelling the engine. Navigation came in two flavors: ORBITAL INTEGRATION PROGRAM updated the spacecraft's state vector mathematically, at infrequent intervals, during *coasting flight*; PIPA READER and AVERAGE-G INTEGRATOR worked together to navigate the LM during the fast-paced periods of *powered flight*.

Yet, all the functions mentioned so far were merely tools for use by the logic in the sections that implemented the mission phases. A list of those sections is given below, but do not study it too carefully because it very soon becomes irrelevant. LM-1 was designed to perform the same series of engine firings as on a lunar landing mission—two each for the descent engine (DPS) and the ascent engine (APS)—but it was a "canned" sequence with no built-in flexibility. The programs for the manned missions to come would be organized on different principles, use a different nomenclature (using terms like P63, P64, P65 and P66 for the lunar landing programs), and be far more adaptable.

```
MISSION PHASE 2 GUIDANCE REFERENCE RELEASE + BOOST MONITOR
MP 3 - SUBORBITAL ABORT
MP4-CONTINGENCY ORBIT INSERTION
MISSION PHASE 6 COAST SIVB ATTACHED
MP 7 - SIVB/LEM SEPARATION
MISSION PHASE 8 - DPS COLD SOAK
MP9-DPS 1 BURN
MISSION PHASE 11 - DPS2/FITH/APS1
MISSION PHASE 13 - APS2
MISSION PHASE 16 - RCS COLD SOAK
```

Mission phase 11 was the most complex. It began with the second firing of the descent engine, guided by the programs that Allan Klumpp and I would write, followed in quick sequence by the casting loose of the LM's descent stage, known as "fire in the hole" or FITH, and a firing of the ascent engine equivalent to a lunar ascent.

And over the next few months, Allan would give me assignments that would lead to the creation of three new log sections:

```
SECOND DPS GUIDANCE
THROTTLE CONTROL
MASS CALCULATOR
```

In theory someone wrote down "requirements" and *then* we wrote the code accordingly. Our requirements document was the Guidance System Operations Plan—the GSOP, pronounced "gee-sop". It defined many of the programs and routines that would need to be programmed in the computer and provided the necessary equations. How the functions would be made to play together happily inside the guidance computer was not addressed. Some necessary functions were not foreseen. It would not be long before the code, keeping the goal in sight, outdistanced the requirements document.

What the GSOP did well was define the language we would speak, and an important aspect of that language was *coordinate systems*.

To fly a spacecraft purposefully you need numbers. What is your position? In three-dimensional space naturally you need three numbers to answer that, one for each dimension. Such a trio of numbers is called a vector. Velocity is another vector: three numbers that express the spacecraft's speed broken down into the three dimensions. Another vector, called thrust, creates acceleration, which allows you to control your velocity and position.

The trouble is, a vector means nothing unless you know its frame of reference, the X, Y, and Z axes along which its three components are measured. Imagine that three mutually perpendicular axes originate at the center of the Moon. Then the spacecraft's position vector is like an arrow from the center of the Moon to the spacecraft, deconstructed into three components referenced to the three axes.

Real life is full of such frameworks. In midtown Manhattan it is streets, avenues, and floors. In Kansas the X-axis is east-west, the Y-axis north-south, and they meet at the crossroads by the radio station. The antenna is 250 feet in Z but only the FCC and the crop duster care about that. These systems are anchored to the Earth, but if you are a U-boat skipper saying "target bearing 1-2-0 degrees," then you are using another sort of coordinate system, one that is defined by your vessel and moves with it.

Now I had three or four coordinate systems to learn about. Consider the LM in orbit around the Moon:

Enclosing all is the celestial sphere of the "fixed" stars. Never mind the expansion of the universe and the swirling of galaxies. The stars are plenty stable enough for going to the Moon, and Newton's three-dimensional physics equally sufficient. We gave the stars their own coordinate system to anchor our math to the actual universe. We called it the *reference* coordinate system because it provided the unambiguous, if arbitrary, spatial framework to which other frames could be related. The precise definition of the reference system varied from mission to mission.

Another coordinate system was defined by the stable member — that lumpy assembly of gyroscopes and accelerometers nested like a Russian doll in the IMU's spherical case, stubbornly holding its orientation no matter how sportily the LM was jockeyed around by some hotshot astronaut. We called this system *platform* or *stable member* coordinates. Acceleration came in platform coordinates because that was where the accelerometers were mounted.

Our diva, the LM, insisted on her own coordinate system as well, X-axis vertical along her spine, that is, along the thrust axis of both the descent and ascent stage engines and vertical as she stood with her not so delicate feet in lunar dust. The Z-axis gazed intently ahead and the Y-axis was her extended right arm, if she had had one. We called this system *body* or *nav base* coordinates. (The *navigation base* was a more or less rigid part of the LM's structure that held the optical telescope and the IMU in a fixed geometrical relationship.)

The interplay of these three coordinate systems — reference, stable member, and body — is the essence of inertial navigation. The inertial sensors on the stable member had a physical relationship on the one hand with the starry universe, and on the other, with the LM's tangible structure. What is more, we had the means to know both relationships quite precisely.

The stable member's relationship with the LM's structure was defined, at any instant, by the angles of the three gimbals in the IMU — numbers that were available inside the computer. That is how the control system knew how to orient the spacecraft, how navigation was able to incorporate radar information from an antenna mounted on the body, and how guidance could point the thrust vector to accomplish some objective.

The stable member's relationship with the starry universe was determined when the IMU was *aligned*, or set to a particular inertial orientation, a process that involved sighting on stars using the telescope. From the alignment process came a matrix — nine numbers in a three-by-three arrangement — that described the relationship between the stable member (SM) coordinate system and the reference (REF) system. The matrix was named REFSMMAT, pronounced "refs mat."

You did not want to lose your REFSMMAT. That is, you did not want to "tumble the platform" or otherwise lose track of its orientation. That would be like a Stone Age man letting his fire go out. You could get it back but only by laborious sightings on stars using the telescope (a device that for that matter can also kindle a fire). If you were starting from a known alignment it was not hard to go to another alignment. That is why astronaut Jim Lovell, after his spacecraft exploded on Apollo 13, hastened to activate the LM and transfer a rough alignment from the Command Module's computer to the LM's.

That was not the end of the coordinate system story. There were coordinate systems fixed to the Earth and to the Moon, essential for specifying landmarks and landing sites. Sometimes a new coordinate system was defined just to make the math easier. The guidance equation for the lunar landing was processed in a special frame that was centered on the intended landing site.

What all these frames had in common was that they allowed you to express things like position, velocity, thrust, attitude, rotational rate — always in threes, three numbers yoked together and called a *vector*. Vectors expressed a direction *and* a magnitude. You could add them, subtract them, multiply them in several ways, and you could transform them from one coordinate system to another.

Now space navigation became easier to understand. Multiply the velocity vector by the time since the last update and add the result, component by component, to the position vector. Presto, your new position — that is, if you are in deep space far from any attracting object. Otherwise, first fold into the velocity vector the computed gravitational effects of the nearby bodies, in our case the Earth and the Moon. If an engines is firing or there is atmospheric drag, add in the velocity change measured by your accelerometers. Repeat at appropriate intervals.

Appropriate intervals. A word about that.

In a real-time guidance computer, like the one in the LM, most computations happen over and over again, repeatedly measuring, calculating and tweaking until the goal is reached. It is called "closing the loop." Inside the computer the interval at which a function is repeated varies from function to function. For example, to control the spacecraft's attitude the control system, or autopilot, must run quite rapidly — ten times per second in our case.

What chiefly distinguishes powered flight from coasting flight is the interval at which the navigational computations need to be repeated. If the spacecraft is in orbit, or on the way from Earth to Moon or Moon to Earth, not firing any engine, influenced only by the gravity of nearby bodies, then it is said to be in coasting flight. Guidance is not engaged. Accelerometers need not be read. They would say zero anyway.

Coasting navigation works by integrating the state vector, a mathematical process that operates on a whole segment of the trajectory, extending from the previous update to the present time, or even a future time, in one gulp. This involves a lot of number crunching, but since the interval at which it has to be repeated can stretch to hours or days, there is no point in making the code run fast.

Powered flight navigation is different. Now an engine is thrusting — the very thing we are controlling to reach our objective. Its effects are not as predictable as celestial mechanics, but they can be measured by the accelerometers and factored into the navigation equation. After that the guidance equation must be processed, because the engine needs to be told in what direction to point. The autopilot must reorient the spacecraft as commanded and throttle control must tell the engine how hard to thrust. Information must be displayed to the crew, and their inputs monitored. And the quicker we can close the loop by repeating this whole process the better.

Coasting flight: serene and philosophical, boring. Powered flight: hectic, on the edge, time is everything, milliseconds matter, can of worms. During powered flight all the necessary navigation and guidance functions had to fit and work together within an "appropriate interval" that was chosen long before I came on the scene.

Two seconds.

It was my luck to have drawn the lunar landing, the phase of the mission when the very most had to be packed into those two seconds.

THE BUILDING

The Instrumentation Laboratory occupied a rabble of superannuated industrial buildings in the postindustrial hinterland behind the MIT campus in Cambridge. The headquarters building, formerly a shoe-polish factory, was situated between the understated MIT High Voltage Laboratory and the obligingly grouchy Sterritt Lumber yard (plagued by the petty needs of students and other amateurs). Not far away was Building 20, the ramshackle structure thrown up during World War II where radar was developed, which stood for another 55 years as the prototype of what we now call an "incubator."

This land was fertile in invention even before the MIT campus crossed the river from Boston in 1916. A few blocks away Alexander Graham Bell perfected his telephone (710 Main Street) and Elias Howe developed sewing machines (55 Cherry Street). Later the chemist Edwin Land founded Polaroid and developed instant photography (730 Main Street). In the 1970s the area became known as "artificial intelligence alley." Then came biotech.

The Apollo work centered on a three-story, yellow-brick building of 66,000 square feet in a prime location at 75 Cambridge Parkway, facing the Charles River. You could enter from front or back. Both entrances had security guards to check badges. At the back door you could catch a shuttle bus that circulated among stops at the MIT main campus and the various Instrumentation Lab buildings. Ours was designated IL-7.

At the front entrance a receptionist greeted visitors and operated a whirring machine that could scan a document and transmit it over telephone lines to a similar machine in Houston. There were loud-speakers throughout the building that broadcast pages, "So-and-so please call 1234." That was a pretty good system for getting through to someone if they were in the building. If not, the Lab phone book listed home addresses and telephone numbers.

Each floor had offices on the perimeter with walls that went all the way to the ceiling and windows that opened to the outside. (Only the computer rooms were air conditioned.) The interior was devoted to clean rooms and labs, and to mazes of cubicles with eight-foot partitions and windows, if any, facing corridors. There were single offices and others with as many as six gray metal desks — none of which bore a terminal or computer of any kind, mind you. (I did acquire a beat-up IBM Selectric typewriter that I found abandoned on the third floor.)

On the second floor was a space called the classroom, which was used for large meetings and later for monitoring missions. Next to that was the hybrid laboratory, where digital and analog computers worked together to create an accurate *real-time* simulation that you could fly from Command Module and Lunar Module cockpits located on the third floor directly above. The cockpit mock-ups were made of plywood but they contained real instruments and controllers. I would eventually fly hundreds of lunar landings in our earthbound LM, but for now the hybrid lab was simply the biggest jumble of wires that I had ever seen.

Near the third-floor room with the cockpits was a big electronics lab that was the lair of the computer designers themselves. Another room was filled with drafting tables. The precise machining of gyroscope components took place in another building, but we had our own machine shop manned by machinists. If you had a private project you could sometimes get some simple milling-machine work done for a smile, and you could scrounge the odd resistor or capacitor in one of the labs. On the second floor there was a small "hackers shop" with a drill press, a metal shear, a bending brake and a few hand tools, which was open to anyone including software engineers. That was the first use of the word "hack," in a tech context, that I can recall hearing. I took the term as referring to the sometimes messy process by which perforations of suitable sizes were made in the aluminum boxes, or chassis, that were used for constructing electronic devices.

The back stairwell led up to a small penthouse with a retractable roof that contained a contraption for practicing star sightings. The experimenter sat in a cutaway cockpit equipped with controls and a telescope and sextant. The cockpit could maneuver in azimuth and elevation. Star sightings were vital to the operation of a practical guidance system with its not-quite-perfect gyroscopes. What the apparatus on the roof had to prove was that the combination of optics, mechanical design and pilot abilities was up to the job. I never saw it in operation—the point had already been made—but a picture of a beaming Doc Draper sitting in the pilot's position with the roof open and the skyline of Boston visible on a crystal clear night, was displayed around the Laboratory.

In the main computer room two Honeywell 1800s ground away night and day, tape drives swooshing, line printers chirping, backed up by the steady hum of the fans that kept it all cool. These were our mainframes, although we did not use the word. On these computers MAC programs like Allan Klumpp's SUSANK were compiled and run. AGC programs were assembled by Hugh Blair-Smith's Yul Assembler. Papers were written using a first-generation word processor built by another Hal Laning protégé, Dave Crocker. And simulations ran in several flavors, including *environmental* simulations where the onboard program was embedded in software that modeled the computer, the spacecraft, and the laws of physics within which they operated.

We submitted jobs using *decks* of 80-column $3\frac{1}{4}$ by $7\frac{1}{2}$ inch IBM punch cards. The deck might be half an inch thick, secured with a rubber band, or it might consist of several thousand cards in boxes. (One box held 2000.) Normally the cards were numbered sequentially in the first few columns so that if you scrambled your deck one of the machines near the computer room could put them back in order for you. Another machine would print the symbolic contents of each card along the top edge so you could read what it said. These machines were hulking gray affairs in the rounded style of the IBM Model B typewriter.

The most important of the gray machines were the ones that gave us the ability (in the absence of anything resembling a terminal) to communicate with the computer: the keypunch machines used to place information on the cards in the first place. This was where our hands touched the clay. It was a tool I was already familiar with, from a brief, dead-boring night job — but this time it was not data entry but creative writing.

You sat down at a small desk with a keyboard. The keyboard was coupled with a transport that took a blank card from a hopper on the right, passed it from right to left through a punching mechanism, then through a reader, and then into an output bin. The tiny rectangular chads dropped into a hopper down below. Since each card passed through the reader as the next one was being punched, you could correct a mistake by holding down the duplicate key until you reached the mispunched column. Then when you finished the card and hit "release," your left hand reached out to intercept the faulty card on its way to the output bin and drop it in the waste basket that was always at hand. It became second nature. You could program the tab key and other functions using (naturally) a punched card of the same type, placed on a spindle.

There were banks of keypunch machines near the computer room. The space was very low and some people attached their crib sheets to the ceiling above their head. Later several keypunch machines appeared in a corridor not far from my office. Some of us wrote out our programs fully on paper forms before we sat down. Others programmed as they punched. I usually started with rough notes and wrote very much as I am writing at this moment. Either way it was the clacking and clunking of keypunch machines that provided the aural background for the creation of the computer programs for going to the Moon.

An onboard computer like the AGC controlled a spacecraft in *real time*. Our earthbound computers operated in *batch* mode; you submitted a job and in due course it would be run. We cared a lot about "turnaround" — the interval between submitting a run and having the output in our hands. There was a priority system, but asking nicely also helped. The best way to get good turnaround was to come in at night and on weekends when there was less competition.

Another way for turnaround to be improved was for a ghost to fix your run and resubmit it. There were many ways for a run to go bad. Some problems might take days of investigation but others were frustratingly banal. You submitted a long simulation to be run during the night. Next day, because of an obvious typo in the initialization, you find a few pages wrapped around the deck instead of the pile of printout you expected.

So at night we spent idle moments looking for such cases in other people's output. When we found one we would fix it and resubmit the deck to be run again. Today this would constitute a breach of etiquette, accounting procedures, configuration control and tidy compartmentalization — but today we have so much computing power on our own desktops that it hardly matters. At that time it was a way to advance our common cause, and a permissible way to show off. Occasionally someone overreached but more frequently time was saved. Blair-Smith may have originated this practice and he would sometimes leave a note signed as the Uneeda Debugging Service — a reference to Cape Cod's Uneeda Termite Service.

The computer room itself was off-limits to engineers but the rule was not always enforced, especially at odd hours. At worst you risked a suffocating bear hug from Cosmo Battinelli or Doug Hook — our chief computer operators tending to be barrel-chested types with an autocratic bent. In time I would gain the cachet of being admitted to the computer room almost unconditionally and would become competent at mounting the $10\frac{1}{2}$ inch reels of $\frac{1}{2}$-inch magnetic tape (each providing 40 megabytes of sequential-access memory) on the refrigerator sized tape drives that stood in rows.

CODING AND DEBUGGING

The second descent engine burn was meant to parallel the lunar landing maneuver as much as possible — except that LM-1 would be flying in Earth orbit with no astronauts onboard. Instead of a spot on the

Moon the target would be an arbitrary position (and velocity) somewhere in the sky. Telemetry data and radar tracking from the ground would reveal how accurately we hit it.

The guidance equation was a straightforward vector calculation: obviously a job for the *Interpretive* language. That was a good thing because at this stage I still found *Basic* intimidating — those little instructions seemed to crawl around on the page.

The strength of Interpretive was that it facilitated the sort of three-dimensional arithmetic that is part and parcel of navigation and guidance in space. Interpretive code was compact, but painfully slow. (Each instruction was carried out by a Basic-language subroutine.) Multiplying two scalars took a millisecond. Matrix-vector multiplication, an operation useful for transforming a vector from one coordinate system to another, took almost nine milliseconds.

Interpretive's peculiarity as a computer language was that it used "Polish" notation, a system devised by the mathematician Jan Lukasiewicz in which operators are listed first, followed by a list of operands. As this worked itself out in the AGC, instructions (with the exception of store commands) were encoded two per word of memory, followed in each case by some number of words, usually one or two, that identified the locations that the instructions would operate on. The Polish angle occasioned a certain amount of in-group levity. For example the Basic-language instruction that concluded the internal processing of each Interpretive instruction was

```
TCF  DANZIG
```

Here is a short, made-up example of Interpretive code, in which vector VREF is loaded, transformed from the reference frame to the stable member coordinate system by multiplication with the matrix REFSMMAT, and finally stored in VSM:

```
VLOAD    VXM       Load vector, multiply by matrix
         VREF      Operand for VLOAD operation
         REFSMMAT  Operand for VXM operation
STORE    VSM       Store vector result as VSM
```

I got the guidance equation coded in no time. I had more trouble with the logic that led up to the point where the guidance equation was engaged, which had to be written in Basic. I started the job, but Allan grew dissatisfied with my architecture — or rather my lack of architecture. "Not sufficient thought has been given these computations to be sure they are free from logical and math errors," he wrote in a private memo written on the back of an AGC coding form. I had written what we would now call spaghetti code. Allan went on to lay out in some detail, as though talking to a child, a much cleaner design.

The concept of software elegance is elusive. There are as many ways to write a ten-word computer program as a ten-word sentence. You need a unifying aesthetic that becomes a personal style and that is something that may keep evolving throughout a long career. This was a first lesson in not giving up on a software problem before finding a clean solution.

I began to grasp how by a series of simple steps, assembled into a kind of pyramid, a spacecraft could be guided to the Moon and back. The guidance code I was writing depended on the navigation and control software, which depended on the computer's operating system. It all depended on the ground apparatus for creating and testing the flight software, which depended on the mission planning. And when the time came for a manned lunar landing, the astronauts aboard the spacecraft, for a busy quarter of an hour, would depend on my code.

But programming the guidance computer was not an exact science. Art, intuition, and trial and error all played a part. Like a house of cards properly constructed, the final structure might be, must be, quite stable, but in the process of getting there catastrophe was inevitable. Catastrophe meant crashing the computer, or the guidance system, or the spacecraft. We had to find a way to do the crashes before flight — and to extract all the lessons each had to offer. And not just the crashes. You needed to be alert for the subtle clues too. Some small oddity might be the only sign you would ever see of something more serious below the surface. Look ahead to the flawed main mirror on the Hubble Space Telescope, or the O-ring leakage that brought down the space shuttle *Challenger*, costly problems traceable to a failure to heed clues. Most of all, you needed to be honest with yourself.

To find the bugs we shook the tree. Since we could not prove by deductive reasoning that a program would work in flight, we ran numerous tests, from simple to complex to absurd. Our tools were simulations and simulators—terms not always distinguished but different in connotation. On the third floor, linked to the digital and analog computers in the hybrid lab on the floor below, we had *simulators*. A pilot could fly the LM or the Command Module in real time from a realistic cockpit.

SUNBURST, however, would fly unmanned. Much more useful to us now were *simulations*, programs running in batch mode on our Honeywell 1800s, and later our IBM 360s. There were two levels of simulation. We could run short bits of code in isolation using what we called *bench test*. I could set up a single pass through the guidance equation, starting with known inputs, and compare the results to a SUSANK run.

More complex was the *environmental* simulation, in which a whole segment of a mission could be flown. Linked to an emulation of the onboard computer were complex programs that played the part of the physical spacecraft and its interaction with the environment, modeling all the relevant LM systems as they reacted to commands from the software and then applying the laws of physics to compute and give back to the software the sensor readings that would result. Using this simulation I could run an entire landing.

As an environmental sim ran on the mainframes a line printer chirped out progress reports, including the numbers on the DSKY and any keystrokes that were input by the simulated pilot. Every two seconds of simulated time, which took much longer, it printed a summary of the spacecraft's state—the home truth, computed with high precision, against which the performance of our onboard system could be measured.

The environmental sim was also called the *statement-level* simulation. (So often we had two or three names for the same thing.) For us on the flight software side it was the environmental simulation, because a realistic environment was provided in which our code could operate. For those on the analysis side it was the statement-level simulator because to their familiar MAC programs was added a statement-by-statement emulation of the onboard code. Sometimes we called it the *all-digital* simulation to distinguish it from the hybrid.

Debugging SUSANK had been straightforward. The MAC compiler caught language errors. After that I could catch functional errors by comparing the numbers I was printing out to data from other runs using the old printout. The MAC compiler put you one long step away from the machine language where subtle bugs could lurk, and MAC programs ran as a single string in isolation from all the factors that could beset and befuddle a program that had to jostle in real time with a raggedy cast of more or less simultaneous actors on a crowded stage.

Debugging flight code was another thing entirely. It was an art I began to appreciate late one evening when I asked Dan Lickly to look at a run that had failed, and watched him pore over several pages of tightly packed numbers at the back of the printout. It was a *dump* of the onboard computer's erasable memory at the moment the simulation ended. With only 2048 words of read-write memory, each represented in the dump by five octal digits, it only took a few pages[*].

When it came to debugging, it seemed, the dump was the first place you looked. That did not mean it was simple. The dump might clearly show the effects of the bug, but clues to its cause or origin were always more elusive.

In most cases a simulation continued to progress before it halted. Suppose your code happened to branch to a stored address that had been clobbered (overwritten) by another piece of code and now contained a number. A random branch would occur and the result would

---

[*] Octal numbers are based on 8 instead of 10. The digits 8 and 9 do not occur. You would count 1 2 3 4 5 6 7 10.... We liked octal numbers because one octal digit corresponded exactly to three binary digits and thus five octal digits gave us a way to represent the contents of our 15-bit words that was both compact and readily translateable back to binary. Consider the constant POSMAX, the maximum positive number that a single word could accommodate, all ones except the sign bit. In octal that is 37777. In decimal it is 16383 and you cannot so easily visualize the bit pattern. For the age of digital computers octal (or base-16 hexadecimal) is a more sophisticated choice than the base-10 system inherited from our finger-counting ancestors. The nerd joke about octal and decimal numbers is that Halloween equals Christmas: Oct. 31 = Dec. 25.

be nasty, but not instant. The software might run haywire for a short time before the sim actually came to a halt. You might pore over the dump and find data that seemed anomalous, but which discrepancies were related to the root cause of the problem and which were side effects? The bug might have created its own smokescreen. Almost every serious debugging session had a moment when what you were seeing in the data seemed impossible.

As I watched Lickly that evening I saw that his method was to trace the steps of the segment of code where the problem was thought to be. The footprints were signs in the data that the code had done what it was supposed to. Where the trail faded was where the error occurred. Instead of looking at what was wrong in the dump he engaged the problem from the other direction, by looking for what was right.

You hoped to debug the program using information from the original run, then use the second run to confirm the diagnosis or test a fix. Sometimes you had to make a third run with new diagnostic tools activated, or perhaps a fourth or a fifth, before you could even develop a hypothesis. Sometimes you woke up in the morning with the answer in your head.

The dump was not our only tool. The environmental simulation let you attach *clocks* to any point in the code, such that when the statement was executed a line of printout appeared. There were points that were routinely clocked, such as the accelerometer reading that kicked off each new pass through navigation and guidance during powered flight. If you had to make a second run you could add new clocks to provide a more detailed picture of the path through the software. You could also turn on a feature called *trace* that printed out every instruction executed by the computer — but that sounds more useful than it was. You needed to pin down the time of the error to a very small interval because even in a machine as slow as the AGC, one second of operation created almost a thousand pages of trace. You could dump additional raw data onto tapes during the simulation. These were the "raw output tapes" that were called MARSROTS — the name a relic from the pre-Apollo period when the Lab was busy designing an unmanned mission to Mars. These tapes could be edited and turned into a printout containing additional data from the run, formatted as you wished to see it. MARSROT data could also be plotted using a pen plotter.

The builders of our simulations must occasionally have resented us who had the more glamorous job of writing flight code. The team that built the environmental simulation was first led by Bill Widnall, then Keith Glick, then Lance Drane. No matter how much they gave us we wanted more. Drane still remembers (although I do not) the day I "stormed" into his office to complain about the plot program's inability to rescale automatically, oblivious to the effort it had taken to provide the capability we did have.

THE GUIDANCE COMPUTER

First, nomenclature. Generically, it was the Apollo Guidance Computer or AGC. The ones in the LM and the Command Module were identical, except for the software, but usually we called ours the LGC — LM Guidance Computer.

As an object, the AGC was a strong-looking, sealed, gold-colored magnesium box measuring two feet by one foot by six inches, weighing 70 pounds and consuming 55 watts. It was mounted on the bulkhead at the back of the LM cabin. Early in the program North American Aviation, who would manufacture the Command Module, wanted to know how big the computer would be. No one had any idea yet. "Well, just tell them it's a cubic foot," said Dick Battin.

As an electronic component, the AGC was a single-string machine vital to the mission. It had to be fast enough, and have enough memory, but first it had to be reliable. The goal was 100,000 hours without a failure.

Reliability would be assured by careful fabrication and testing. Yet, in one of those paradoxes by which technology leaps forward, the only way to meet the goals for speed, weight, and power consumption, not to speak of Battin's one cubic foot, was to use a type of component whose reliability at that time was anything but established:

the integrated circuit. Eldon Hall, the AGC's principal designer, has written a riveting account of the decision to use ICs. Hall quotes the following doggerel by a hardware designer named Jayne Partridge:

The transistor's a marvelous invention
Replaced the tube convention
Found its niche
To amplify or switch
Whatever the designer's intention.

But the breakthrough was the IC
Integrated monolithically
It became pivotal
As computers went digital
With increasing complexity.

Inside the computer's case modules about ten inches long, but variable in other dimensions, were packed like cordwood. Inside the modules were 2800 integrated circuits of identical type. Each "chip" contained two logical devices called *triple input NOR* (not or) gates. Such a gate, if any of its three input is a one, outputs a zero, otherwise a one—the two values indicated by voltage levels. In high school, after learning about truth tables, James Chambers and I had experimented with similar devices composed of relays mounted on a piece of plywood. What we would not have believed was that a whole computer could be built up from such simple components.

No one knew whether chips were going to catch on and there was a concern about procurement risk. Not only the computer but most of the ground support equipment was designed using the same logical type precisely to create enough demand that the manufacturer would not lose interest in making it. Program Manager Ralph Ragan estimated in a 1966 interview that "Building four or five prototypes consumed 60 percent of the country's production of integrated circuits."

Conversely, the supplier, aided by Hall's team, could concentrate on perfecting the manufacture of a single type. Every failure was documented and analyzed. New ways of testing were devised. Leaks were detected by weighing chips before and after bathing them in Freon, with enough precision to detect any contaminant that had found its way inside. Ten years before, MIT's Whirlwind had gone through much the same process to perfect the vacuum tube. It was a milestone in computer history when in 1952 Whirlwind achieved seven consecutive hours of error-free operation. Now, in one cubic foot instead of a two-story building, we aimed at no errors at all.

Chips caught on after all. Today thousands of Apollo Guidance Computers could be implemented on a single integrated circuit.

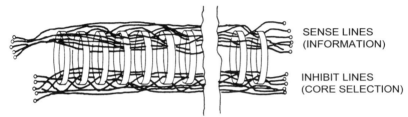

SENSE LINES
(INFORMATION)

INHIBIT LINES
(CORE SELECTION)

Core-rope memory. The ferrous cores act as transformers such that a current is induced in a sense line that passes through an energized core. Inhibit lines determine which core is activated. Sense lines that bypass the activated core are read as zeroes, those that go through are read as ones. The memory address determines which core is energized and which sense lines are read.

In the AGC's read-write *erasable* memory (RAM in modern terms) information was stored in magnetic doughnuts called *cores* that could be energized in either of two states corresponding to one and zero. For the AGC's read-only *fixed* memory (ROM) a very conservative direction was taken: a primitive but durable form of memory called *core rope*. In this case the ferrous cores acted as transformers such that a current was induced in any *sense line* that passed through an energized core. Information was encoded by weaving the sense lines either through or around the cores. To look at, core rope memory was a tangle of thin copper wires. That is why a program that was released for manufacture was called a rope, as in "the Apollo 11 rope" — revision 99 of LUMINARY.

Ropes were manufactured at Raytheon's plant in Waltham, where technicians, using a special loom, laboriously threaded the copper wires either through or around the cores, guided by a mylar tape produced by the Yul Assembler and testing as they went along. The technicians were ladies of a certain age who came to be regarded almost as royalty. It took about six weeks. The end result, for each mission, was six modules, each about the size and shape of a ten-inch plank of one-by-five (teak for the weight) with a 96-pin connector at one end, which were slid into slots in the computer itself.

For the logic designers, the AGC was a computer defined by two almost irreconcilable numbers: a word length of fifteen usable bits, and a total memory, for the SUNBURST version that flew on LM-1, of 34K words. Of that total, 2K was the read-write memory we called *erasable*, and the remaining 32K, which contained the programs we were writing, was read-only *fixed* memory[*]. (Later, 4K words of fixed memory were added, bringing the total to 38K.)

Their problem was how to encode, within fifteen bits, both an operation, and the address to which the operation applied. The operations were actions like add, subtract, multiply, divide, jump, branch, and so on, that were needed to write meaningful software. The more such operations the language could provide, the easier the computer would be to program.

Suppose that three of the fifteen bits were allocated to the operation code. That would be enough to encode eight different operations. If the remaining twelve bits were allocated to the address, that would be enough to address 4K words of memory. Yet the designers provided, for us who would wrote the code, a rich instruction set of over thirty machine-language operations having access to 34K (and later 38K) words of memory. The dodges by which they did it are an object lesson in draining the cup of ingenuity. For an inexperienced software engineer it presented a perilous learning curve as complications were wrapped in solutions, and vice versa, until one hardly knew which was which.

---

[*] AGC memory sizes, here and elsewhere, are given in terms of *words*, each consisting of fifteen usable bits plus one additional bit (called the *parity* bit) used for error checking. The letter K here denotes a unit of 1024 words. The version of the AGC that flew the lunar landing missions had an additional 4K words (four banks) of fixed memory, for a total of 38K. That equals 76 kilobytes, but we did not use the word *byte* in connection with the AGC.

The designers first made a virtue of the necessity that memory be packaged in *banks*. There were eight banks of erasable memory at 256 words each and 32 banks of fixed memory at 1024 words each. They developed an architecture in which some memory banks were always "visible" (making them especially precious) but others had to be switched into place by setting additional bits located in a separate register. Switching between banks added complication (minimized by how memory was allocated) but twelve bits were now enough to address any memory location. And, in another coup, since only ten bits were enough to address any location in erasable memory, two additional bits became available for encoding operations such as TS (transfer to storage) or XCH (exchange) that by definition could only operate on read-write memory. By these means the instruction set was roughly doubled.

And it was doubled again when the designers created a second class of instruction that had to be immediately preceded by a special instruction named EXTEND, which set an internal bit to be added to the operation code of the following instruction. This made the code bulkier, but it would have been bulkier still without the additional operations. The intriguing part was that it was possible to change the operation of a future instruction by skipping over the EXTEND state-ment—a trick I would one day find occasion to use.

As something to be interacted with, the AGC was present throughout the cockpit. Numerous buttons and switches were wired to the com-puter: mode switches for the control system, the throttle, the ren-dezvous and landing radars, the abort buttons, the ROD switch for controlling rate of descent during the final phase of the landing, and so on. Each crew position had two joysticks: a *translational* hand con-troller (THC) that doubled as a manual throttle, and a *rotational* hand controller (RHC) used for maneuvering and also for "redesignating" the landing site during the visibility phase. The computer received inputs from both sticks and knew how to interpret them by the posi-tions of the mode switches.

In the other direction, the computer gave information back to the crew by means of several ingenious mechanical indicators: an *eight-ball* (properly the FDAI) to display attitude information, tape meters for altitude and altitude rate, and an instrument called the *cross-pointers* that we used to indicate the spacecraft's horizontal velocity during the final stage of the lunar landing.

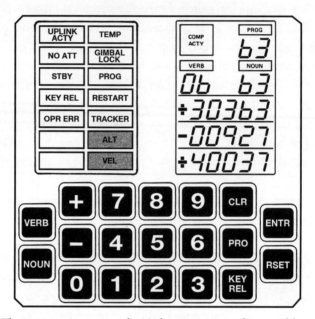

The DSKY as it was seen by Neil Armstrong and Buzz Aldrin on Apollo 11 at MET 102:37:26. The LM is at an altitude of 40037 feet and is losing altitude at the rate of 92.7 feet per second. The ALT and VEL lights are lit, indicating that the landing radar has not yet locked on to the surface.

But there was another place where human interaction with the computer went beyond digital imitations of analog controls and instruments—where the interaction took the form of a grammatical conversation. That was the computer's display and keyboard unit, the DSKY. Physically the DSKY (rhymes with "whiskey") was an eight-by-eight inch panel located between the two astronauts. It had 19 keys, a numeric display with a total of 21 digits, and a bank of 14 indicator lamps. Some of the indicators were specific to the LM, such as the ALT and VEL lights used to signal landing radar lock-on, and some were in both spacecraft, such as the light marked PROG that would light up to signal a program alarm. The keys were large squarish things designed to be operable with a gloved hand. The DSKY's in the simulators usually had worn keys so you could barely read the labels.

The numeric display is where it gets interesting. At the top were two digits that indicated the current program mode. At the bottom in three rows were three five-digit registers, each with a plus-or-minus sign, which were our only general-purpose way to deliver information.

Between the program number above and the three registers below were indicators, two digits each, labeled VERB and NOUN. Similarly, the keyboard had VERB and NOUN keys.

The *verb* and *noun* were our language for two-way communication between man and computer. The idea came from Ramón Alonso. It may be cute but it worked quite well. The set of functions we called Pinball handled the mechanics, responding to astronaut inputs on one hand, and providing the software with the ability to talk back on the other.

Verbs were actions, and nouns designated specific collections of data to be displayed in the three general purpose registers. To view the codes for any pending alarms, for example, the astronaut—normally it was the LM pilot who operated the DSKY—would key in

VERB 5 NOUN 9 ENTER

where Verb 5 meant "display octal" and Noun 9 meant "alarm codes." Other verbs did not require nouns. To initiate the landing sequence the LMP would key in

VERB 37 ENTER 63 ENTER

where Verb 37 meant "change program" and P63 was the program being selected. In response, Pinball would schedule a job named P63LM, the program mode display would change to 63, and after a moment of computation the software would respond by posting Verb 6 Noun 61 on the DSKY, where Verb 6 meant "display decimal" and Noun 61 included a countdown to descent engine ignition—the first of a series of communications initiated by the software as the landing progressed. A display needing a response, such as a request to authorize an automatic attitude maneuver or an engine firing by keying PROCEED, would be flashed on and off.

69

If the crew needed to see information not included in the default display they could use Verb 16, which meant "monitor." Other verbs enabled the crew to reach deep into the computer to change any bit of any word. That was rarely done in flight, especially during an engine firing, but it would get Apollo 14 out of a tight spot.

For the mission planners, the guidance computer was a device capable of performing various functions that could be summoned up using the DSKY, ranging from small tasks like displaying information, to large functions such as the programs that conducted the lunar landing. The lunar goal of the mission forced a certain progression in the calling up of major modes, but there was considerable flexibility in what the LM's (or the CM's) computer could be asked to do in an off-nominal or (worse still) contingency situation or (worse still) contingency situation for which there was no advanced planning.

For the two astronauts in the cockpit, the computer was almost a colleague, doing the things it could do best—flying an economical trajectory, controlling attitude, computing the sequence of maneuvers that led to a rendezvous, providing information to the crew and mission control—while they did the things the human could do best, such as looking out the window and choosing a landing site. It was not something that happened without training but with enough rehearsal the team was harmonious. Flying the LM in the simulator at Cape Canaveral, John Young would giggle through the lunar landing about how "smart" the computer was—while asking for more, of course, another story for later.

From its own point of view, as we were the best qualified to say, the LM guidance computer was the almost-conscious center of an electronic web.

Information came in from keyboard and switches, from which to know the crew's intentions; and from sensors, to be chewed and filtered and folded into that plane of information, jittering forward through time, that was the spacecraft's self-knowledge. To that knowledge, method was applied and the information that resulted went out to displays, to radars, to the ground by radio; and it was acted upon, with commands to engines and maneuvering jets. Between the ins and the outs was SUNBURST—and one day LUMINARY—that big block of green-bar paper come alive.

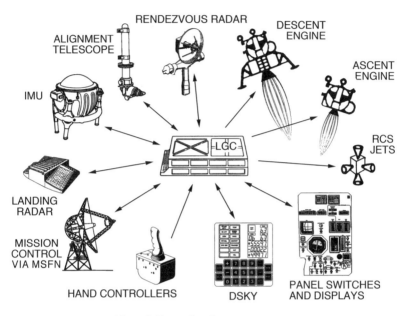

The LGC's circle of connections.

That was where we came in—we who wrote the flight code. The program was a piano roll punched with music we composed, with its characteristic rhythms and polyphonies, but with a melodic line that might sometimes surprise us as the internal logic, based on the immediate situation, selected among the alternate pathways that we made possible. Our computer was a player piano that could improvise. When it flew, our experience would be that of a composer attending the performance of a work he created, not listening like a member of the audience but living the music internally.

Our life in the LGC was less authentic than that of the neurosurgeon's patient, who experiences his brain from the inside, but it was more intimate than the experience of the surgeon. Using language and logic we lay down pathways for the computer's inanimate thoughts and in simulations we literally traced those "thoughts." We did not so much humanize the LGC as assume it as an identity. We thought in code when we were awake and sometimes we dreamed in code asleep.

THROTTLE CONTROL

Next Allan Klumpp asked me to program the throttle control function that was the link between the guidance equation and the LM's descent engine.

The descent engine, the DPS, was a very unusual rocket. Its unprecedented feature—achieved by varying the cross-section of the injectors that spewed fuel and oxidizer into the combustion chamber—was that it could be throttled through a range of thrusts.

You had to have variable thrust to land on the Moon. A missile only needed to pass through a given spot and then explode. The LM had to blast down from lunar orbit and then act like a helicopter. It had to be right side up and moving slowly when it got near the surface, and it needed the ability to hover under the control of a pilot. Rockets that come down are very different than rockets that go up.

The guidance equation, every two seconds, produced a "desired" acceleration vector. If the desired acceleration could be provided, the LM would find its way to the Moon. The direction of the vector, as translated by a routine called FINDCDUW written by Allan, told the autopilot how to orient the LM. The magnitude (or length) of the vector told the engine how hard to thrust.

The job of throttle control was to compare the acceleration required by guidance to the present acceleration as measured by the accelerometers, multiply the difference by the mass of the vehicle to get a thrust change, convert that to up or down pulses, and send them out to the throttle electronics.

That was my assignment and at first it sounded simple. "Not so fast," warned Allan—because in the last paragraph there were two traps: "as measured by the accelerometers," and "mass."

The readings that came from our exquisite accelerometers did not actually measure acceleration, it seemed; they measured the net velocity change since the previous reading two seconds before. That was not the same thing, especially when, part way through that two second period, the actual acceleration was changed by the previous throttle command. Furthermore, the previous throttle command was not instantaneous. It took time for the throttle pulses to be sent out, and it took time for the engine to respond to the pulses. These were effects that had to be accounted for. Allan led me through the physics. I was annoyed by the clutter of compensation terms that resulted, but with the aid of plots produced by the environmental simulation I got it working.

As for mass, I looked around to see where that was being calculated — and found to my surprise that it was not. The LM's mass at the start of the mission was known, but that was only a starting point because the spacecraft steadily became lighter as it burned fuel. Suddenly I was not just building a throttle controller, I was building a mass estimator.

You could estimate loss of mass if you knew a measure of the engine's efficiency called *specific impulse*, ISP for short. It was expressed in seconds. Think of it as how long the engine can make a unit of fuel last while delivering a given thrust, the longer the better. A longer ISP is achieved by expelling the same amount of gas at a faster velocity. The DPS had an ISP of around 300 seconds — compared to 450 for the extraordinary hydrogen-oxygen main engines of the Space Shuttle — but it varied depending on thrust. I programmed a table where the mass estimator could look up the ISP for the current throttle level.

It was a good exercise in Basic-language programming but Allan may have pointed me to this approach to teach me a lesson about gilding the lily. By the time I coded the corresponding routine for the lunar landing missions I knew that a much simpler mass estimator, without the ISP table, would suffice. The compensation terms remained. Unknown to us, they harbored a near-fatal flaw.

The only "secret" document I saw during the Apollo program was one that showed the curve of specific impulse versus thrust level for the LM's descent engine. I placed this and my other information on the engine in a binder I labeled "Indecent Engine Book," and, per regulation, locked that in my otherwise empty file cabinet using the combination padlock I was issued when I started work.

The stock room had paper with a broad red border and the word **SECRET** at the top and bottom. For a while I enjoyed writing personal letters on that stationary.

I had quickly become comfortable with the Interpretive language that I had used for the guidance equation, but throttle control and the mass estimator were jobs for Basic. Basic took longer to master but the reward was greater.

The thing about Basic was that it operated in very small steps. In some computer languages, to compute a sum, you could write

```
X = Y + Z
```

In Basic that would require three sequential steps:

```
CA      Y       Load number at address Y into accumulator
AD      Z       Add number at Z forming sum in accumulator
TS      X       Transfer result to storage at address X
```

And to code the equivalent of

```
IF P = Q THEN GOTO TAG
```

Would take four steps:

```
CA      P       Load number at address P into accumulator
SU      Q       Subtract number at Q, result in accumulator
EXTEND
BZF     TAG     Branch to TAG if accumulator is zero
```

As you see, the special register called the accumulator, at address zero, was the hot center of the AGC's operation.

This was bewildering at first but confusion is a stage of learning. The saving grace was that the ultimate authorities were readily available. The lair of the hardware designers was somewhere upstairs, but Hugh Blair-Smith, creator of the Yul Assembler and author of the AGC programmer's bible, Memo #9, was highly accessible.

Blair-Smith combined a smart person's hauteur with an unfailing willingness to oblige. He was patient with the bumpkin I must have seemed in those days, equally ready to teach or gab. One night in his office, over pizza, I wondered aloud whether computers might, as they became more complex and interconnected, spontaneously acquire personality and a will of their own, just as we presume organisms acquired a consciousness at some point in the evolution of the physical brain. I had been thinking about the snarl of wires in the cable trays overhead, connecting lab spaces where the wires came and went from mysterious boxes and sometimes seemed to bubble out of bursting seams. Blair-Smith sneered at the question. Computers had not even begun to approach the level of complexity where that could be considered.

In truth we were far closer to the breadboard of relays that I built with James Chambers in high school than to the turbulent and unprincipled flow of information that characterizes our brave millennial world, so smart and so stupid at the same time.

As we entered 1967 the goal of landing a man on the Moon in 1969 seemed very distant, but also uncomfortably close for the amount of figuring-out and coding and testing that remained. From my position the contours of the path ahead were not visible. It was hard to know what pace was needed but Allan Klumpp and I worked long days and measured ourselves against the other parts of the mission. We seemed to be ahead of Larry Berman who was programming the ascent and abort phases. There were two of us but our task was much larger.

FIRE ON THE PAD

John McCarthy had said that at the Lab making it work was the only thing that mattered. Management's job was to stay out of the way. It was our tradition. It was years beyond this book before I ever saw an organization chart at the Laboratory. "They hid them," Norm Sears said.

Sears had been present at a meeting with high ranking military officers about a system Doc Draper proposed to build for them. One of them asked Doc how the effort would be organized. Impromptu, he drew a neat organizational chart on the blackboard. When the meeting was over and the brass hats had gone away he picked up an eraser and started erasing. Someone protested, "No, don't erase that!" But Doc kept on, saying "Never mind, you'll figure it out."

I never figured it out. I was hired by George Cherry, but I worked with Allan Klumpp who had a sort of sibling rivalry with Cherry. But Jim Miller was the one to consult, if I thought I needed to, when I wanted to put some new code into the SUNBURST assembly.

Miller was a tall, courtly man with a Ph.D. in computer science at a time when there were not many of those. He admitted to keeping a listing of SUNBURST under his bed as a sleep aid, "But sometimes, boy, I see something that wakes me up." It was Dan Lickly who would occasionally stop by my office to ask when some piece of code might be ready. Lickly was often to be found in Miller's office, slouched in a chair in the narrow space between a table and the wall. I picture them head to head, bent over a listing.

We responded to requests, not orders. I knew who I was working with, but not exactly who my official boss was. We focused on the goal and our bosses, whoever they were, gave us the freedom to do so creatively. I would never have been able to reconstruct an organization chart from my own experience. Much later I figured out that I "reported" through three different chains of command, all of which, however, led to Dick Battin and his deputy Norm Sears.

Certainly no one was monitoring our hours. Often I gave myself Friday afternoon off and queued up to buy rush seats for the Boston Symphony Orchestra, then led by Erich Leinsdorf.

Symphony Hall had been a refuge during my college years, when the saving grace of many a lonesome week was the BSO on a Thursday or Friday, or a Sunday afternoon recital by a soloist whose records I had grown up with. Now I had a creative job on an immense, important, imagination-catching project. In that domain I felt smart again — but in matters of the heart I was, as ever, naive, hesitant, bemused, becalmed.

For me the Apollo years were an era of exploration in a every sense, and the way to the Moon seemed no more unsolvable than the mysteries of love. I was lucky to be in time for the Apollo project, and I was lucky again to live at a time of cultural experimentation, of the casting off of the conventions I had grown up with — a time when Eros was celebrated and women were becoming more free to express and act on their own pent up appetite for experience, which ran parallel to mine.

The first of the happy relationships that enriched the main years of this story emerged almost as if from a reverie, as I sat on the left side of the sparsely occupied second balcony at Symphony Hall on a Friday afternoon, absorbed in the music and in some thought or daydream—awaking to the quiet figure sitting alone opposite me, across the width of the hall, her long honey-colored hair over one shoulder, her long, tanned legs extending from a short, loose dress. She was there again the next time (her cello teacher, a member of the orchestra, got her in). The third time, I maneuvered to cross her path and she probably wondered what took me so long.

Her name was Sally. On our first date, on a very cold night, she wore her mother's leopard coat on the back of the Yamaha. In the spring we played tennis late at night in the tennis shed at the Country Club in Brookline—once during a violent thunderstorm. In June the Beatles' *Sergeant Pepper's Lonely Hearts Club Band* came out and we listened to it for the first time, with two of her girlfriends, in a house on Brattle Street. Afterwards we all climbed a tree in a cemetery in Harvard Square and spent an hour watching the human parade on a nearby sidewalk. We went to bed but only played at making love, our inexperience a piquant impasse.

The Boston tradition of shifting apartments in September, sometimes every September, is a convenience for the rememberer, who can arrange events in time according to the real estate they are associated with. With 148 Marlborough Street, first floor front, I associate Sally, and cashew nuts—from the nights I spent by the fireplace, provisioned by S.S. Pierce, reading eclectically—*John Aubrey and His Friends*, *The Secret Agent*, *The Confessions of Felix Krull*, *The Awkward Age*, *The Proud Tower*—or juggling computer code in my head as I looked for a neat solution for a problem, or a problem to match a neat solution— firelight flickering on the high walls.

On January 27, 1967, fire broke out in the Command Module during a simulation on the launch pad at Cape Canaveral and killed the astronauts Virgil Grissom, Roger Chaffee, and Edward White.

We knew, intellectually, that we were dealing in men's lives—and doing so very publicly. We joked blackly that a bad line of code could land us in the hot seat of a Congressional committee—but the fire brought it home. It was much harder for the older guys who knew the dead men personally. They had visited Cambridge to use our hybrid simulator before the more elaborate rigs in Houston and Cape Canaveral came on line.

Malcolm Johnston, later our liaison with the astronauts and operational planners in Houston, had a drink with Gus Grissom, who was sitting alone in a bar in Cocoa Beach and seemed to want company, just before the fire. Grissom "unloaded" at length on the condition of the spacecraft, saying, "What we have here is a Heathkit."

After the fire, no one at MIT would have believed that Kennedy's goal could be met. In fact, as has often been told, by prompting a rigorous and intellectually honest review of the spacecraft and their systems—and by reminding us what we were doing—it was probably this sacrifice that made achieving the goal possible.

WHAT IF WE LOST POWER?

The futility in Vietnam continued to drain resources and lives and optimism. When the astronauts Neil Armstrong and Dick Gordon had toured Latin America in October 1966 they were met with enthusiasm about the space program, but also by anti-war chants.

Early on April 15, 1967 I drove with Allan Klumpp and several others to New York to join a peace march called the Mobilization to End the War. We gathered in Central Park and marched toward United Nations plaza under waving banners, carried along by the surge of the crowd. At the UN Martin Luther King and Benjamin Spock spoke—not that we saw or even really heard them, but we helped swell the crowd to a reported half million.

We drove wearily back to Boston, punster Bernie Goodman mining a piscatorial seam ("I thought there was something wrong with my tuna, but it was my herring"), and on my shoulder, sound asleep, the head of a girl we had met in the crowd, who needed a ride back to Boston.

—

What does your computer do when the lights flicker? Shuts down. The briefest interruption is enough. What about our guidance computer, bouncing around in its flivver of a LM? A power transient during the landing was not the unlikeliest event you could imagine. Yet, if your guidance computer shut down during a lunar descent it could spoil your whole day. As usual, we had to fix it in the software.

This should be a footnote, just another wrinkle that cropped up while I was working on SUNBURST — but it comes up again later. It took me by surprise. Were we really expected to write the software in such a way that the computer could pick up seamlessly after a power outage? Charley Muntz had reacted the same way on a Friday during the summer of 1963 when

> One of the senior hardware designers came into the software area and announced that "We have to face the fact that the power will probably fail sometime between here and the Moon. The computer should recover from such a failure and resume its steering and display tasks."

Muntz's first job at the Instrumentation Laboratory was as a janitor — he was a math major at MIT and it was a summer job. Trundling from office to office emptying waste baskets gave him a taste for the sort of projects Doc Draper's lab was tackling and the Lab, for its part, was glad to hire him as a software engineer as soon as he graduated.

Meanwhile Hal Laning had withdrawn, guru-like, from direct responsibility for the Apollo flight software. In the early days of the Apollo contract no one had worried about the software. "Hal will take care of it," was the refrain. But Laning did not care for large projects and hated meetings. Now Muntz was charged with turning his legacy of ideas and prototype code into flight software.

For Muntz, the requirement to recover from a power transient marked the end of his apprenticeship. He had already coded the first version of the onboard software that implemented the Interpretive language, but this new problem was different. Hal Laning had not already solved it. Muntz was on his own. "I found myself confronting the bull in the ring," Muntz remembers. Olé.

What he came up with was called *restart protection*. For each vital string of computation a waypoint, called a restart point, would be kept track of. If the power fluctuated, the saved information would be used to reconstruct each of the protected computations, starting at its most recent restart point. (Our erasable memory was of a type that could survive the loss of power without losing information.)

The person doing the coding had to set the restart points. The key was to avoid computations that would produce an erroneous result if you jumped back to the previous restart point and looped through the computation a second time. If the computation of a variable was in some way based on the previous value of the same variable, you would have to code something like

```
NEWX = X + Y
set restart point
X = NEWX
```

Restart protection was easy enough once you got the hang of it. There remained a few places that seemed impossible to protect from a restart, such as the instant, every two seconds during powered flight, when we read and then zeroed the accelerometers. The unavoidable chinks lasted only a few microseconds so the odds were greatly in our favor — but it was a game of chance.

In the hybrid lab, on the front of the equipment rack that contained the guidance computer, was a button that would trigger a restart. Sometimes we pushed it just for kicks. The LM always stayed on course.

A power transient was not the only condition that could bring the restart logic into play. For example, if one of those hair-thin wires in our woven core-rope memory happened to break, a *parity failure* might occur. Each of our fifteen-bit words of memory actually had an additional, sixteenth bit, called the *parity* bit, which the assembler set to a one or a zero to force the total number of ones among the 16 bits to be odd. When the computer accessed a word of memory it counted the bits that were set to one and if the result was *not* an odd number it would trigger a restart. Another mechanism called TC Trap could detect a one-instruction endless loop. Night Watchman monitored a special location that the software had to access at frequent intervals. There were several other checks performed in hardware. In each case, if trouble was detected, a restart was triggered.

But to the taxonomy of restarts Charley Muntz was about to add a new family, the *software restart*.

Laning had created prototype versions of the functions called *Executive* and *Waitlist* that provided the AGC's operating system. Together they gave us the tools to build a flexible, robust system that got the most out of our rather meager computational resources. It was up to the prolific Muntz to turn Laning's prototypes into flight code.

Waitlist let us schedule short bits of software called *tasks* that had to occur exactly at a given time. Executive was for scheduling larger blocks of software, called *jobs*, that were executed in an order determined by the priority we assigned them. Executive and Waitlist worked together. Typically a task would be scheduled to make a measurement at a specific time, such as reading the accelerometers, and then the task itself would schedule a job to do further processing based on the measurement.

Waitlist tasks—limited by fiat to five milliseconds—always executed to completion. Jobs could be of any size, and could be interrupted at any time by another, higher-priority job. If that happened certain information had to be preserved for when it picked up again. Laning had laid out blocks of erasable memory where the information could be saved. The blocks were of two sizes. Every job needed a *core set* of 12 words. Jobs that used the Interpreter needed an additional *vector accumulator* (VAC) area of 44 words. In the version of LUMINARY that went to the Moon there were enough core sets for eight jobs to be scheduled at one time, and enough VAC areas for five of them.

But what if a new job was requested when all the spaces were occupied? Here was a loose end for Muntz to deal with. In fact it was an explicit challenge, laid down by Laning in a comment imbedded in the prototype code:

WHAT TO DO WHEN THERE'S NO ROOM FOR A NEW JOB? (APPROXIMATELY)

What indeed? Take up again the matador's sword and cape! Muntz might have said, if the software is properly coded and tested there will never be that many jobs competing for memory. Instead he asked, what if there were?

"Assume everything is screwed up," opined his office mate.

"Just like when there's a restart," thought Muntz.

With that, he realized that the appropriate response to an overload of the Executive queues was already at hand, in the procedure he had created to recover from a power outage or an endless loop — only now the software would undergo the procedure electively. Again the solution for one problem found a more general application.

How would the code initiate a software restart? Why, by intentionally misbehaving. I might have said, by phoning in a bomb scare, except that the immortal line of code that Muntz programmed, and the comment he added, borrowed from T.S. Eliot, was

```
WHIMPER    TC    WHIMPER        NOT WITH A BANG...
```

The instruction at tag **WHIMPER** transferred control to the instruction at tag **WHIMPER**, whereupon **TC** Trap would detect the endless loop and trigger the restart.

There was an extra payoff in provoking a restart when the Executive storage areas were overloaded. It might cure the problem by shedding load. If a computation was vital to keeping the **LM** on course, we would restart-protect it. Non-vital functions were not protected. These would be swept away by the restart and the burden on the Executive would be eased.

The restart software continued to evolve. In the version that went to the Moon the tag **WHIMPER** was retained, for sentimental reasons, but it no longer referenced itself and the comment was expunged. Software restarts were handled entirely by software without resort to triggering the hardware mechanism.

In the **LM** there were ten conditions in all that caused software restarts, each with its own alarm code. We called these **BAILOUT** alarms, after the tag in the alarm and aborts section to which control was transferred to begin the process. If the Executive found that **VAC** areas were all used up, it called **BAILOUT** with alarm code 1201; if no Core Sets were available, the alarm code was 1202.

Ed Copps, in an August 1968 paper, estimated that about 4 percent of the AGC's fixed memory was devoted to restart protection, not counting the 6 percent, one bit in every 16, that was devoted to parity checking. Considerable extra testing was entailed. Was it worth it?

> In a total of over 25 hours of space flight, the computer has yet to have a transient failure from which the restart feature could be called on to demonstrate its worth. This could well be the experience for the whole Apollo program. We have seen that the provision for restart in the computer program complicates the generation and test of the program. We have seen that there is a significant class of transient failure events which restart will probably fail to cure. And yet only one successful recovery by restart might save a mission.

Ed Copps wrote that about one year before the LM's computer experienced, and withstood, five software-initiated restarts during the most critical phase of the Apollo 11 mission.

THE HYBRID

One summer during college I had taken a part-time job as guide at an 1860 Victorian row house on Beacon Street called the Gibson House that was open as a museum. The house had made few concessions to Twentieth Century frippery, other than electric lighting, but was chock full of Nineteenth Century frippery. Visitors were sparse. I spent my time reading in the comfortable window seat facing Beacon Street or sipping tea in the formal dining room with the Scottish lady who came by to dust.

My most interesting visitors were two attractive sisters who stayed for hours, fascinated by the dense collection of knickknacks, the chandeliers and sconces, glass-fronted cabinets full of books, Chinese and Persian rugs, wallpapers French and Japanese, sculptural objects in bronze and porcelain, fans, jewelry, fine china...

Marjorie Shepatin and I were never lovers, but we became (and have remained) very close friends, and now the apartment on Commonwealth Avenue, where she and her sister Paula presided over a stream of visitors that almost amounted to a salon, became the hub of my social life.

Marjorie had a friend who lived in a tiny apartment in a tiny house on Beacon Hill, and that is where I smoked marijuana for the first time. Nothing happened, but I tried it again and soon came to regard it as one of nature's amenities. Back at the sisters' apartment it was like a ritual when the pipe came out and the pungent aroma of cannabis mingled with that of cat litter.

That a government could outlaw a simple thing of nature, given to all of us equally, outraged my sense of the natural rights of man.

At home alone in the quiet of the night I would smoke and listen to the Goldberg Variations, or the string quartets of Beethoven—but under Marjorie's influence my musical tastes were expanding. One Friday night she took me to the rock-and-roll club called the Boston Tea Party. As we ascended the stairs from Berkeley Street the music seemed to envelope us like a liquid through which we floated upward, and in the auditorium, a broad, high room with lively acoustics, fantastic shapes were conjured up by light passed through tinted fluids. The band that night was the Velvet Underground.

SUNBURST Revision 120 was released for manufacture in December 1967, just in time to be transformed into core-rope memory and loaded aboard the unmanned lunar module that flew in January on the mission we called LM-1 — later designated Apollo 5.

Months before that, a new program named SUNDANCE was created as a version of SUNBURST. The testing of SUNBURST continued, but the development of the new software needed for manned operation could proceed on SUNDANCE. The program that would go to the Moon would be spun off from SUNDANCE a few months later. That was LUMINARY.

In the interim Allan Klumpp and I used SUNDANCE as a test bed to press on with our work on the lunar landing. I quickly coded up the actual lunar-landing guidance equation and added the LPD (landing point designator) capability, the feature that told the astronaut where guidance was taking him and allowed him to move that point. SUNDANCE would fly only once, on the Earth-orbital Apollo 9 mission in March 1969, commanded by Jim McDivitt. Our lunar landing software was in the computer but access to it was disabled.

Now that we were coding for the Moon one thing that had to change was *scaling*. The AGC was a fixed point machine. That meant the decimal point was fixed—or rather the binary point. We had to be careful to scale our numbers so that there was room for the maximum value that could be anticipated, allowing for extreme cases, while sacrificing no more precision than necessary at the other end. Of course we had to understand how the scaling carried through any computations we had to perform.

The numbers in question were things like position, velocity, acceleration, force, mass. Most of them were in double-precision, that is, they were made up of two fifteen-bit words, each with a sign bit, providing 28 bits of precision.

During the lunar landing we scaled our position vectors at 2^{24} meters to comfortably accommodate the lunar radius of 1,737,400 meters, plus an ample allowance for the spacecraft's altitude. That meant that each component of the vector, when all ones, was equal to one bit less than 2^{24} meters, and the *granularity*, the value of a single bit, was 1/16 of a meter. In other words, any value between zero and just shy of 16,777,216 meters, positive or negative, could be accommodated.

Another thing that changed, now that we were writing code for manned missions, was that we spent more time in the hybrid lab on the second floor. It was not as chaotic as it looked when viewed from the corridor because the boxes and equipment racks tended to turn their messy backsides toward the windows. There was a working area of relative order inside.

The hybrid simulator was important because we could control a mission just as the astronauts would, using the computer's display and keyboard. At first we used the DSKY mounted on an equipment rack in the lab. Later we flew lunar landings from the LM cockpit—constructed from plywood but fully equipped with keyboard, eight-ball, displays, switches and control sticks—on the third floor directly above.

Because the hybrid simulator was built around an actual AGC it provided an important cross-check on the simulation programs that ran on the Honeywells and later our IBM 360s. The AGC itself sat out of sight in the bottom of an equipment rack. I did not even know it was there until late one night when Peter Adler and I were chasing a bug. We had traced the problem to a faulty output channel, or so we thought. We set a bit, but when we examined it afterwards it was still zero. To allege a hardware failure was no light thing, but eventually we skulked up the back stairs to the Systems Test Lab to seek advice—and the first living thing we saw was the imposing figure of Al Hopkins himself, one of the AGC's main designers. He was immediately alert. Never overlook a clue.

Hopkins's approach was to grab another computer, lug it downstairs, and plug it in in place of the one in the hybrid lab. We repeated the test. Same result. That ruled out a hardware failure. But what was going on? Back upstairs Hopkins unfolded a huge circuit diagram and after a moment said, "There's no flip-flop on that bit." The signal was getting out. Not seeing its reflection was as expected. Very good and slightly bad. A genuine hardware failure would have shaken things up. On the other hand Peter and I had to find another explanation for our bug.

When Hopkins plugged in the second AGC it was by means of the large connector through which all information flowed in and out of the computer: in, from a simulation of the spacecraft's sensors and controls; out, to a simulation of the spacecraft's effectors. Closing the loop between the effectors and the sensors were computers that modeled the dynamics of the spacecraft as it interacted with Newton's laws.

The challenge was to keep up with real time. On the Honeywells our environmental simulations took several hours to run a fifteen-minute landing. That improved as our mainframes were upgraded, but they were still too slow to run a simulation with a "man in the loop." The hybrid could do it because it harnessed together two fundamentally different technologies—digital computers and analog computers. The digitals, Scientific Data Systems 9300s, stored information in ones and zeroes and did their work by means of successive operations programmed in a language—not so different from our guidance computer except they were housed in big tan boxes with arrays of flickering lights instead of a modest case. Their job was to initialize the simulation, feed data between the AGC and the analogs, and capture information for analysis.

The analogs, a pair of Beckman 2133s if you are taking notes, were another thing altogether. They stored numbers as voltage levels, operated as electric circuits, and were "programmed" on a plugboard that resembled a large square platter of multi-colored spaghetti. A stored "variable" was literally a potentiometer whose setting could be changed by a complex mechanical linkage. Because as an electrical circuit it operated instantaneously, the analog computer could model the dynamics of the spacecraft and its environment rapidly enough for the simulation to keep up with real time. We could watch what it was doing on chart recorders of the classic type with a jittering stylus squiggling lines on moving paper.

As I write this, digital devices can *imitate* analog functions far more cheaply and almost as quickly as an analog system can *do* them. That is why more people listen to music on MP3 devices today than on vinyl records and don't know what they're missing. In 1967 we were still placing the needle in the groove and pumping the vibes through 6L6s—and analog computers were a good way to build a real-time man-in-the-loop simulation.

Speaking of 6L6s (and other vacuum tubes) they were much in evidence. The hybrid simulator needed 800-hertz power because the LM's systems required it, and someone figured out that McIntosh audio amplifiers, fed by oscillators, were an economical way to supply it.

No simulation was perfect. Confidence came from crossing a range of initial conditions with a variety of simulators and simulations, each with its own strengths and weaknesses. With a program like SUSANK, written in a compiler language, you could test a concept. On our hybrid simulator you could run real-time tests involving interaction between the astronauts and a real guidance computer. If you did not need real-time operation or man-machine interaction the environmental simulation running on our mainframes gave you exact, repeatable insight into what was happening in the computer.

That was just the beginning. The LM simulator at the Grumman Aircraft Company facility in Bethpage, Long Island, where the Lunar Module was built, used actual flight equipment to the maximum extent possible. NASA had LM simulators in Houston and at Cape

Canaveral whose main task was training astronauts. These had cockpits that were authentic to the last detail and magnificent out-the-window displays good enough to train for landing at a particular spot on the Moon. There was also, for developing pilot skills, the airborne simulation of the LM's flying qualities nicknamed the flying bedstead: a strange combination of jets, rockets and maneuvering thrusters that allegedly flew like the LM.

If you want names, the Grumman simulator was the FMES, for Full Mission Engineering Simulator, NASA's were each called the LMS, for LM Mission Simulator. I would fly hundreds of lunar landings on the one at the Cape. The flying bedstead was the LLTV, for Lunar Landing Training Vehicle. I would see it in action once.

At MIT, formal test plans were developed and new people hired to run them. That lay beyond the first line of defense, the tests less tightly controlled or carefully documented, but perhaps more focused and sincere, that were run by the original designer-programmer to satisfy himself that his code worked as he intended.

Always, happenstance was to be respected and serendipity courted. Even if you made a gross mistake in the initial conditions you wanted to understand how the software reacted to it. You hated cliffs. Maybe you misplaced a decimal point and initialized the LM below the lunar surface. You hoped to see the guidance equation attempt to plot a course. You did not want to see the software go irretrievably off the rails. Software that tried to perform reasonably in an absurd situation, we thought, was more likely to perform reasonably in an unforeseen situation.

THE RIVALS

There was no such thing as overtime. The building was always open and the computer room was almost always manned. There was one small perk for working into the evening: the Lab would pay for dinner. Allan Klumpp and I often found ourselves at Simeone's, an Italian restaurant in Central Square.

Allan's father was a prominent physician and his mother was the daughter of a man who sold short before the Crash. She was a punter herself and soon enough had departed for Greenwich Village and another man. Allan stayed with his father and his maids Rosa and Mahala, where the Model-A Ford that Rosa and Mahala drove him around in may have kindled his destiny as an engineer. That happy interlude ended when his mother swooped in and took him away to a ranch in Mt. Shasta, California where Allan milked the cows and slept in an unheated cow stall that he shared with large spiders.

Doc Draper came to MIT for *mens et manus*. Allan came for a dame. He dreamed of marriage as an escape from chaos and lovelessness. When he finally met Sue he was very direct, and had partial success, but college threatened to separate them. Sue planned to go to Pembroke College in Rhode Island. Allan was set to go to the University of Southern California. It was already September.

It was Allan's luck that his mother's sister's husband's father was Horace Ford, Senior, the Treasurer at MIT. What is more, Horace Ford, Senior, had heard about the prototype record changer Allan had devised that played 78s, 45s and 33s even if they were intermixed on the spindle. (Conductive labels on each disk signaled the apparatus which rotation speed was required and where to drop the needle.) Allan's grandmother made the call. Were there any places open in the entering class? There were two. "I'll take one!" she cried, and put Allan on a train. As he tells it, Sue was not overjoyed when he popped up just 40 miles from Providence. Allan tends toward self-deprecation in cases where he succeeds in the end.

He graduated from MIT with a degree in mechanical engineering, worked two years for Douglas Aircraft in California, and returned to MIT to earn a masters degree in control theory; then back across the country to the Jet Propulsion Laboratory, and back again to Washington D.C. where he served on a panel that helped NASA choose the lunar orbit rendezvous method for going to the Moon. Allan authored a reliability study that concluded that ten crews would perish for each one successfully landed on the Moon and brought back to Earth. He was swiftly hired by MIT and put to work discrediting his own prediction.

If it was a determination bred of heartache and arachnophobia that drove Allan, it was the US Army and the brains he did not even know he had that saved George Cherry. He too had grown up without parental support, but on the other side of the tracks.

George graduated at the bottom of his class at Southwest High School in Saint Louis and found himself in Chicago, broke and homeless, when epiphany came in the form of an Army billboard. After testing his IQ the Army offered him Officer Candidate School, but he chose the guaranteed technical education that came with serving in the ranks. When he graduated from radar repair school at the top of his class the Army offered him his choice of assignments. George took a job teaching the Nike surface-to-air system at the Redstone Arsenal in Huntsville, Alabama, Werner von Braun's shop.

"The Army saved me from being a bus driver," he said. After the Army, he earned a bachelor's degree in physics at Syracuse University, and six months after graduating attended a lecture by Dick Battin, MIT's astrodynamics guru and the person responsible for the Apollo flight software. George was hired and by the time I came on the scene five years later he led the LM software development.

Along the way he had not only cooked up the guidance technique, called E-Guidance, that was the basis for the lunar-landing guidance equation, but he had also found time to advance the state of the art in autopilot design.

The LM's autopilot was the software that controlled the spacecraft's attitude, or orientation. A conventional autopilot design at that time would work by firing the maneuvering jets repeatedly as it tweaked the spacecraft through an attitude change. The jets would go

pif-pif-pif-pif-pif

That kind of autopilot had to operate very rapidly. It either had to be implemented by an analog system or by a digital computer capable of sampling the attitude and taking action one hundred times per second. The AGC could only handle that if it was the only thing it had to do. Apparently a separate system would have to be provided for attitude control. But George saw another way.

Supported by the Lab's then-generous tuition reimbursement policy, he had become acquainted with concepts in optimal control theory that were being worked out academically at MIT but which were not yet in circulation in industry. In his concept, the autopilot only had to operate ten times a second. On each pass it would check the spacecraft's attitude and rotation rates and compare them to the current command, as generated either by crew action or by guidance. If the difference exceeded some threshold, called the *deadband*, two jet firings were computed, each involving some combination of the maneuvering jets. Timers were set so that the jets would fire at exactly the right times. The first firing started the maneuver and the second ended it. The jets went

    puff..........puff

In between, as George liked to say, Isaac Newton was in control. It was jujitsu. Minimal force was applied at just the right moment and in just the right direction. The deadband could be adjusted to vary the sensitivity.

NASA selected the MIT concept for a digital autopilot (DAP) after a face off against BellComm and Grumman, who together favored building a separate, analog system for attitude control. George Cherry led the Instrumentation Lab team. MIT's concept used less "gas" (astronaut-speak for RCS propellant) and it could be processed in the computer at a pace that left some time for guidance and navigation.

Thus attitude control was added to MIT's responsibilities and our system became the Primary Guidance, Navigation *and Control* System, not just PGNS but PGNCS. As I came aboard, the DAP was in full throes of implementation and the subject of a great deal of chatter and scurrying. It needed to be ready when we were ready to start running simulations of the guidance phases like the ones I was working on.

However you read the pattern of Allan Klumpp's early life, it had produced a person who was direct, methodical and tenacious. He was a tall gangly man with strong features and big hands and feet. He frequently rode to work from his home in the distant suburb of Wayland on an old big-tire bicycle and then used the only available shower in the building, located in the women's room on the third floor. He liked 1954 Fords, and wore the same tie every day—square ended, with horizontal stripes.

George was quick, articulate, tightly-wound, a flashy dresser. His suit jacket was carefully hung on the back of his office door. I cannot picture him laughing or smiling. His ambitions took him from the technical role in which he had imagined the digital autopilot and originated the lunar landing guidance equation to the management role in which he hired me—head of flight software for the LM, reporting to Battin. Allan also reported to Battin, but not through George.

Allan's considerable ego was matched by a need to be understood that you could see in his slightly stooped posture—as though he were seeking acknowledgement in the eyes of someone shorter. He stressed simplification, making the right approximations, and above all intellectual honesty. Never overlook or rationalize away an anomalous result. Allan would say, "If it's worth doing it's worth doing right." George, as manager, held with Voltaire that "The better is the enemy of the good." The apothegms were not really in conflict—the trick lay in recognizing the point where the return for further effort diminished—but the personalities were.

Allan was the tortoise, slow but sound, George was the hare. If Allan brought a well thought-out proposal, George seemed automatically to take an opposing position, and since he was the better debater he might win the argument on points even when he was wrong technically, to Allan's intense frustration. George needed to be in control; Allan only wanted to be understood, but it was almost the same thing.

George and Allan had finally collided when George asked Allan to figure out what the astronauts would actually see out the window during the visibility phase of the landing. Allan used the pen plotter to draw on paper successive views of a stylized lunar landscape as viewed through the LM's triangular window, then photographed the frames on 16mm movie film. (This rates, I believe, as a very early application of computer graphics.) To capture the view he had to simulate the landing, so George Cherry handed him a deck of about 300 cards—"one seventh of a box," Allan remembers—that comprised George's guidance simulation using his equation to control the LM. This deck was the seed from which Allan's SUSANK grew.

George Cherry's work was focused on the visibility phase of the mission (which became P64), the final approach that began at an altitude of about 7600 feet and ended at 400 or less. George assumed that some other guidance method would deliver the LM to the correct initial conditions—but Allan made a simplification. He realized that George's visibility-phase guidance equation, set up with different target parameters, could be used by the braking phase as well. He programmed it in SUSANK and it worked.

"Are you trying to take over the whole landing?" shouted George (as Allan related it). And thus, by the time I arrived, Allan owned the whole landing, from orbit to surface, and in the afterglow of their collision I was there, almost as George's delegate, to take care of parts that Allan could be persuaded to throw me—and Allan was generous.

AX*SR*T, BURNBABY, AND TWIDDLE

Saving memory and time, and trading them off against each other, became our obsession. We browsed the program listings looking for opportunities to save one or the other, whether in our own code or some one else's. Especially valuable was the 2048 words of unswitched read-only memory, which we called *fixed-fixed* memory. To save five words of fixed-fixed was be a big score.

When it came to time, the kind we cared about was not the time we lived and worked in, nor the time since launch; it was the two seconds that lay between successive accelerometer readings. During that span, during the lunar landing, we had to fit in navigation, landing radar readings, guidance, throttle control, attitude output, and display—with the digital autopilot, downlink, and a great deal else operating in the background—while trying to leave a healthy margin just in case.

I saw that in SUNBURST we were already close to the margin and I knew that a great deal still had to be added before we could go to the Moon. I set up some runs to narrow down where the time was going and the result was surprising.

Sometimes it was necessary to transform a vector from the body coordinate system to the stable-member frame, or vice versa. One case was when we incorporated landing-radar data measured by an antenna mounted on the body into the inertial state vector. The transformation depended on the attitude of the spacecraft at any given moment as defined by the angles of the three gimbals that connected the stable member with the structure of the spacecraft.

I discovered that the subroutines that were provided to perform these transformations were eating up more time than the lunar landing guidance equation itself. They had been coded in Interpretive for compactness not speed by someone who had the Command Module in mind and did not anticipate that they would be needed by the LM during a high-intensity phase of the mission.

I set out to rewrite these subroutines. My idea was to speed them up dramatically by recoding them in Basic, and I thought I could do it at little or no memory cost. The core of my new transformation routines was a new version of the routine AXISROT that I called AX*SR*T.

AX*SR*T was convoluted. The core of the problem was three by three: there were three components in the output vector, and each component contained a contribution from each of the three gimbal angles. That called for a loop within a loop—but each of the nine passes had to do something different.

I installed AX*SR*T in SUNDANCE and it worked fine. Then I installed it in the current Command Module program and the next morning my name was Mudd. I had overlooked a problem caused by the time-sharing of erasable memory. Until I fixed it no one's CM simulations were working.

I was a wild child from the LM side. The CM side was a tighter ship and could afford to be because their software was nearing maturity while ours was still helter-skelter. COLOSSUS did not even need the faster code. I was showing off and I overreached. Allan remembers having a discussion with George Cherry over whether to fire me. George denies it. I suspect Allan's discussion was with Fred Martin, Cherry's counterpart as project manager for the Command Module software. Martin had greater reason to be annoyed and he called me in for a door-closed talk about it. I felt secure enough but my spirits were dampened.

By mid-afternoon AX*SR*T worked perfectly. Compared to the old version execution time was cut in half and fewer than ten additional words were consumed. The problem could have delayed us seriously later. No one asked me to deal with it and in a more regimented environment I would not have been able to. That in miniature is how the system created by Doc Draper operated so successfully.

I moved into a new cubicle that I shared with Peter Adler and a graduate student who came and went.

The GSOP had organized the mission software into a series of programs—also called *major modes* or sometimes *mission phases*. The programs that conducted the lunar descent were known as the P60s. While I worked on those, Peter programmed the P40s, the orbital burns, which came in varieties that used the maneuvering jets, the descent engine, or the ascent engine. We thought of ourselves as the LM powered flight guys and became friends. Meanwhile Larry Berman worked on the ascent program (P12) that would whisk the astronauts back to Moon orbit.

Peter and I quickly realized that during the period preceding the engine's time-of-ignition (TIG) these mission phases had a lot in common. All started powered flight navigation at TIG minus 30 seconds, most performed a preliminary ullage burn using the maneuvering jets at TIG minus 7.5, all required the astronaut to push the PROCEED key during the last five seconds before ignition. In other ways they differed. The nouns displayed on the DSKY contained different data. Different guidance had to be switched in. RCS burns and the APS burn from the surface did not need ullage. For descent engine burns the engine was started at 10-percent throttle and had to be throttled up 26 seconds later.

Each mission phase could have had its own customized logic. That would have cost a lot of memory. Execution time would have been saved, but only during a period, the countdown to ignition, when time was not yet at a premium. Peter and I decided to write something to handle it all: a general purpose ignition routine for use by every powered-flight phase. To accommodate the variations we turned to the same concept Allan had used when he ripped out my spaghetti code in SUNBURST: jump tables. We defined a variable in erasable memory that we named WHICH, and set it to indicate which of the powered flight phases was in progress. At each decision point **WHICH** pointed to the table entry that would show the way forward.

The section began with a crisp description and directions for use, and then we saw fit to add:

HONI SOIT QUI MAL Y PENSE

The phrase meant "shame on you if you disapprove" (the motto of England's Order of the Garter). The reason for that was the transgressive name we gave the routine, in allusion to the 1965 riots in the Watts section of Los Angeles. "Burn, baby, burn" was shouted by the rioters as they set fire to looted storefronts. We named the section "Burn, Baby, Burn" and the entry point, since tags were limited to eight characters, was **BURNBABY**. After about a year on the job the use of the word "burn" for a rocket engine firing was deeply embedded. It did not cross our minds that not so long before we wrote **BURNBABY** three astronauts had died by fire on Pad 34 at Cape Canaveral.

It was not long after the AX*SR*T flap — not that I am drawing a straight line — that NASA applied the scourge, in the form of Howard W. Tindall. Tindall was a tall man with a ginger crew-cut and a sunny disposition, but in a knock-heads meeting with Ed Copps, Alex Kosmala and Fred Martin he imposed new rules: better definition of interfaces, a new committee to resolve conflicts in the use of erasable memory, constants controlled to avoid duplication and make sure everybody used the same lunar radius (for example), internal design reviews, changes to be added in blocks not piecemeal, and finally:

> Much tighter assembly control will be exercised with all program modifications being monitored and reviewed by a higher level of MIT management. Only those changes really necessary will be permitted. New assemblies will only be produced once a week as opposed to the much higher frequency hitherto.

The new rules were applied more easily on the sedate Command Module side. On the LM side the pace remained quicker. We continued to produce new assemblies several times a week. It was true that our changes were now going to be "reviewed by a higher level of MIT management"—in the sense that they would be reviewed by *some* level of MIT management. In fact a new position was created to perform the function, or at least a new title: Assembly Control Supervisor. The more common term was *rope mother*. That seemed just right for the nurturing role that she played (whatever her gender), and the term even had a touch of glamour.

The Assembly Control Supervisor collected changes from various sources, coordinated them, ran the assemblies that incorporated the changes into the program, and issued a memo that described the changes in each revision. She did not decide whether a change would be made, but she might decide when. Her responsibility was to the rope as a whole; her special concern was how the parts of the program interacted inside a machine so limited in memory and computation time. The most dangerous case was when two functions inadvertently shared the same location in erasable memory at the same time. With so little of that type of memory to go around erasable assignments might be stacked as high as six deep.

The title was new but not the role. Jim Miller and Dan Lickly took a maternal interest in SUNBURST, but it was not really "assembly control" then because we ran our own assemblies. As the job became more formalized and the programs more mature Jim Kernan and then Craig Schulenberg collected and documented the changes to SUNDANCE and LUMINARY. After Apollo 11 Dana Densmore took on the job and saw it through to the ultimate LM rope, LUMINARY 210, which flew on Apollo 15, 16, and 17.

The good thing about this system was that the Assembly Control Supervisor was not your boss. You could concentrate on landing on the Moon, for example, without having to justify every change to an otherwise superfluous manager. Managers there were, but in the tradition of Doc Draper they tried not to get in the way. Really they had no choice but to trust us, if we were to accomplish the goal at all. For me management was like a cloud, distant and indistinct, usually benign, containing personalities but not much structure. I may have been more oblivious to it than others but I was permitted, even encouraged, to be oblivious to it.

As for Bill Tindall, he headed up something called Apollo Data Priority Coordination. That name became a serious misnomer later when missions were being flown and Tindall's panel became the hotbed of operational planning and his famous memos, called Tindallgrams, delighted and informed the whole community.

My nocturnal ruminations by the fireplace on Marlborough Street led to another bit of code, which I called TWIDDLE.

It had to do with the function called Waitlist that we used to schedule tasks, like reading the accelerometers, that had to execute at a specific time — and *tasks* was the word we used, to distinguish these speedy lightweights from the *jobs* that did the heavy lifting. The input to Waitlist was a two-word address that contained both the memory location and the fixed and erasable bank information for the task. Waitlist would look for the address in the two words of memory that followed the "TC WAITLIST" statement.

It occurred to me that in many cases only one word was really required because the task being scheduled used the same memory banks as the code doing the scheduling. That led to TWIDDLE, a prologue to the Waitlist routine that could be called with a one-word address. TWIDDLE used five words of valuable fixed-fixed memory, but it saved ten. Potentially it saved as many as forty words elsewhere.

That was very nice, but that is not what TWIDDLE was really all about for me. For me, it was a triumph in the lapidary art of assembly-language programming because of the way it exploited one of the more esoteric characteristics of the AGC's instruction set.

The obvious approach would have been to build a second version of the start of Waitlist for the one-word case, but that would have taken more words than it was worth. TWIDDLE simply led into Waitlist, but found a way to modify the operation of the code that followed it[*].

---

[*]   The transfer to storage operation (TS) would skip the next instruction if the number being transferred was too big for 15 bits to contain, a condition called *overflow*. By intentionally creating an overflow I made a TS instruction skip over an EXTEND instruction, thus transforming a double-precision operation to fetch the two-word address into a single precision operation.

When I was sure TWIDDLE worked I asked our lovely and capable young secretary Jenny Flaherty to put out a Sunlighter, number 57 in the series. It was our least formal type of memo, usually a single hazy, blue-ink mimeographed page. The next day, to my delight, the building was full of doubters. As I passed Jim Miller's office I saw that he and Dan Lickly, in their usual positions, were examining a copy of Sunlighter 57 that lay in the middle of the empty table like a biological specimen they did not want to touch.

"How do you like my new lead-in to Waitlist?"

"It's fine except it doesn't work," drawled Dan.

"You don't think it works?"

"No, it doesn't work."

With that I whipped the confirming printout out of my back pocket and waited in silence while Lickly and Miller examined the trace. "Oh yeah, Q has an overflow bit also," Lickly muttered. I watched realization dawn and that was all the reward I wanted. Miller offered me a figurative gold star and permission to put TWIDDLE in the rope.

I thought it prudent to make one more experiment. The tests I had run never touched a real flight computer. I had used the bench-test simulation that *emulated* the complexities of the flight computer's instruction set using our ground-based mainframe computer. It allowed you to print out a trace that showed in precise detail the operation of each instruction. That was the printout I showed Lickly and Miller.

Bench test had never been wrong. On the other hand TWIDDLE depended on one of the computer's more obscure features. I needed to see TWIDDLE work on an actual Apollo Guidance Computer — such as the one in the hybrid lab*. The AX*SR*T flap, whether or not I might have been fired over it, was something I did not want to repeat.

I put together an off-line version of SUNDANCE that used TWIDDLE to schedule the count-down to the landing burn. That

---

* As a matter of fact the all-digital simulator did harbor a very subtle bug, also related to the overflow bit in the central register Q, that was only discovered four years later.

evening I loaded the program into the hybrid simulator and selected P63. The countdown began on schedule. After that came the pleasure of proving, to skeptical audiences, over and over, that **TWIDDLE** worked.

Actually, the reviews are still coming in. In 2011 Jim Miller had occasion to praise my contributions to Apollo but added, "not counting your code that took different paths when control did or didn't pass through a certain **EXTEND** instruction." Well at least he remembered it. In 2012 Hugh Blair-Smith was referring to **TWIDDLE** when he wrote, "I did stumble across your cute trick in **LUMINARY** 131, and admired it enormously. Shoulda guessed it was yours."

THE PUSSYCAT TEAM

In September 1967 I moved to an apartment in the building next door on Marlborough Street. The living room was less grand but there was a separate bedroom. That fall the Red Sox won the American league pennant. After the clinching game on the first day of October, with several baseball-mad neighbors, I joined the crowd estimated at 3500 that surged around the city, celebrating undestructively for several hours.

One night I woke in the wee hours to sounds of activity in the alley behind my bedroom, and a strange light. I quickly dressed and went out and found the First Unitarian Church, one block away, fully engulfed in flames, fire companies still arriving and burning embers flying in the stiff breeze. I knew the building from my unsuccessful stab at being a New England Unitarian. In fact I had played its pipe organ to an empty sanctuary, inflicting my piano-lesson repertoire on the fine old Aeolian-Skinner instrument whose spectacular destruction I was now witnessing.

Boston Unitarians had not been quite what I expected after the free-thinkers I had consorted with in Memphis. I had lost interest in organized religion, but I was sad to see the old building destroyed.

In our ignorance we thought of astronauts as bland, unintellectual, interchangeable. We joked about "idiot proofing" our programs. By "we"

I mean us youngsters, the most recent new hires, who didn't know any better. Our attitude changed immediately when we encountered astronauts face to face. For me that was November 6, 1967.

A big meeting was in progress in the classroom—the second meeting of an ad hoc group of MIT and NASA people first called the Tiger and now the Pussycat team. The earlier meeting had been about what to throw out. Today was about what we still needed to put in. Allan Klumpp came to get me when the lunar landing phase came up for discussion.

Our guests from Houston and the senior MIT people sat around tables arranged in a wide U. I took a chair next to Allan on the sidelines. I had heard that astronauts would be attending. But where? There was not a flight-suit to be seen. Negative snazzy knitwear.

I assumed at first that the short, balding man in a snappy glen plaid suit, who was chairing or at least dominating the meeting, was a particularly buoyant NASA manager. He turned out to be the astronaut Charles Conrad, known as Pete—or by his fellow astronauts as Tweety. Conrad at that time held the record for distance from Earth, 850 miles, on Gemini 11 with Dick Gordon. Later he would go 235,000 miles farther still on Apollo 12 and be the third man to walk on the Moon. Also at the table were Neil Armstrong, who would be the first—his Gemini mission had ended in a harrowing abort—and Jim Lovell, who would test his luck by twice approaching the witchy orb, but never touch it.

Armstrong brought up the cross-pointers, a meter in the LM cockpit, driven by the computer, that indicated the LM's horizontal velocity during the very last phase of the landing. The instrument had two crosshairs, one of which moved up and down to indicate velocity forward or backward, and another that moved right or left to indicate lateral velocity. This was important information because you wanted to land with very low horizontal velocity, yet the surface itself might be invisible because of dust kicked up by the descent engine. Armstrong's point—which I did not fully take in at the time—was that ambiguity was created by the fact the cross-pointer instrument was meant to indicate velocity in the horizontal plane, but was mounted in a vertical position in the cockpit. You can sense the potential for confusion if you consider that on an overhead high-way sign an arrow pointing up and one pointing down both mean "go straight ahead."

The discussion moved on to another topic that was closer to home: the information to be displayed to the crew on the DSKY during the landing. The DSKY had three, five-digit lines where numbers could be displayed. During the lunar landing we always used the second line to display the LM's rate of descent (also called altitude-rate, sink-rate, or H-dot), and the third line to display the spacecraft's altitude. Altitude and altitude-rate were essential throughout the landing. That left the top line for other purposes. During the first part of the landing, the braking phase, we used it to display total velocity relative to the Moon, a value that steadily decreased as the LM slowed.

But then came P64, the visibility phase, where with only one five-digit line available on the DSKY the discussion settled on two numbers that the astronauts needed, or wanted, to know. One was the LPD angle that told the mission commander where to look to see the landing site that the guidance system was aiming for. The other number was the time remaining during which redesignation of the landing point was still possible — essentially a countdown to the end of the visibility phase. We had not anticipated the need to display the time remaining. It was another window into astronaut thought processes.

Suddenly it came to me that I could construct an artificial five-digit number in which LPD angle would show up as the first two digits and time remaining as the last two or three. That way two numbers could be displayed in the space of one.

I cleared my throat and said, "I think there's a way to have both."

Allan seemed startled and at the table necks craned around to see who had spoken. I explained my idea. The geometry of the landing was such that the LPD angle always had two digits. The time remaining to redesignate would be somewhat more that 100 seconds when the visibility phase started, but to avoid running the two numbers together it was acceptable to truncate the time at 99 seconds until it got there.

"Are you sure about this?" asked Conrad.

"Definitely, if you don't mind having a zero between the two numbers." (I had not yet confirmed that the display software would let me display two unrelated numbers separated by a blank.)

With that, Conrad turned to the other astronauts at the table and said, "We should have had this guy at the meeting last week."

I left the meeting with Conrad's quip ringing in my ears, and spent the next nineteen days in the Massachusetts General Hospital. I had returned to the Lab that evening to check on a simulation. On my way home on the Yamaha, just before midnight, I was struck from the left side by a turning car.

ROSENCRANTZ AND GUILDENSTERN

The left front corner of the car caught my left leg. When I came to rest on the pavement I saw that the leg, at a point about halfway down my thigh, was displaced to the left by about thirty degrees. So you have finally broken a bone, I thought, and it's a big one.

Not that I was thinking clearly. I thought I needed to straighten the leg out to minimize the damage the jagged bone might be doing inside. The pain started when I grasped my leg by knee and calf and reduced the angle. I was lying in Mt. Vernon Street near the tiny firehouse where Engine Company 10 was based. Quickly the firefighters came to my assistance. One of the city police vans that doubled as ambulances arrived and took me to the emergency room at the nearby Massachusetts General Hospital where I heard someone diagnose my "fractured mid-shaft left femur" while I was still in motion. I was wearing new brown corduroys that I hated to see being cut off me.

Next morning Dr. Robert Boyd presented the options and I took no time at all to opt for the alternative that did not involve three months in bed: the surgical implantation of a stainless steel rod down the middle of my femur. I would be able to walk on crutches immediately and the pressure of doing so would accelerate the healing. Boyd said the procedure was invented by a Luftwaffe surgeon named Gerhard Küntscher to get injured pilots back into the air sooner. American orthopedists learned about it when prisoners of war returned home after receiving the treatment in Germany. Until its advantages were understood it was regarded as unethical medical experimentation.

"I'll try to get an OR for this afternoon," said Boyd, and I woke up vomiting in the ICU with an eight-inch gash in my left thigh where the bone had been brought out and reamed in both directions (penetrating the greater trochanter) and a smaller incision in my hip through which the intramedullary rod, 36 centimeters long, 11 millimeters in diameter and C-shaped in section, had been hammered home. I liked being at a teaching hospital because with students present when I was examined I got the straight scoop.

After a few drowsy days on injected Demerol (they said) I began to adjust to a way of life that would continue for two more weeks. On Boyd's order I got a satisfactory breakfast of bacon and eggs. The other meals were grim but the floor kitchen had an unlimited supply of ginger ale, milk, and Arrowroot cookies. At night I took to hanging out at the nurses' station or reading medical books in the resident's office. After breakfast, and nursely ablutions, I caught up on sleep.

The orthopedic ward was full and I shared a four-bed room on a medical floor with an old man who was silent except when he coughed up the residue of his former occupation, and an anything but silent, bowel-preoccupied middle-european who was interesting for a few days (only) because he had lived through much of the modern European history I had studied as part of my program of learning as little mathematics as possible.

The fourth bed had transients. A guy of about thirty with a very florid complexion lay there for a few days, attracting a parade of interns, residents and senior cardiologists who listened intently to his chest for long periods with stethoscopes, trying to understand what was happening there. A group would move off but one or two would always straggle back for another listen. One morning the man was taken down for a cardiac catheterization, at that time an experimental procedure. As he described it, he lay on a cold slab in a Frankenstein's laboratory of noisy esoteric devices, surrounded by a squad of Igors and crowds of leering onlookers, with a mysterious figure in the background calling the shots, while his heart did acrobatics in response to the probing of the catheter.

I had a cast on my right wrist because I had also broken that. I know what I was working on then because I still have copies of flowcharts that I wrote in the hospital with my left hand, for two tiny routines identified in the GSOP as R11 and R13 — which I was pleased to dub ROSENCRANTZ and GUILDENSTERN, names from *Hamlet* that swam into my consciousness because Tom Stoppard's *Rosencrantz and Guildenstern are Dead* was then playing on Broadway. (I had to split the names between two lines because of the eight-character limit.)

GUILDENSTERN monitored the switches that the astronaut could use to switch to the manual or semi-manual mode for the final stage of the lunar touchdown. That logic would continue to evolve. ROSENCRANTZ monitored the two big buttons on the LM's control panel that the astronauts would push if it were necessary to abort the landing. ROSENCRANTZ was never called on for an actual abort but it figures in the story of Apollo 14.

Within weeks I abandoned crutches for a cane. At six months I was playing tennis. Finally something to thank the Luftwaffe for.

DANA

Dana Densmore came on the scene just before my sojourn at Mass General. It was afterwards that we became lovers.

Dana, along with Phyllis Rye and several other capable women, had been hired wholesale from a consulting company and put to work on *services* — those functions common to the LM and Command Module software that provided support for the *applications* that contained the mission-related capabilities. Her first assignment was to recode part of the restart logic that Charley Muntz had originated. Now restarts that arose because of a software condition, such as when the Executive's queues were overloaded, would be handled without resort to a real hardware restart.

After that she made herself an expert on the telemetry programs that we called *uplink* and *downlink*. In the up direction, mission control could send information to the guidance computer in the same verb-noun language that provided the onboard human interface. Meanwhile, in a cycle that repeated every two seconds, downlink transmitted to the ground a list of data items to be displayed on the consoles at mission control—two words every twenty milliseconds, two-hundred words in all.

This did not have much to do with me. In the computer, uplink and downlink ran in the background and its only impact on my code was the computation time it consumed. It was not until later, when Dana became the Assembly Control Supervisor for LUMINARY, that we worked together.

At the time, for me, Dana was a short haired gamine with dimples and curves whom I began to glimpse in the corridors—wearing a minidress that might have come from Carnaby Street—and soon tracked to her office. It was the era of Twiggy, and Mrs. Peel on the TV and Barbarella on the silver screen, and we called young women chicks with never a twinge of irony. Skirts and dresses were so short that a minor lapse in uptightness might reveal the streamlined shapes of inner thigh in their armor of Lycra Spandex—a phenomenon that was not without its effect on me. As if that were not enough Dana was smart, which hardly needs saying, and wholly engaged.

Dana's journal opens a window on our first encounter. I am sitting at a keypunch machine in the hallway and I greet her with evident pleasure or interest. She notices my "long pretty hair," my wire-rimmed glasses, my mustache. I was still on crutches then. Some time later—using a cane now—I was sitting in a chair near the door of Allan Klumpp's office when she passed by and impulsively reached in and touched my head. I reacted "electrically" (Allan was also agitated), and

> After the incident with his hair, he came into my office all the time. I flirted with him, spoke softly to him, asked him questions about the Integration program, didn't pull my hand or my knee back if it touched his, and generally fell somewhat in love with him. He was flattering, he was entertaining, he was a great help to me with my work....

I learned to my disappointment that Dana was married, but I also began to see that she did not appear to be bound by the usual conventions. In fact she was radical from birth. Her father, Russell Allen, was an official at the AFL/CIO and, according to her sister, Dana knew the words to "Union Maid" before she turned two:

There once was a union maid, she never was afraid
Of goons and ginks and company finks and the deputy
*   sheriffs who made the raid.*
She went to the union hall when a meeting it was called,
And when the Legion boys come 'round
She always stood her ground.

Her mother, Donna Allen, along with Benjamin Spock and Russell Nixon, had during Dana's childhood been investigated by the House Un-American Activities Committee because of their public stand against nuclear weapons. In response Donna Allen gathered information about the Committee's unsavory activities and lobbied Congress to abolish it.

Dana had graduated from St. John's College in Annapolis, where they taught students to think, she said, by bombarding them with weighty tomes with minimal preparation. It was, "Here, see what you make of this." Aristotle, Newton, Kant. That was not bad preparation for making sense of the snarl of flight software that she was now dealing with.

A group of five or six of us often went out for lunch. We frequented "small" Joyce Chen on Massachusetts Avenue, the No Name Restaurant on Fish Pier in Boston, and the MIT Faculty Club in the Sloan Building, where we dined on tablecloths (and ran up bills) in a room thick with Nobelists—but one day Dana and I found ourselves at Cronin's in Harvard Square by ourselves. The way she squirmed in the booth opposite me.... It was the first time that I understood, non-verbally, in real time, that I was desired by a woman.

Still, I did nothing—shy of her marriage, not knowing yet that by agreement it was an open one—but the next weekend, on a wintry night, she had tickets to a play, and afterward in my apartment big wet kisses led quickly to clumsy embraces on the floor, the flinging off of garments, and clumsy lovemaking on the bed.

Sometimes we smoked and listened to Bob Dylan entwined on the vinyl sofa in the living room of her apartment—stoned enough to construe "The Ballad of Frankie Lee and Judas Priest" as a chronicle of Christianity, Judas representing the betrayal of Jesus by the church founded in his name — while her husband studied at his desk in the bedroom. More comfortably, back on Marlborough Street, we crawled around on the bed, nuzzling and grappling like jungle cats, as the hundred-watt radiation of the bedside lamp fell on our stimulated skin like the equatorial sun.

Stanley Kubrick's *2001* came out in April 1968 and soon after, with the customary cannabic preparation, we saw it in the original version at the Boston Cinerama on Washington Street. As the arriving shuttle matched its roll rate to the rotation of the great ring station in Earth orbit and entered its docking bay to Johann Strauss's "Blue Danube Waltz," we were equally alive to the operational subtleties of the maneuver and the erotic subtext.

I sold the Yamaha and bought an Alfa-Romeo roadster in the 1600cc version, body by Pininfarina, five-speed gearbox, aluminum double overhead camshaft engine with steel inserts, top speed about 110 mph. Red. The Alfa was delicate, both mechanically and cosmetically, but so sweetly responsive, so harmonious in its vibrations that it ranks in my mind among the most precious of those old-technology experiences now lost. Cinerama with analog sound is another.

One day we walked around town with my Pentax camera. The pictures show Dana in a toggle coat, me in a corduroy jacket with long hair, mustache and wire rims — my look less hippie or beatnik, perhaps, than Bloomsbury. Several times we drove the Alfa to Brattleboro, Vermont to work in a friend's darkroom, sometimes spending the night, sometimes driving back in the wee hours.

Very late one night we rolled through Groton, Massachusetts at a velocity that was perfectly comfortable in the Alfa but high compared to the statutory limit. Completely unknown to us town cops gave chase. By the time they came within sight their blood was up and after I stopped they came towards me with large revolvers drawn and pointed.

I was accused of being "all over the road." Certainly the clumsy cruisers chasing me were. It was a "thickly settled area." Hardly, at three in the morning with nary a light in the whole mean town.

Then one of the cops turned to Dana and asked if she had felt safe doing eighty on a twisty road.

After a slight hesitation Dana said no; in the interval I had half-feared something more defiant. Was she sensibly trying to mollify persons who looked like they were ready to shoot one of us and have their way with the other? Was it a knuckling under to male authority so explicitly displayed? Or was she, as usual, telling the simple truth? A deer might have jumped out. Had she said anything about it to me? No, Dana replied. She was having too much fun she said later, deer or no deer. My license was suspended and I endured several spring and summer months as the owner of a lovely sports car that I could not legally drive in Massachusetts.

We spent a hot summer weekend in Greenwich Village — or rather in the narrow bed by the front window of a second-floor apartment on 6th Avenue, in sticky embrace, with scarcely a peek outside and certainly no Broadway theatre or fine dining. That was our apex not our end, and our intimacy was never exclusive, but it was in the persona of disappointed lover that in August 1968 I took a bus to western Massachusetts, where Marjorie was enrolled in an art program near the Tanglewood Music Center. I slept at an inn in Lenox and spent days at the swimming beach on the Stockbridge Bowl and nights on the lawn when there was a concert. One evening at dusk, with a new friend, walking across a field from the lake to her dormitory, we saw an unknown object fly parallel to the horizon, trailing a long blue flickering flame.

After fifty years one can almost forget that over all our work and fun hung the war in Vietnam. Dana's husband was contemplating a move to Canada that would have posed an unwelcome dilemma for her. She thought of joining the draft resistance movement, and one evening I accompanied her to a meeting in a dark apartment near Central Square. There was food, unseasoned rice and beans, and the talk was hardly less dreary. Dana remembers it the same way, but at the time, with my convenient space-program deferment, I could hardly be snide.

Through her mother, who was a friend of Bernardine Dohrn (future cofounder of the Weather Underground), Dana had already felt the rumblings of the female liberation movement. Now it all clicked. Why were women working for everyone else's liberation instead of their own?

Now in the draft resistance movement she saw another example of male entitlement. Naturally the movement was led by men because women were not drafted, but did that mean that a woman's role was limited to cooking the rice and beans? The problem was not so much the overt discrimination, but society's expectations, amplified by the media, that bred aggrandizement in men and helplessness in women.

Dana took up martial arts, not so much to fight off an attacker, which might never come up, as to overcome the latent intimidation. She led a snow-day rebellion against the unwritten dress code for women of dresses and skirts, but she guarded equally her freedom to wear a minidress. She flatly rejected the notion that there was any contradiction between enjoying her own sexual freedom and standing against the objectification of women.

Late in 1968, Dana founded *No More Fun and Games, A Journal of Female Liberation*. Six issues were published and the last, in May, 1973, had 192 pages. Only recently have I looked at these volumes. For the first issue Dana wrote an essay titled "On Celibacy" that began:

> One hang-up to liberation is a supposed "need" for sex. It is something that must be refuted, coped with, demythified, or the cause of female liberation is doomed.

Dana wrote that while, or soon after, we were practicing non-celibacy together, but her perspective on sexuality was stronger and more nuanced than it may sound.

> This is a call not for celibacy but for an acceptance of celibacy as an honorable alternative, one preferable to the degradation of most male-female sexual relationships....

I think she meant that once the sense of helplessness is overcome by recognizing that sex is neither a necessity nor an obligation, anything becomes possible, not excluding short skirts, knee-bumping, playing with gender roles, and happy heterosexual lovemaking between equals. Maybe it boiled down to, "Better no man than a boorish man."

Reading these passages today, the prose seems angular, jagged. It is easier to recognize the softer contours of the woman I knew, who had achieved or at least asserted a measure of liberation for herself, in the drawing by her sister Indra Dean Allen that decorated the cover of the same issue. A young woman, naked, seems to have thrown off the ligatures that bound her and made them into a place of comfort where she stretches languorously. Her arms are clasped above her head and she seems ready, in her posture and her appraising eyes, to welcome a lover.

INDRA DEAN ALLEN

PART TWO ⚓ FLYING

FIRST MANNED MISSIONS OF THE LM

APOLLO 9
March, 1969
Jim McDivitt CDR, Dave Scott LMP, Rusty Schweickart CMP
LM-3 — SUNDANCE 306
Earth Orbit

APOLLO 10
May, 1969
Tom Stafford CDR, John Young LMP, Gene Cernan CMP
LM-4 — LUMINARY 69
Lunar Orbit

APOLLO 11
July, 1969
Neil Armstrong CDR, Buzz Aldrin LMP, Mike Collins CMP
LM-5 — LUMINARY 99
Sea of Tranquility (0.674°N, 23.473°E)

APOLLO 12
November, 1969
Pete Conrad CDR, Alan Bean LMP, Dick Gordon CMP
LM-6 — LUMINARY 116
Ocean of Storms (3.012°S, 23.422°W)

APOLLO 13
April, 1970
Jim Lovell CDR, Fred Haise LMP, Jack Swigert CMP
LM-7 — LUMINARY 131
Lunar Flyby after Accident

APOLLO 14
January-February, 1971
Alan Shepard CDR, Ed Mitchell LMP, Stuart Roosa CMP
LM-8 — LUMINARY 178
Fra Mauro (3.645°S, 17.471°W)

The Pussycat Team had firmed up the lunar requirements. The new GSOP was written and reviewed. At the very end of March 1968 LUMINARY was created as a version of the latest SUNDANCE.

The new name was a break from the solar style that had given us programs named AURORA, SUNDISK, SUNBURST and SUNDANCE. Now, by agreement with NASA, Command Module programs would begin with the letter C. Variations of COLOSSUS and COMANCHE would fly the lunar missions. LM programs would begin with L, hence LUMINARY, a word meaning a source of light, a heavenly body, or a prophet.

A new memo series was established, the Luminary Memo, and in No. 6 George Cherry announced our assignments. We already knew them of course; he was writing for NASA's benefit.

I was listed as responsible for the automatic landing phases (P63, P64, P65) and throttle control, plus the aborts monitor (R11) and the manual-modes monitor (R13). Craig Schulenberg was assigned the manual and semi-manual final landing modes (P67 and P66)—although I soon acquired these too. Bob Covelli would code the complex landing radar routine (R12). Larry Berman got ascent and aborts (P12, P70, P71). Peter Adler would rework the orbital maneuver phases (the P40s) so they would work either in Moon or Earth orbit. The landing analog displays (R10) were assigned to someone who I will not name because he did a bad job, which I eventually had to fix, and never enters the story otherwise.

Maybe it was a reward for helping create the first iteration of LUMINARY, or compensation for what appeared to be the heaviest work assignment, or recognition for being injured on my way home from work at midnight. I was invited to join a group going to the Cape to view the second launch of the Saturn V, known as the AS-502 mission, or later as Apollo 6. Cape Canaveral at this time was officially

Cape Kennedy but to us it was simply "the Cape." I suppose we were the only people in Massachusetts for whom that did not automatically mean Cape Cod.

The first Saturn V had flown the previous November. It was an "all-up" test, a big, necessary gamble, rewarded when all three stages functioned perfectly. I was in the Massachusetts General Hospital in a fog of injected pain drugs. Apollo 5, in January, the LM's first flight, was another sort of anticlimax. Software written by me was blamed for shutting the descent engine down unnecessarily. No one had informed us of a last-minute procedural change that made the engine slow to start and therefore the Delta-V Monitor concluded the engine had failed. The primary guidance system was turned off for the remainder of the mission. Allan Klumpp and I lost our only chance for a rehearsal.

That was another reason someone might have thought I needed a bracing dose of tangible rocketry.

I shared a car with George Cherry. We checked in at a motel in Cocoa Beach and drove into the Federal reservation from the south, passing the gantries of the Jupiter, Atlas and Titan launch pads visible off to the right as we drove north, then turned left to cross the causeway that led to the Kennedy Space Center itself. After a stop at the MIT office in the headquarters building we drove a few miles further still to visit the structure that had dominated the landscape ever since Cocoa Beach: the Vertical Assembly Building, known as the VAB. Inside the vast jungle gym that was the interior of this huge cube we boarded an elevator with a glass wall, and as we ascended the equivalent of thirty stories we could glimpse through the platforms and work structures the narrowing shape of the rocket that was being assembled for the Apollo 8 mission.

That was the third Saturn V. The second was on Pad 39A, three miles away, giving off white vapor as it was loaded with the substances that made it go. The substance that made the onboard computer go was the program SOLARIUM, and the computer itself was a preliminary version of the one that would go to the Moon. The guidance system navigated but did little else. No crew was aboard. The mission was simply a second test of the mighty Saturn launch system.

The next morning I sat with Phil Felleman and Norm Sears in the covered grandstand of the press area near the VAB, watching the giant countdown clock that stood in the field between the grandstand and the waterway by which rocket segments were delivered by barges named *Palaemon, Orion,* and *Promise*—and beyond that, hazy in the morning mist, the slender rocket poised for flight.

There was trepidation in our anticipation. The first Saturn V had set the pad on fire and shaken the press grandstand more than anyone expected. Ceiling tiles had come down around Walter Cronkite's ears in his private studio. I eyed the roof over our heads. Meanwhile Doc Draper, who attended every launch, worked the house, taking pictures with his Minox camera.

At zero, huge plumes of smoke exploded left and right from the flame pit and after a few seconds the 360-foot rocket lifted majestically from the pad. The five F-1 engines on the first stage generated enough thrust to lift 7,500,000 pounds—but in the first few seconds after the holddown clamps were released the stack gained only a few feet because it weighed almost that much. As the rocket rose it unreeled a quarter-mile flame that licked at the end like a blowtorch. When the sound arrived, after a delay of fifteen seconds, it seemed to beat against our chests, stronger than thunder ever is after a count of fifteen.

As fuel burned, acceleration increased. When the rocket tilted to drive downrange a new, hard, crackling rose above the tremendous pedal note. When, still visible, the first stage dropped off and the second stage's J-2 engines took over, the rocket was already 50 miles away and moving at 6200 miles per hour. When the second stage finished, only a short burn by the third stage's single J-2 engine was required to place the spacecraft in Earth orbit.

However exciting for observers, AS-502 was a success only if you judge by the number of problems it uncovered. On the first stage, pogo oscillations were measured—so named because an astronaut in the Command Module would have felt that the whole rocket was bouncing on end like a pogo stick. Pogo is a chronic problem in rocket engines, caused by uneven burning. It is both uncomfortable and dangerous. In the worst case the vibrations could interact with the resonant frequencies of the structure and tear the whole stack apart.

This time pieces fell off the shroud enclosing a dummy Lunar Module. Then two of the five engines on the second stage shut down prematurely. The third stage took up the slack, placing the spacecraft in orbit, but it balked when commanded to fire a second time to simulate the burn that would boost the spacecraft out of earth orbit on a path to the Moon.

Happily, the problems with the booster were not ours to fix. We drove back to Cocoa Beach, this time taking the road that passed near the old gantries where the Mercury and Gemini missions had been launched. At one point a sign warned "Caution, Nitrogen Fog on Road."

The date was April 4, 1968. Back in my motel room I turned on the television and learned that Martin Luther King had been shot dead at the Lorraine Motel in Memphis.

My flight back to Boston connected in Washington. In the aftermath of the killing of Dr. King, 4000 regular army troops had been brought into the city. As we landed at National Airport I saw the tidy rows of tents on the Mall—like a scene photographed by Matthew Brady—and felt a gulf of loss and foreboding.

ELIMINATING LINEAR GUIDANCE

I moved into a new office, a cubicle of my own in the warren of eight-foot partitions on the second floor. Allan Klumpp moved to another cubicle perhaps forty steps away and around a couple of corners, which seemed about right. Peter Adler, Dana Densmore and Phyllis Rye were nearby. Next door was a large office occupied by Dave Moore and Sharon Albert, smart new hires who came along too late to do much coding but who contributed in many other ways, especially testing.

My office was on a corner. One wall had a door and another a large glass window facing the corridor. As everywhere the walls were an institutional light brown. I visited the paint department at Sears and during the night I painted two walls an aquatic green, one salmon, and the fourth a sort of lavender. I thought the effect, through my window, would be like an aquarium. The next morning (while I slept) everyone from Doc Draper on down came by to take a look. Allan was beside himself, said it was the best thing I had ever done.

Two nights later Peter added to the fun by painting his new office in a bold red, black and yellow. Others were probably studying their paint chips, but at that point the union painter—a fine gentleman who could paint a wall in a busy corridor with a drop cloth folded to be just a foot wide—filed a grievance. Dan Lickly, Peter and I attended a meeting with the union representatives, chaired by James Fandel of the MIT Department of Personnel Relations. The discussion seemed to hinge on the fact that by long agreement engineers were allowed to do technician's work like soldering, and the fact that the offices were painted, as we affirmed, for "aesthetic reasons." The union was assured that software engineers were not taking on the maintenance function as such. In a letter that was a masterpiece of bureaucratic non sequitur Fandel denied the grievance. Our offices stayed colorful, but there would be no more painting.

In theory Allan Klumpp did the analysis and I programmed the guidance computer—but it was never that simple. Allan wrote some important portions of code for the lunar landing missions, including the landing time-to-fly computation and the routine, known as FINDCDUW, that derived attitude commands for the autopilot from the "desired" thrust vector calculated by the guidance equation.

I was no match for Allan's ability to derive an equation, something he could do right in front of you with a sharp pencil on a pad of paper labeled with his name and the date. On the other hand it fell to me to incorporate the equations Allan designed into the temporal structure of a computer that had to do many other things at more or less the same time.

Although it may seem like the tail wagging the dog, one can learn things by coding an algorithm for the computer that might elude a more theoretical approach. If something seems dissonant, or awkward to code, that may be a sign that it is backward, or upside down, or unnecessary. How you felt about what you were writing was a metric. You wanted your solution to a coding problem to have felicitous proportions. In that way we were Platonists.

In the SUNBURST version, the lunar landing had a brief sub-phase at the end of the braking phase whose only function was to maneuver the LM to the starting attitude for the visibility phase. This in-between phase annoyed me. Was it really necessary? We issued a new attitude command every two seconds anyway. Could FINDCDUW not handle the step change in the attitude command when we switched to the visibility phase targets?

Allan agreed. We wrote a Program Change Request (PCR) to eliminate the phase, NASA approved it, and we recovered a significant amount of memory. Allan gave me credit for the idea in his memo describing the changes. We began to feel that with our complementary talents there was no problem we could not tackle.

THE DOCTORS

It goes without saying I was among smart people.

I was okay. I had breezed in and out of Mensa when I thought it was to my advantage, but one in fifty can do that. I held my own at the Lab despite a not very good education, but that was only because I did software, a thing that was at once literary, and mechanical, and only after that, mathematical.

If you asked yourself who was the smartest of them all it was easy to eliminate, starting with my whole generation, but harder to settle on. It is only a parlor game, but you would have to choose between Doctor Laning and Doctor Battin — or rather, not choose.

For us who were programming the guidance computer, Hal Laning and Dick Battin were the poles between which we were held in tension. Laning represented the practical side: the languages we used and the real-time operation of the computer as it coped with many jobs and tasks at essentially the same time. Battin personified the legacy of Kepler and Newton, the equations that it was our job to embed in the context conceived by Laning.

They became good friends but they differed in temperament. Laning took modest pride, Battin liked to strut his stuff. Laning's lair was a cul-de-sac behind the keypunch area on the first floor. Battin had a big office on a busy corridor. Laning hated meetings; Battin hosted them—but when one went on too long he would end it by puffing on his pipe and skating a few perfect smoke rings across the table.

The men met in 1951 when Battin joined the Instrumentation Laboratory to work with Laning on guidance for the Thor and later the Polaris ballistic missiles. At that time computation was still done on mechanical calculators by young female operators called "computers." Whirlwind was about to change that.

Whirlwind was a bulky machine that used vacuum tubes and had only 2048 sixteen-bit words of memory, but it was the direct ancestor of our one-cubic-foot guidance computer. It was the first digital computer to attempt real-time control, having been intended originally for flight simulation. To achieve processor speed it operated on multiple bits simultaneously. Whirlwind's developers, led by Jay Forester, invented magnetic core memory. Not fifteen years later those technologies were going to the Moon.

Whirlwind even supported a primitive form of computer graphics, using an oscilloscope, exemplified by a program called "bouncing ball" that prefigured the arcade game Pong (released 1972).

In 1952, a scientist wanting to use Whirlwind first had to learn the esoteric language the machine was wired to understand. Hal Laning thought of a way he could write something resembling ordinary algebra instead. Using Whirlwind's "native" language he wrote a program that read and parsed the programmer's algebraic input—as punched on paper tape by a sort of typewriter called the Flexowriter—and translated it into strings of instructions that the machine could understand directly. The program was called a *compiler*. Laning named it George and the first code it ever executed was

```
X = 1
PRINT X
```

Laning said the name came from the expression, "Let George do it"—the title of a radio drama featuring a detective who boasted, "If the job's too tough for you to handle, you've got a job for me, George Valentine." Laning was born on February 14, 1920 so there was a resonance in that explanation.

At the time Hal created George, his real job was developing guidance equations for intercontinental missiles. Laning was simply creating a tool to make their lives easier, but he understood what he had accomplished:

> Nearly everyone who has had a problem to solve on a large-scale digital computing machine has probably felt that it would be indeed convenient if one could give the machine his problem in ordinary mathematical language with perhaps a suggestion for a method of solution. We have been motivated by a sympathy for this feeling in writing a program for Whirlwind I that will constitute, we hope, a useful step in the indicated direction. The effect of our program is to create a computer within a computer...

A great deal of modern computer science stems from those statements. Laning's compiler predated the better known compiler language called Fortran. John Backus, who led the team that developed Fortran, consulted with Laning during the planning of his system. In a 1991 letter, recommending Laning for the National Medal of Science, Backus wrote

> Dr. Laning was the first person to conceive of and implement what we would now call a true compiler—a program that converts a description of a computer program into a real machine-language program that a computer can then execute whenever desired.

Unaccountably, Laning was not awarded the National Medal of Science, and he was prohibited by the rules from receiving the Charles Stark Draper Prize for engineering achievement. It is Backus who in 1993 got the prestigious Draper Prize, with a gold medallion and $375,000, for developing what was cited as "the world's first practical general-purpose, high-level computer language." Maybe whoever wrote that thought they could get around Hal Laning with the weasel words "general-purpose" but I do not buy it.

Another of Laning's inspirations was the real-time operating system for the Apollo Guidance Computer, which we knew as Executive and Waitlist. These complementary services gave us everything we needed to organize the numerous functions that had to operate together, seemingly simultaneously, inside the computer—while making maximum use of meager resources, and remaining robust in the presence of perturbations.

Harder to describe is Laning's quiet influence on the people he worked with. Years later, when several of his protégés formed a company to create a new language for the IBM computers on the Space Shuttle, they named the language HAL—as well they might since in essence the new language was created by combining MAC, an evolved version of Laning's George, with a real-time operating system resembling the one Laning thought up for the Apollo computer.

After the book and movie *2001* came out we liked to think that Arthur C. Clarke was among the cognoscenti who understood Laning's accomplishments and was winking when he christened the malevolent (or badly programmed) computer aboard the space station, but Hal, the person, had the sweetest personality in the world. Many years later I had the pleasure of partnering him at tennis once a week, sometimes with Dick Battin across the net.

Battin had breezed through every available level of school and had become indisputably the greatest astrodynamics man on the planet. At the Main Institute (as we called the academic institution of which we were nominally a part) Battin taught a famous course to generations of students, including three who later walked on the Moon. Meanwhile, at the Laboratory, he oversaw the translation of astrodynamics into software—at the time more often spelled "softwear." When Battin told his wife Marjorie that he had been put in charge of software she said, "Please don't tell any of our friends."

In October 1957 the Russians launched Sputnik. The event caught Battin flatfooted: he had just decamped to the consulting firm Arthur D. Little in search of greener pastures. Back at the Instrumentation Lab, Laning, Elmer Frey and Milt Trageser were galvanized. They set to work on a paper titled "Preliminary considerations on the instrumentation of a photographic reconnaissance of Mars." That audacious 1958 paper defined, not just a better Earth-orbit mission or even a flight to the Moon, but a round-trip, photographic flyby of the planet Mars by an unmanned spacecraft.

> The main idea in the nonstop trajectory is that of a vehicle which makes two circuits around the Sun while the Earth makes three, passing near to Mars in the process.

That paper brought Battin back to MIT posthaste. He set to work with Laning and others to turn the "preliminary considerations" into a proposal for an actual mission. Laning and Battin were the principal authors of a report titled "A Recoverable Interplanetary Space Probe" that defined a system with an inertial sensor, optics, a digital computer, and rockets for maneuvering — all the elements, except the crew interface, that would be needed to guide a manned mission to another orb. That work would be a major factor in winning the Apollo contract, that plum of plums, for the MIT Instrumentation Laboratory.

In January 1961 — Kennedy's rousing speech still four months away — Battin was still pondering the Mars mission. He showed, with the trajectory to prove it, that it was possible for a spacecraft to travel from the Earth to Mars by way of Venus. The gravitational attraction of the cloudy planet would bend the spacecraft's course from the downhill path it took from Earth to a new outbound trajectory aimed at Mars. The beauty of it was, that required much less fuel than going directly from Earth. Battin credited Laning with pointing the way in this statement from the "preliminary considerations":

> The possibility at once suggests itself that by guiding the vehicle to the rear of Mars instead of in front of it, a gain in energy will occur and that a reduction in the required velocity in leaving Earth might be achieved.

Battin had formulated the "first realistic multiple fly-by mission ever designed," the technique that has made possible the tours of planetary exploration that followed Apollo. It is not quite free. The maneuvers have a reciprocal effect on the planet that is used as a slingshot, either speeding it up or slowing it in its orbit around the Sun — albeit infinitesimally. I have enjoyed asking Battin why no environmental impact statement is required.

Kennedy spoke, and three months later the Instrumentation Laboratory won the contract to create the primary guidance system for both Apollo spacecraft. Battin made much of the date, 1961. It reads the same upside down. That had not happened since 1881 and we must wait until 6009 for the next occasion. Noting that Apollo, *ex post facto*, could be made to stand for "America's Program for Orbital and Lunar Landing Operations," Battin maintained that the Sun-god of the ancient Greeks, patron of the Delphic Oracle, predicted through his own name that it would be America that went first to the Moon—but how do we know the god did not mean Atlantis?

Doc Draper's Lab had won the Apollo contract, but then the position had to be defended as industry groups lobbied to take the job away from us. A university could not build production hardware. A non-profit laboratory could not be held accountable like a real company. We were a bunch of prima donnas. Dick Battin turned back one assault with a flash of cold steel.

> An industry group... was, obviously, probing to find our weak spots. I presided at the conference table and was absentmindedly toying with a pair of scissors when an annoying fly flew past. Suddenly, with one slash of the scissors, I cut that fly in half in midair.

With the fly on the table in two parts the tone of the meeting changed in the Lab's favor.

THE SCB, THE LLTV

The next time I saw Pete Conrad was at a meeting of the Software Control Board (SCB) in Houston.

The Manned Spacecraft Center (later renamed the Johnson Space Center) resembled the campus of a newly founded state college, built on flat, low-lying land between Interstate 45 and the funky communities of Seabrook and Kemah that lay along the upper reaches of muddy Galveston Bay. There was little hardware on view. The buildings were nondescript, except that several of them had enigmatic windowless wings with large doors.

The bones and muscles of the manned space program were at Huntsville and Canaveral. The central nervous system was at MSC in Houston. It was the home of the astronauts, the Flight Operations Directorate, and the Mission Planning and Analysis Division.

Christopher Columbus Kraft was the head of FOD, the chief of the flight controllers. He was also in charge of us, since the flight software was considered part of operational planning. Kraft represented the high-voltage upper-level decision-making of the Apollo program. He came across as prickly and dangerous.

Kraft was both chief critic and top defender of the flight software. At a review held shortly before Apollo 7, the prime crew, led by Wally Schirra, were represented by a member of the backup crew who, when his turn came, stated that the crew "had no confidence in the flight software." Everybody knew that came from Schirra, and noted that he had ducked saying it to Kraft's face. Steve Copps was there:

> Kraft said, in so many words, that if they [the prime crew] were ready to fly then he didn't understand what they were saying. He then said that if they weren't ready he would replace them that minute. He then declared the software ready for flight.

The SCB was Kraft's instrument for managing the flight software. Proposed changes came in the form of Program Change Requests to be discussed and approved, disapproved, or deferred. PCRs might come from anywhere — but where the LM was concerned, mainly from NASA, Grumman, and us. The SCB met in a large conference room in the headquarters building. Some 20 or 30 managers and engineers attended. Some sat at a large table, others in chairs along the wall on either side. This was my first time and I sat beside George Cherry at the table with a degree of pride.

Kraft hosted an open meeting but not an indulgent one. A consensus was sought, but Kraft made the final decision: yes, no, defer — then it was press on, or just press, as it was said, to the next topic.

During the meeting Pete Conrad came in and sat down behind George and me, and after it adjourned Pete and George fell into conversation while I and Clint Tillman from Grumman listened in. Conrad had been doing a lot of flying in helicopters because they handled somewhat like the LM, but the gold standard for simulating the LM was the Lunar Landing Training Vehicle. In fact he was going to fly the LLTV at Ellington Air Force Base the next morning. Did we want to come watch?

It was barely first light when George had a few words with the guard at the Ellington back gate. Conrad had probably fixed it informally. In heavy fog we wound our way to a remote corner of the airfield. We began to hear ungodly whooping sounds. A small hangar, and what looked at first glance like a particularly interesting junkyard, emerged from the murk. There, mounted on a sort of pylon that allowed it to rock and spin, an LLTV lurched violently as its maneuvering jets shrieked. Tillman called it a scene from *Faust*.

We drove on to find another LLTV sitting on a runway near a small communications trailer. The LLTV was called the "flying bedstead" because that is what it looked like. It had four legs, maneuvering jets at the corners, a jet engine and rockets in the middle, and on one end a little porch where the pilot sat in the open air. The LLTV was intended to simulate the dynamics of the lunar landing. The jet engine supported five sixths of the vehicle's weight. Throttleable rockets supported the one sixth that corresponded to the strength of lunar gravity. Why that combination was thought necessary (or sufficient) to create the impression of lunar flight I never understood, but it was a flying machine that could hover on a reaction engine and maneuver using thrusters and that was unique enough.

Conrad turned up in an olive drab flight suit, jaunty enough but more serious than the day before and like us short of sleep. The fog burned off and Conrad walked out to where the LLTV was waiting, fully fueled. He flew several landings, rising to about 100 feet and descending, controlling both attitude and throttle manually. After one landing the support crew reported that there was enough rocket fuel for ten seconds more flying. With George Cherry muttering "Don't do it, don't do it," Conrad took off again and landed safely. It took two hours to prepare the craft for a new session so Conrad went to eat breakfast. Tillman said he would have eaten first.

In May, a few months after we watched Conrad, Neil Armstrong lost control while flying the LLTV and had to eject. Not long after that I turned a corner in our maze of cubicles and came face to face with Pete Conrad, talking in the corridor with a couple of control system engineers. I joined the conversation and asked Conrad if he had flown the LLTV since Armstrong's crash. That got him started.

"The LLTV is hard to control in any sort of wind and that's how Neil got in trouble, but it has one hell of an ejection seat. With all the big boosters and all that, the LLTV is still the hairiest vehicle in the whole damn program." Another time I heard Conrad say, with a malicious twang, "I love watching first flights on the LLTV."

After a test pilot crashed another LLTV, again ejecting safely, NASA management tried to ground the machine but the astronauts insisted that it was vital for their training. In my opinion they loved the contraption not because it was realistic but because it was challenging.

One of the regulars at the Software Control Board was a man named John Norton who worked for TRW. Norton was tall and severe, always in a dark suit, humorless, almost cadaverous, seemingly haunted by the software error that ruined his life.

Norton had been in charge of the onboard software for the unmanned Mariner I spacecraft that was to have begun the exploration of the planet Venus. Its Atlas booster went off course and had to be destroyed. The problem was traced to a software error and the software error was traced to a hand-written equation in which a vital symbol had been omitted.

Norton took responsibility for the mistake and, as the legend went, resolved to serve Apollo not in a creative role but as one who would catch the errors of others. He wrote reviews of our code that I believe were useful to NASA management, and he produced an accurate gloss on the flight software that the flight controllers could use instead of reading the code itself.

For the catching of errors, Norton practiced a sort of mental simulation known as "eyeballing" — in other words he read the code. The method was not effective at catching the subtle and dangerous problems that concerned us the most, usually having to do with timing, but it bore a rich harvest of minutiae. Norton wrote excruciatingly detailed critiques of our documentation, of our code (sometimes based on preliminary versions) and even of the non-functional comments with which we annotated the code — to all of which we were obliged to respond.

Norton took himself too seriously for us to respect him fully. In one case where in a comment I had misspelled the word "angle" as "angel" he criticized the "inconsistency." I remedied the inconsistency by changing all the spellings to "angel." There was no reaction.

Norton certainly was pettifogger enough to understand my point. Steve Copps was not so lucky. It had fallen to Copps to pull together an early version of the GSOP, our requirements document:

> I remember being proud of the product and more or less thought of it as my baby. I was young. Imagine the shock when within 24 hours after [Houston] received it we got a multipage memo written by John Norton... I couldn't believe it. I must have seen it as a challenge because I decided that if John Norton could find all those faults in a day then I could fix them in a day.... Around five in the morning I was finished and had incorporated the comments which were pretty much valid but for the most part were not substantive.

> After proofing it as best I could I decided that it would be fun to tease John a bit and insert a little comment which I assumed would take him days to find, and would make him laugh if he ever did find it. In the middle of P52 I wrote in tiny letters the words "Norton needs glasses."

Norton saw it immediately and did not laugh. Quite the contrary. Copps caught hell, even if the chewings out came "in all cases with a wink and a smile."

In 1971 it was enough for Norton to hear at second hand that Russ Larson had said that Norton was "working with us" at MIT on a User's Guide document, to touch off another episode. In a memo to his NASA boss, Jack Garman, Norton accused MIT of trying "to drag my name into their excuses to NASA as to why the document is lousy," adding,

> MIT still has their millions and I still have the post-midnight hours. As I told you yesterday, I've been working for 6 years on Apollo, and NASA doesn't have much to show for it.

After Apollo, Norton, still with TRW, worked on a project to computerize the distribution of hydroelectric power in the Northwest. He was still writing his painfully detailed critiques of other people's software. As it happened, a high school senior named Bill Gates came to work for him as a programmer. Gates has credited Norton with being among his best software teachers. Norton surely learned more from reading our code than we learned from him. Users of Microsoft software might wish he had learned more.

So far as I know, John Norton never detected a consequential bug in the Apollo flight software, but it was clever of him to parlay the software error that destroyed Mariner I into a reputation as a programming expert.

APOLLO 7, 8, 9

I went to meetings of the Software Control Board several more times during this period. I upgraded my wardrobe at the Harvard Coop and Filene's Basement. At the same time my hair was getting longer and after a brief experiment with a beard I settled on a mustache that I kept almost to the Millennium, except for a few shave-offs at Halloween.

One of my first Houston trips coincided with the splashdown party for Apollo 7, held at a barnlike saloon on NASA Road 1 called the Flintlock Inn. Splashdown had been early in the morning, Houston time, and the party had been going on for some hours when we got there. Soon after I walked in a NASA manager named Phil Shaffer suggested I get a haircut. That was the only such comment I ever heard and soon enough sideburns, mustaches, longer hair, and even bell-bottoms began to be seen around the space center.

If you read the Apollo 7 transcripts you can see why those involved needed a drink. Wally Schirra's crew seemed unprepared for the mission and Houston seemed unprepared for the crew. The flight ended with a running battle over whether the crew would wear their helmets during reentry. Finally the three astronauts—who all said they had stuffy noses—reneged on an agreement mission control understood them to have made, whereupon Deke Slayton said to the crew:

> You better be prepared to discuss in some detail when we land why we haven't got them on. I think you're too late now to do much about it... It's your neck and I hope you don't break it.

Apollo 7 qualified the Command and Service Modules for flight but disqualified the crew. None of the three ever flew again for NASA. For future missions a balance would have to be found between spam in a can and brats in a can.

———

Never mind. Apollo 7 was CSM-only in low Earth orbit. Allan Klumpp and I hardly noticed. We were nine miles from the lunar surface, figuring out how to go the rest of the way.

I was working the irregular hours, shifted towards night, that suited my metabolism and the job at hand. Often I would go to work around noon, work all afternoon, go home for the evening, then return to work at eleven or twelve—sometimes leaving a person asleep in my bed—to enjoy the late night hours when the computers were not so busy and I could get output within a few minutes. The first morning arrivals were my signal to go home, unless I stayed for the day. When I slept I slept very well, thank you.

Apollo 8 was Frank Borman's mission. It was only the third flight of the mighty Saturn V and the first since the launch I had witnessed on the day Martin Luther King was killed. That mission was marred by pogo vibrations and engine failures. Nevertheless, a month before its scheduled launch, NASA announced that Apollo 8 would go to the Moon and enter orbit. With the LM not yet ready to fly, why waste a Saturn V on putting one little spacecraft in Earth orbit?

The decision was an eye-opener—after LM-1, after the fire, after AS-502, after Apollo 7—a stunner. Evidently the people running the space program were of a bolder stripe than I had quite realized. It was intoxicating.

The booster functioned perfectly, as did the spacecraft and the guidance system. The crew excelled. Photographs taken of a distant Earth forever changed our view of our home planet. The poetry of the *King James Bible*, on Christmas Eve from lunar orbit, raised goose bumps on atheists. All at once a lunar landing in 1969 seemed possible again.

During the mission Jim Lovell used the Command Module's sextant to make dozens of star-elevation measurements using Earth and Moon horizons. The measurements were incorporated in the state vector using an ingenious algorithm called a Kalman filter that allowed incomplete information to be incorporated as it was collected, each time improving the navigation estimate a bit more. The system was so accurate that at the crucial junctures of lunar orbit insertion and Earth reentry the onboard navigation was perfect—proving that the system could have navigated safely to the Moon and back, completely without help from the ground, just as it was designed to do.

That is why, for many at MIT, Apollo 8 was the giant leap, the great fulfillment. We had ventured to another orb, seen its secret side, and done so by precise intention using a guidance system they had designed in their dreams — a thing of greater importance than the landing, that mere detail, left to the student. Well, Allan was that student and I was his apprentice, our business was landing, and the LM still had not emerged from her dressing room.

Soon she did, yet even Apollo 9 did not distract us. It was an Earth-orbit mission with both spacecraft, the only mission to fly with SUNDANCE. For the first time the LM flew with men onboard and cut loose from their ride home — another step out on the limb. No burn corresponding to the lunar descent was planned. Instead there was a six minute firing of the descent engine to prove that the LM could propel the stack with the heavy Command and Service Module attached.

The mission's main objective was to prove that the Lunar Module and the CSM could successfully rendezvous, preferably with the LM as the active vehicle. Three rendezvous solutions were computed: one in the Command Module, which was tracking the LM optically; one on the ground using radar data; and the solution that was acted upon, the one computed by the guidance computer in the LM based on onboard navigation. The computations agreed and the rendezvous was successful.

Something happened during Apollo 8 that would matter to us. Pete Conrad and Neil Armstrong had been in competition to command the first mission to attempt a landing. We had seen that at the Pussycat Team meeting a year before, where Armstrong was taciturn and Conrad irrepressible. But which quality did NASA value more? Two days before Christmas, with Apollo 8 in route to the Moon, Deke Slayton asked Armstrong if he wanted to command Apollo 11 with Buzz Aldrin as his LM pilot.

Aldrin was a fighter jock with West Point and Air Force roots. He had a doctorate from MIT (where Dick Battin was one of his teachers) and was happy to wear the nickname he had earned, both for his operational specialty and his intellectually-superior attitude toward the other astronauts, of Doctor Rendezvous.

I later heard how Conrad was informed of the decision. Bob Pearson ran the LM Mission Simulator at Cape Canaveral (the LMS) and he was on the console, with Conrad in the LM cockpit, flying landings, when Slayton and Alan Shepard arrived and climbed up to the cockpit. Conrad unplugged his headset so Pearson could supply no direct quotations, but Conrad would say anything to anybody, said Pearson. Conrad emerged from the cockpit, put on his shoes, walked straight out of the building, and drove away in his Corvette.

Armstrong himself was unsure, until Apollo 9 and Apollo 10 flew, whether Apollo 11 would even get to make the attempt, and Michael Collins, from the detached position of the astronaut who would wait in orbit, was "a little pessimistic about our chances to carry the whole thing off." Smart money might still have bet on Pete Conrad and Apollo 12.

THE LANDING RADAR

Bob Covelli built the software that operated the landing radar during the lunar descent. After navigating through hundreds of thousands of miles it was impossible to know the spacecraft's position and velocity, relative to the lunar surface, with enough accuracy to ensure a safe landing. On top of the other uncertainties there were the *masscons*, irregular concentrations of lunar mass that would have an effect on the LM's orbit that we could not accurately model.

The solution was to equip the LM with a radar that could measure the distance to the surface and the velocity across it. The data from the radar would be folded into the inertial navigation and any error in altitude or relative velocity would be corrected.

We expected the landing radar to lock on and begin measuring altitude when the LM was about 40,000 feet above the surface, and a bit later to begin measuring velocity. As the landing began, two lights on the DSKY labeled ALT and VEL were illuminated. Covelli's software indicated each data acquisition by turning off, first the ALT light, then the VEL light.

We were too jealous of our hard-won inertial state vector to expose it to raw measurements without due diligence. When the radar locked on, Covelli's code began computing a number called DELTAH (delta-height), the difference between the altitude derived from our inertial position vector and the altitude measured by the radar. DELTAH might be as much as a few thousand feet. Radar data was not accepted until the crew, and the ground, agreed that it looked reasonable. Houston had the number on their consoles via telemetry. For the crew we defined a new noun, Noun 68, which displayed DELTAH, scaled in feet, along with two unrelated items.

The LM pilot, who had the job of operating the DSKY during the landing, would key in

VERB 16 NOUN 68 ENTER

to call up this display. If DELTAH looked good he would authorize the incorporation of radar data by keying

VERB 57 ENTER

And even then, Covelli's software only slowly drew the state vector into agreement with the radar, and stayed alert for anomalous measurements. Nevertheless, our simulations showed that by the time the LM neared the surface we would know our altitude and relative speed quite accurately.

Only two things spoiled this pretty picture. The radar was completely unable to correct any error in the LM's horizontal position. The only device on the LM that could recognize a particular spot on the Moon was the human eye. The other limitation was that the software assumed the Moon was a smooth and round, like a billiard ball. The areas around the landing sites chosen for the first attempts would do their best to conform to that ideal, but if we ever needed to pass over a mountain range or a deep valley on the way to the landing site, something would have to be done.

In September 1968 I moved again to a bigger apartment, two large rooms spanning the first floor of a Marlborough Street brownstone two blocks from Massachusetts Avenue.

I upgraded my sound system, acquiring an AR-2 speaker and a Dynaco amplifier and preamp to go with my AR turntable. I was still playing my classical albums, but sometimes, in the dead of night, in a large chamber with no rug and little furniture I would put on the Doors, or Cream, and let the analog sound take me to the mystical place where that music seemed to originate.

The drawback, I soon found out, was that the landlord lived in the basement, immediately below me. After three months of complaints I broke the lease and found a new apartment at 2 Lime Street, on the flat part of Beacon Hill between Charles Street and the Charles River, where I lived for the rest of this story.

But it was during the three months at 358 Marlborough Street that Ruth first worked her magic on me. We met in Cambridge at the design store where she worked and we turned out to be neighbors in the Back Bay. Ruth was a serious person and a great beauty. There was something about her that made me think of the actress Bette Davis, some combination of a sensual languor and a flair for the dramatic. The first time we went out we ended up in my apartment and I lit a fire in the fireplace. I remember that she seemed indifferent to my advances, but a little later she left the room for a moment—and came back through the arched doorway breathtakingly naked.

At Christmas, with Apollo 8 in lunar orbit, we bought a Christmas tree in Haymarket and marched it the length of the Back Bay to her apartment, where we lay in front of the fireplace in the scent of balsam. On New Year's Eve we attended the opening of a new club called The Ark, located in a cavernous space on Lansdowne Street, in the shadow of Fenway Park's left-field wall. Beacon Street Union opened, followed by the California band Spirit. The light show may have outdone the Boston Tea Party in wattage but in this badly-proportioned space the effect was disappointing.

Most of our stepping out was more highbrow. We were melted and stirred by Franco Zefferelli's *Romeo and Juliet*. In June we dressed up for the Royal Ballet at the Music Hall. Rudolf Nureyev and Margot Fonteyn danced a sensuous *Pelleas and Melisande*, choreographed by Roland Petit to a score by Arnold Schoenberg with the corps de ballet in camouflage leotards. When the performance was over, with the crowd spilling onto the broad sidewalk in front of the theatre, Nureyev and Fonteyn themselves strode by in Cossack boots and puffy jackets, enjoying the worship of the throng, glowing as though there were a follow-spot on the roof, and perhaps there was.

Joan and Charlie Jones, last seen in Brattleboro, Vermont when Dana and I visited to use their darkroom, had moved back to Boston. Ruth and I visited them in their apartment in the South End, on the top floor of one of the first houses on the Chester Square block of Massachusetts Avenue to be recovered from dilapidation. We explored the contiguous hulks by crossing the roof and entering through their roof hatches. For a few decades in the nineteenth century these had been the grandest homes in Boston, high-ceilinged, gothic-portaled, rococo-plastered, corniced and medallioned—now a shambles, peopled by ghosts if you wanted to spook yourself out. Several of the houses had observatories on the roof, once-lovely small rooms with windows on four sides and a view over the rooftops to downtown skyscrapers in one direction, and to the south and west the hills of Milton and Newton.

Ruth was capricious, seductive, demanding, ellusive and substantial at the same time. She operated at a higher temperature than I had experienced before. She had another, less-presentable lover and made no secret of it. I was the one she took along when she visited her sister in Wellesley. Still, I was unjust when after three seasons I accused her of taking advantage. It would have been a better complaint if I had enjoyed it less.

Marjorie found a paying job at the Starr Bookshop in the Harvard Lampoon building in Harvard Square, where she created order in a collection that had taken on the hue and contours of dust. As 1969 began, Marjorie and I heard Led Zeppelin at the Tea Party on their first American tour—Robert Plant's voice like nothing I had ever heard in any rock club or opera house.

Time was our great preoccupation. Numerous functions had to be executed at the same time inside the computer. Of course they did not really happen "at the same time," but a combination of hardware-triggered interrupts, scheduled software interrupts called *tasks*, and a priority structure for allocating the non-interrupt processing in units called *jobs*, gave the illusion that it was all happening at once.

Ten times a second the digital autopilot operated to control the attitude of the spacecraft. It responded to attitude commands by firing RCS jets, and during thrusting flight by pivoting the engine. Every twenty milliseconds, in another hardware interrupt, the downlink program sent two sixteen-bit words of telemetry data to the ground. These (and others) were "background" activities that were not of great concern to Allan Klumpp and me, except for the time they consumed.

Navigation and guidance calculations repeated every two seconds during powered flight. Each pass started with the reading of the accelerometers, which took place in a *task* called READACCS that was scheduled using Waitlist. After reading and resetting the PIPAs the task rescheduled itself for the next cycle and then invoked the Executive to schedule a *job* called SERVICER, which contained the bulk of the processing.

That much was common to all the powered flight phases, but SERVICER itself was a sort of parade in which different floats participated, depending on which mission phase was being celebrated. By the way it was not pretty. Many hands had contributed to SERVICER, even before I came on the scene. It was logically tight enough but it was not easy to follow in the code.

SERVICER always began with navigation. It ran the so-called average-G equation that incorporated the velocity change measured by the accelerometers, along with the calculated velocity change due to lunar gravity, into the position vector. During the landing, measurements from the landing radar were also incorporated. Next came guidance.

For the orbital and mid-course burns controlled by Peter Adler's P40s, guidance was very simple because the spacecraft did not maneuver during the engine firing; during the lunar landing phases, the P60s, it was much more complex. After guidance came the processing of throttle commands (if the descent engine was being used), and the output of attitude commands to the autopilot. Finally, data was sent to the DSKY for display. Then the SERVICER job would end and wait to be rescheduled by the next READACCS.

Everything SERVICER did was vital to achieving the lunar landing, but it carried the lowest priority of all the jobs that were active. That was necessary because SERVICER was so bulky and time-consuming. It had to have a low priority so the other jobs needed during the landing, all of them much shorter, would have a chance to run at all. That meant, of course, that if there was not enough time it would be the SERVICER job that would fail to complete.

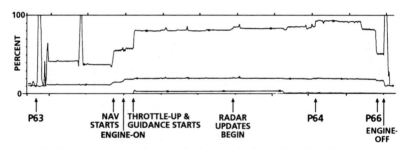

Guidance computer duty cycle during the lunar landing, from a simulation of the Apollo 11 landing programs.

We thought of the aggregate of all the interrupts and tasks and jobs in terms of *duty cycle*. We worried about how much processor time was left when all these functions were operating. We needed a margin for several reasons. For one thing, there would always be minor variations in how long the program took to run depending on the branches taken by the code.

More significantly, there were ways in which computer time could be "stolen" by the computer's auxiliary electronics. Information from the IMU, and from other sources such as the rendezvous radar, were sent to the computer by means of analog-to-digital converters known as CDUs, which worked by triggering actual computer operations.

Each CDU increment or decrement cost one memory cycle of 11.72 microseconds. Vibration concerned us. Could vibration, by mimicking changes in attitude, flood the computer with counter increments that would shrink the time available for the operation of our programs?

We aimed for a margin of 15 percent. That number was another of those guesses that stood up, like Dick Battin's one cubic-foot computer and the two-second guidance period. The number came from Charley Muntz, who wrote the Interpreter and co-invented restart protection. He brought it up with Allan Klumpp in the hallway and found him unreceptive: "I have a whole computer to use, and I'm going to use it."

Allan did not tell me about this conversation but he must have given it further thought because 15 percent was the number he announced to me as our goal. We achieved that during the early part of the braking phase (P63), up to the point where navigation began to incorporate landing radar data, but during the busiest part of the visibility phase (P64) our margin was barely 10 percent.

The environmental simulation allowed us to measure and plot duty cycle during the landing. It also allowed us to set a parameter called TLOSS so we could study how the software reacted under varying degrees of time stress. We came to use the term TLOSS in a more general way, to refer to the loss of processor time available for executing the code, whatever the cause.

TRAINING APOLLO 11

It was getting exciting. NASA was flying missions at intervals of barely two months. We had released LUMINARY 99, the rope that would fly on Apollo 11, and we were tumbling toward the first attempt at the summit.

First came Apollo 10, running LUMINARY 69. We monitored the mission from the second-floor classroom where the SCAMA link had been moved. Veteran astronaut Tom Stafford commanded. His crew included the future commanders of the final two Moon-landing missions, John Young and Gene Cernan. Leaving Young alone in the Command Module in lunar orbit, the LM separated from the CSM and performed a short burn of the descent engine to lower its perilune—its orbital low point—to about 50,000 feet. The object was to get low enough to test the landing radar and to rehearse the landing procedures, stopping just short of committing to an actual landing.

Pete Conrad might wander around the halls at MIT chatting with programmers, but the formal occasions for our interchanges with the astronauts were the crew training meetings held before each mission. It was our chance to instruct them in how to use the computer programs—the finer points, because every crew would already have flown landings in simulators—and to hear feedback from the most acute judges of our designs. For the crews it was a chance to cross-examine us, and, we hoped, gain confidence in the software we provided. Some of these sessions were more fun than others.

For Apollo 11 the crew-training meeting was in Houston, spread over two days, heavily attended and somewhat formal in atmosphere. A U-shaped arrangement of tables was set up in a large NASA conference room, MIT on the left wing, astronauts and NASA folks on the right. George Cherry made a presentation on the crew interfaces during descent, based on a memo we had written together. I took no formal part and sat at the back of the room, straining to hear the dialog taking place up front. Among the astronauts Buzz Aldrin did most of the talking.

Sometimes engineers say things that *sound* alarming. It came up that if an excessive number of landing site redesignations in the downrange direction were entered, then guidance could potentially plot a path that dipped below the surface. It was something you could do in a simulation but wanted to avoid in real life. I made an association between that and the fact that the presence of Chief Astronaut Deke Slayton entered the room soon after and lingered for a while. Neil Armstrong said he did not plan to use the redesignation capability anyway. At most he would put in one click to show us it worked.

There were undercurrents. It had emerged publicly that Aldrin was asking NASA to decide which astronaut would climb out of the LM and walk first on lunar soil. In fact he seemed to be campaigning, in concert with his father, for it to be him instead of Armstrong. It may have had something to do with the honor of the Air Force. My reaction was "Good grief." The decision had really been made years before when the LM's designers put the commander on the left and the hinges of the inward-opening hatch on the right. It would not have been impossible for Armstrong and Aldrin to switch positions before egress, but it would have been a clumsy, unnecessary procedure. The issue may have preyed on Armstrong a little. Malcolm Johnston recalls a conversation in which Neil seemed to be asking his opinion, which he gave—that of course the mission commander should go first. The "decision" in Armstrong's favor was announced the month before the crew training meeting.

Actually it was worse than we knew. After the decision, "Buzz's attitude took a noticeable turn toward gloom and introspection," according to the mission's level-headed Command Module Pilot Mike Collins. Gene Cernan remembers that Aldrin "was met at every turn by angry stares and muttered insults from his fellow astronauts." Not a pretty picture, three months from the Moon.

On the other hand, if there was one person you could rely on to stay cool, it was Neil Armstrong. He had shown us that on his only previous spaceflight, although it ended in an abort. That was Gemini 8, flown in March 1966 with Dave Scott in the other seat. A rogue thruster was spinning the spacecraft at an increasing rate. Nothing they tried fixed it and they were at the point of blacking out. "Well, we've got the re-entry system," Armstrong commented.

"Hit it, boss," Scott replied. That stabilized the spacecraft but committed it to an immediate return to Earth. On the way down on parachutes they were not sure whether they were over land or water. If land they would have to eject. Armstrong held a mirror up to the window to see downward. It was water, the South China Sea, running fifteen-foot swells as they soon found out. The destroyer *Leonard Mason*, making almost forty knots, reached them in three hours. "Gemini was not a good boat," Scott recalled.

During a break in the meeting a NASA engineer named Jim Alphin introduced me to Armstrong as we stood around in the hallway. I took the opportunity to talk up the redesignation capability. I assured him it was well tested and urged him to use it if he saw a spot that looked "interesting." He replied very pleasantly that anywhere he could touch down would be "interesting." He had no intention of trying anything the least bit "fancy."

I used the wrong argument. I should have said: first landing, lumpy Moon, probability of navigation errors. You could be heading into unexpected terrain. If you use the redesignator early in the visibility phase to improve the site you won't have to burn up so much fuel sashaying around at low altitude, and maybe you won't have to scare us all half to death.

If I had only known what was going to scare us all half to death.

APOLLO 11: IGNITION TO HIGH GATE

Once more we have gathered in the classroom for a mission. Binders six-inches thick containing the programs for the flight computers, and smaller volumes containing copies of the same checklists that are aboard the two spacecraft, lie open on long tables. A squawk box carries the conversation between the spacecraft and the ground. Open lines link us to the guidance system support room at the mission control center in Houston.

Launch was smooth, trans-lunar injection exactly on course, the long coast to the Moon uneventful. On the backside the joined spacecraft performed a lunar-orbit-insertion burn that left them in a circular orbit at an altitude of about sixty miles. Mission Commander Neil Armstrong and LM Pilot Buzz Aldrin entered the LM and took their positions, Armstrong on the left, Aldrin on the right. They activated its systems in the order prescribed in the checklist. The LM separated from the Command Module and performed a short retrograde burn to lower its orbital low point to an altitude about nine miles above the lunar surface.

Now Aldrin, using the display and keyboard unit that sits like a car radio between him and Armstrong, keys

VERB 37 ENTER 63 ENTER

Pinball understands that Verb 37 means "select program" so on the final keystroke it schedules a job called P63LM. On the DSKY the PROG register changes to 63 and the Computer Activity light goes solidly on as we begin the first wave of calculations.

First the ignition algorithm figures out the orientation the LM should be in at the start of the descent, and the exact time that the engine should be ignited. That is the first hurdle. The ignition algorithm is an iterative calculation that has to converge. If the initial conditions are seriously out of whack it might not.

BRAKING PHASE TTF (MIN-SEC)

TIME FROM IGNITION (MIN-SEC)

CROSSRANGE (XXXX.X NAUT MILE)

Simulation data.

The crew knows that the ignition algorithm has succeeded when the display starts flashing with a new set of data called Noun 61, the first of a series of nouns that will appear during the landing, each displaying its information in the DSKY's three general-purpose registers.

The first register displays the length of the braking phase, almost ten minutes from throttle-up to High Gate; the second gives the time to ignition, still more than twenty minutes away. The third register contains the crossrange distance – the distance the intended touchdown point lies from the plane of the LM's orbit. There is no decimal point. The astronauts have to know that crossrange is displayed in tenths of a nautical mile.

The display is flashing — the signal that a response is needed from the crew. The crossrange distance and burn time are deemed reasonable. Aldrin keys PROCEED.

Next come a series of calls and responses. Do you want to do a fine alignment of the IMU? The present alignment, performed two hours ago with sightings on Antares and Acrux, is adequate. Key ENTER to bypass. Shall we do an automatic maneuver to the burn attitude? The display gives three angles that will match the eight-ball when the maneuver is complete. Key PROCEED to authorize, ENTER to approve once the maneuver is accomplished. Then a curve ball, an alarm indicating that the landing radar antenna is in the wrong position. Aldrin resets the landing radar circuit breaker and the indication disappears.

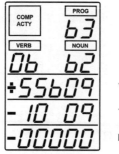

Apollo 11 flight data at MET 102:22:56.

Now **BURNBABY** takes charge — the routine Peter Adler and I wrote when we realized we were duplicating each other's code for the sequencing that led up to lighting an engine. The first thing **BURNBABY** does is call the orbital integration subroutine to calculate the **LM**'s orbital state vector as it will be exactly 30 seconds before the time of ignition (**TIG**), the moment powered flight navigation will begin. The crew knows the calculation has taken place when Noun 62 appears on the **DSKY**. The top number is the **LM**'s orbital velocity of 5560 feet per second, equal to about 3800 miles per hour. The middle register counts down to ignition, now scarcely ten minutes away. The bottom number is the accumulated velocity change (we call it delta-V) as measured by the accelerometers in the **IMU**. Delta-V is certain to be zero now because we are not yet reading the accelerometers.

The display requires no response and the count goes on. At about five minutes before **TIG** the ground gives the go for **PDI**, powered descent initiation. At **TIG** minus 35 seconds the display goes blank... then reappears. That is a signal that powered flight navigation has begun. Every two seconds, from now on, a task called **READACCS** will read the accelerometers and then schedule the **SERVICER** job.

If you picture **SERVICER**, repeating every two seconds, with the autopilot and housekeeping functions such as telemetry running in the background, then you have in broad strokes a picture of the computer activity during the landing. **SERVICER** is the scaffolding for a succession of functions. It runs during every powered flight phase, but the burden varies. During the landing, SERVICER is a pack camel whose load is piled higher and higher at each oasis. So far the load is light, just navigation and a bit of code to send information to the DSKY. Guidance is not yet engaged.

About thirteen seconds before ignition Aldrin flips a switch to arm the engine. At TIG minus 7.5 BURNBABY triggers a firing of the RCS jets to settle the fuel in the descent-stage tanks. At TIG minus 5 the display flashes and Verb 6 changes to the much more emphatic Verb 99 — "key PROCEED to enable engine."

It is about 4:05 in the afternoon of July 20. Four days, six hours, and 33 minutes have elapsed since launch. The LM is about a quarter of a million miles from Earth and nine vertical miles from the Moon. Huge stores of treasure, energy and brainpower have brought the mission to this point. Now the consent of two brave men in the cockpit is required. Aldrin keys PROCEED.

Allan Klumpp and I edge closer to the loudspeakers and the others seem to give way. We have worked together for three years to reach this moment. We have watched while other phases of the mission met their first trials. We have even seen bits of code we wrote exercised on previous missions — my AX*SR*T, his FINDCDUW — but it is now that we will finally be tested.

We are, however, powerless. Out of the loop. From here on events will unfold too rapidly for us to have any influence from Cambridge. Decisions will be made by mission control with support from the experts manning other rooms in the same building. In the AGC Support Room are NASA hotshot Jack Garman, and our man Russ Larson.

At zero BURNBABY sets bit 13 in output channel 11. Valves open and fuel and oxidizer meet and take fire in the combustion chamber of the descent engine. Noun 63 appears on the DSKY. Inertial velocity, as before, is joined by two new numbers that will be in every display from here on down: altitude-rate (also called rate of descent) and altitude. Just before signing off BURNBABY schedules a task called ZOOM to execute exactly 26 seconds after ignition.

The throttle is at 10 percent. The engine is delivering a thrust of about 1000 pounds. The LM's mass is about 34,000 pounds. At an acceleration of 1/34 G Armstrong and Aldrin hardly feel the engine. During this period the autopilot adjusts the descent engine gimbals so that the thrust vector passes through the center of mass of the spacecraft.

		VELOCITY (XXXX.X FT/SEC)
		ALT RATE (XXXX.X FT/SEC)
		ALTITUDE (XXXXX. FEET)

Apollo 11 flight data at MET 102:38:13.

Even now, SERVICER's load is light. The only additions at ignition are R11, the little routine that monitors the abort and abort-stage buttons, and the Delta-V Monitor, now adjusted, that had yelled "no fire" on the LM-1 mission.

Twenty-six seconds after ignition, ZOOM wakes up, opens the throttle to maximum, and activates guidance. SERVICER's load becomes much bulkier. Now the guidance equation has been added, along with a surprisingly complicated routine to send out throttle commands to the engine, written by me, and a deceptively simple one (FINDCDUW), written by Allan Klumpp, that passes attitude commands from guidance to the digital autopilot.

Now the engine is thrusting at its maximum, about 10,000 pounds, producing about 1/3 G in the cockpit. Hardly a kick in the pants, but enough. Ten seconds after throttle-up the LM is already on a trajectory that will "intersect" the surface if the engine fails. The LM is thrusting directly against its forward motion but the spacecraft is free to rotate around the thrust axis and right now the windows face the lunar surface. Picture yourself flying feet first, face down, wind in your petticoats.

Bill Tindall had expressed skepticism that monitoring the lunar surface early in the descent had any utility, likening it to "a low altitude pass over an unfamiliar desert at Mach 3 with lots of other interesting things going on inside the cockpit," but Armstrong finds it easy to recognize landmarks below and he is timing when he flies over them. About three minutes into the burn he says, "Our position checks down range show us to be a little long." From this he knows that if the error is not corrected the LM will land beyond the intended site.

About a minute later, with the LM still above 40,000 feet, Armstrong rotates the spacecraft to a windows-up attitude. Now the LM faces in the general direction of Earth but that is not the point. To land safely you need a radar. After a quarter-million mile journey and several orbits of a body with a lumpy gravitational field, no inertial navigation system is good enough to make a delicate touchdown without local measurements of the altitude and velocity relative to the surface. The position of the landing radar antenna requires the LM to be in a windows-up posture—or, as the LM maneuvers, increasingly windows-forward—from now on. Just shy of five minutes into the burn the indicator light labeled ALT goes out. That means that the radar has locked on to the lunar surface and is providing altitude data.

SLANT RANGE (XXXX.X NAUT MILE)

BRAKING PHASE TTF (MIN-SEC)

DELTA-HEIGHT (XXXXX. FEET)

Apollo 11 flight data at MET 102:38:13,
just before the first alarm.

But is it good data? Bob Covelli's "reasonableness" check will stop grossly bad information from contaminating the state vector, but the crew and the ground must still make a judgment call before allowing radar updates. The basis for the decision is DELTAH—the difference between the altitude calculated by the inertial system and the altitude measured by the radar. DELTAH is visible on the ground, via telemetry, but we have also provided a way to monitor it onboard, and so, about five minutes into the landing, passing through 35,000 feet, Aldrin keys

VERB 16 NOUN 68 ENTER

Verb 16 means "monitor" and Noun 68 names the new set of data that now populates the DSKY's three general-purpose registers: DELTAH looks reasonable: about 3000 feet. There is no reason not to incorporate radar data, but it is here that the lunar descent goes off the rails.

Aldrin: Altitude light out. DELTAH is minus 2900.

Houston: Roger. We copy.

Aldrin: Got the Earth straight out our front window.

Armstrong: Houston, you're looking at our DELTAH?

Houston: That's affirmative.

Armstrong: Program alarm.

Houston: It's looking good to us. Over.

Houston means the landing radar looks good. Mission Control has not yet reacted to the program alarm. The crew sees the display change back from Noun 68 to Noun 63. Aldrin quickly keys

VERB 5 NOUN 9 ENTER

to bring up a display of the alarm code.

Armstrong: It's a 1202.

Aldrin: 1202.

There follows a pause of over fifteen seconds, one of those occasions when time seems to simultaneously speed up and slow down. I suppose the intensity of the experience increases the space, per unit of clock time, that it takes up in our memory.

In Cambridge someone looks up the alarm code and announces, "executive overflow — no core sets." The alarm occurs when the Executive's queue is full. It has been asked to schedule a job but has no memory left to allocate. Core sets are groups of twelve registers that contain the vital information that must be preserved if a job is interrupted by a higher priority job. There are eight core sets so as many as eight jobs can be scheduled at the same time. Normally that is plenty.

But why, why is this happening?

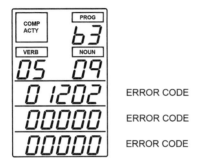

Apollo 11 flight data at MET 102:38:27

We know that when this alarm occurs the computer goes through the same restart sequence as it would follow if it lost power for a moment. All computations are flushed and then reconstructed using information in the restart tables. Charley Muntz's insight in 1963 is being tested. (Listening at home, he knows it.)

Is vibration a problem after all?

In mission control, guidance officer Steve Bales keys the line to his back room and asks a different question. Go or no go? Garman and Larson are suddenly very much on the spot.

Onboard, it did not escape Aldrin's notice that just before the alarm the ground approved the radar. He releases the alarm-code display and keys

VERB 57 ENTER

to authorize navigation to incorporate landing radar data. That adds another load on SERVICER's back. It is time-consuming because range and speed are measured by an antenna fixed to the LM's structure. The radar data has to be converted from the body coordinate system to the stable-member frame used by navigation.

Meanwhile Armstrong eyes the abort button. Can the mission continue? Is guidance still in control? Maybe he remembers the abort on

Gemini 8. When he finally breaks the silence there is an edge in his voice that comes across clearly on the squawk box.

Armstrong: Give us a reading on the 1202 Program alarm.

Jack Garman is accustomed to looking at the guidance system from the outside and he has developed confidence in its robustness. He has seen this alarm before. When a big simulation was aborted because of another obscure alarm Gene Kranz had ordered a review of the "impossible" alarms like the one that had just occurred.

Garman consults his handwritten notes. 1202 is a go as long as the alarm does not recur too frequently and the trajectory looks okay. Larson acquiesces with a thumbs up because he is too dry to speak. Garman says Go. Bales says Go. Kranz says Go.

Houston: Roger. We got ya—We're GO on that alarm.

That is the Capcom, Charlie Duke, the only man in mission control who talks to the crew directly. Was he about to say, "We got you a Go," as though a case had been argued and won?

Thirty seconds have elapsed between the alarm and the Go from Houston. The LM is approaching 30,000 feet, descending at about 130 feet per second. Aldrin wants to watch DELTAH decrease as radar data is gradually mixed into the LM position vector, so once more he keys

VERB 16 NOUN 68 ENTER

DELTAH is down to 1772 feet. Aldrin watches it decrease: 1629, 1348, 907. The radar is doing its job. Then the alarm indicator on the DSKY lights again. Again Noun 68 disappears and Noun 63 returns. Again Aldrin calls up the alarm code and again sees "1202."

Aldrin: Same alarm, and it appears to come up when we have a
             16 68 up.

Houston: Roger. Copy. We'll monitor your DELTAH.

Again our computations have been flushed and reconstructed and apparently the LM is still flying. In Cambridge someone says "Something is stealing time." Aldrin's Verb 16 is not the cause of the problem but merely the final straw that tips us into deficit. Something is stealing time. Some dreadful thing is active in our computer and we do not know what it is or what it will do next. Unlike Garman in Houston I know too much. If it were in my hands I would call an abort. I remember the anticlimax of the LM-1 mission.

About 400 seconds have passed since ignition. The spacecraft is at 23,000 feet, sinking at about 100 feet per second, pitched back 67 degrees. Armstrong's heart rate is 120. Then something very good happens.

Aldrin: Ah! Throttle down.

Armstrong: Throttle down on time!

Houston: Roger. We copy throttle down —

Aldrin: You can feel it in here when it throttles down. Better than the simulator.

Four times in four seconds. It is as though after all the agitation about the alarms they just love saying "throttle down." In Cambridge we savor it too. In the present situation they are about the sweetest words that we could possibly hear because throttle down, occurring just when expected, is a strong indication that navigation and guidance still know what they are doing. In the official transcript of the air-to-ground communication during the landing those are the only exclamation points.

At the beginning of the burn the imperative was to shed forward velocity, so the LM began by thrusting full bore with the engine aimed straight ahead. Now we are lower and slower and the spacecraft is six tons lighter than at ignition. Full thrust is no longer required—but the reduction cannot be gradual. We must not operate the engine in the region between 63 percent and maximum thrust because the nozzle will erode excessively. Throttle down occurs in one swoop when the thrust level commanded by the guidance equation first comes below about 57 percent, allowing room for it to build up slightly without violating the upper boundary and returning to maximum thrust.

One thing though. Armstrong now knows the LM is straying into unknown territory. If guidance had known about the down-range error he had noticed earlier when the LM was windows-down, throttle down would have been late as the LM tried to pull up short by applying additional thrust.

All the while the LM has been gradually pitching forward and just before the braking phase ends the spacecraft is pitched back only 55 degrees. By craning over the bottom of the window Armstrong can glimpse the lunar surface ahead. Inside the guidance equation, TTF, the computed time to fly before reaching the current targets, is getting smaller and smaller; but TTF figures in the denominator and if we let it get too small the equation will become overly sensitive. By design we automatically declare High Gate when TTF reaches about 60 seconds.

APOLLO 11: HIGH GATE TO TOUCHDOWN

Guidance automatically switches to Program 64. The equation is the same but now we are flying to a new set of target conditions called Low Gate. The spacecraft begins pitching forward. A job named HIGATJOB repositions the landing radar antenna. The DSKY switches to Noun 64.

The top register contains two distinct numbers—my suggestion at the Pussycat Team meeting in November 1967, the first time I saw an astronaut in person and the day of the night I broke my leg.

REDES TIME (SEC) — LPD ANGLE (DE(

ALT RATE (XXXX.X FT/SEC)

ALTITUDE (XXXXX. FEET)

Apollo 11 flight data at MET 102:41:31.

The number on the right, 70 degrees just after entering P64 with the pitchover maneuver not yet complete, is the LPD angle. LPD means landing point designator and it is how we tell the astronaut where the LM is going. The angle is referenced to a vertical scale, marked off in degrees, on Armstrong's window. Calculating the angle has lashed yet another burden on the back of SERVICER. The number on the left is the number of seconds remaining during which Armstrong may tweak the aim point.

Over about ten seconds the LM pitches forward until it is canted back only about 40 degrees from vertical. The lunar landscape fills the windows. Armstrong does not recognize the landmarks he got to know in training. Aldrin may steal a quick glance but he must keep his eyes in the cockpit, watching the DSKY and the other displays.

When the automatic pitch maneuver is complete Armstrong switches to ATT HOLD, the autopilot mode in which deflecting the joystick in his right hand (the RHC) commands a rotation and releasing it stops the rotation and holds attitude. Armstrong wants to get a feel for the LM's handling qualities. He puts in small commands in roll and yaw, comments favorably, and switches back to AUTO. The spacecraft is nearing 3000 feet.

Houston: You're go for landing.

Aldrin: Roger Understand. Go for landing. 3000 feet. PROGRAM ALARM.

After three minutes of alarm-free operation it comes as a jolt. Again the computer goes through its restart procedure. Again Aldrin keys Verb 5 Noun 9. This time it is a 1201 alarm—not "no core sets" but "no VAC areas"—another indication that something is clogging the Executive queues. Our heads are spinning.

Houston: We're go. Same type. We're go.

Does Houston know more than we know? Well, yes. They have telemetry that shows the LM is still precisely on trajectory. It is as though a terrible screech is coming from the front of your car, but the engine is still running, the steering still works, and you are getting very near your destination.

One minute into P64, with the LM passing through 2000 feet, Armstrong becomes interested in the LPD.

Aldrin: 2000 feet. 2000 feet.

Armstrong: Give me an LPD.

Aldrin: 47 degrees.

Armstrong: Give me an LPD.

Aldrin: 47 degrees.

Armstrong: 47. That's not a bad looking area. Okay.

Aldrin has already keyed PROCEED to enable the redesignation capability. Armstrong had said he did not intend to redesignate, but that was before he knew he was going into terrain that is less familiar and perhaps less hospitable. Now if he wishes he can shift the landing site using the same hand controller that he just used for attitude control. Being ready to react to this signal adds the final birdcage to SERVICER's bulging load. Here is Armstrong's recollection a few days after returning to Earth:

> Normally, in this time period, that is, from P64 onward, we'd be evaluating the landing site and checking our position and starting LPD activity. However, the concern here was not with the landing areas we were going into, but rather whether we could continue at all. Consequently, our attention was directed toward clearing the program alarms, keeping the machine flying, and assuring ourselves that control was adequate to continue without requiring an abort. Most of the attention was directed inside the cockpit during this time period and in my view this would account for our inability to study the landing site and final landing location during final descent. It wasn't until we got below 2000 feet that we were actually able to look out and view the landing area.

It is odd that Armstrong portrayed 2000 feet as the point where the distraction clears because at about that moment something new happens. The DSKY goes blank. Stays blank for about ten seconds, at which point, at an altitude of 1400 feet, just 24 seconds after the previous alarm, the alarm light flashes once again and the DSKY comes back to life. It is another 1202. Houston says go. No one comments on the blank DSKY. After the mission they will laugh about it. Other cockpit indicators driven by the computer are still functioning.

Just 17 seconds later, near 800 feet, it happens again, another 1202, although this time the DSKY is only blank for a second or two. Armstrong's heart rate rises to around 150.

For the fifth time the onboard software has taken itself apart and put itself back together again. NASA is trusting our programs to an extraordinary degree—possibly more than they know. Go has become reflexive. Really it is out of Houston's hands. Out of Earth's hands. With the LM below 1000 feet only Armstrong and Aldrin are in a position to react fast enough if the LM suddenly stutters or bucks or freezes or gives any definitive sign of a loss of control.

Whatever his heart rate, Armstrong seems to have become blasé about the program alarms. He may be too focused on the Moon to even notice. At times that bracket the last alarm Armstrong asks for, and receives, an LPD angle:

Aldrin: 700, 21 down, 33 degrees.

Armstrong: Pretty rocky area.

That is not a great advertisement for our LPD system. Only 30 seconds ago the LPD angle pointed to "not a bad looking area." But we have at last guided the LM to an altitude, and a velocity, from which a semi-manual takeover is practical.

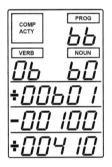

HORIZ VELOCITY (XXXX.X FT/SEC)

ALT RATE (XXXX.X FT/SEC)

ALTITUDE (XXXXX. FEET)

First display in P66. Apollo 11 flight data at MET 102:43:21.

The rest of the story has often been told. It is too late to stop short so Armstrong decides to land beyond the rocky area. At 650 feet, with a sink rate of about 20 feet per second, he switches to ATT HOLD, taking attitude control away from the guidance equation. He maneuvers to a more erect posture to preserve his forward velocity. Ten seconds later, down to 430 feet, he blips the ROD (rate-of-descent) switch. This triggers a transition to P66, the semi-manual final landing mode. The LM is still moving forward at about 40 miles per hour.

In P66, guidance is much simpler than in P63 or P64 because Armstrong, not the guidance equation, is controlling horizontal motion. The computer's job is to operate the throttle in response to attitude changes and inputs from the ROD switch. The net effect is a considerable lightening of the computational load.

As one minute in P66 turns into two a new apprehension takes over. Fuel. Onboard, the low fuel light comes on. That means that 30 seconds of fuel remain. There may be more but only 30 seconds is promised.

Finally, after almost 150 seconds in P66 and a series of maneuvers that Neil Armstrong will later characterize as "spastic," as he tries to stop the LM above a smooth spot despite the blowing dust that confuses his perception of his motion across the surface, the contact probes touch the surface. Indicators light up in the cockpit. Armstrong switches the engine off. The LM plants her four feet in lunar dust.

Houston: We copy you down, Eagle.

Armstrong: Houston, Tranquility Base here. The Eagle has landed.

Houston: Roger, Tranquility. We copy you on the ground. You got a bunch of guys about to turn blue. We're breathing again. Thanks a lot.

Aldrin: Thank you.

They are in a very remote place where we have sent them in a rickety jalopy that is their only way back to civilization. At least they are polite about it.

WHAT JUST HAPPENED?

Allan Klumpp grabbed my hand and pumped it. "We did it," he said, but congratulations were brief. In the manned spaceflight business you do not truly celebrate until the guys are in the ocean and at this moment we had concerns about achieving that. What caused the alarms? Was the computer healthy? Would ascent work?

Some things we knew. We understood how the alarms were triggered. More jobs were being scheduled than were completing with the result that the Executive's storage areas ran out. When the Executive was asked to schedule a new job but did not have storage available, it had no recourse but to trigger a software restart by transferring control to the tag BAILOUT in the Alarms and Aborts section, accompanied by an alarm code.

The temporary storage areas were of two sorts: *core sets* of twelve words, which all jobs needed, and *VAC areas* of forty-four additional words required by jobs that used the Interpreter. There were five VAC areas and if one was requested when none were available a 1201 alarm was generated. There were eight core sets and if they ran out a 1202 alarm was generated.

We believed that jobs were stacking up because something was stealing time. We had no idea what that was but we understood how it would affect the landing software. SERVICER was the biggest job that was running, scheduled each time by the READACCS task that came around like clockwork every two seconds to read the accelerometers. If for some reason SERVICER had not finished by the time READACCS rescheduled it, then it would be scheduled again. The new job would start executing, but the stub of the previous SERVICER would keep possession of its core set and VAC area. If it kept happening, one or the other type of storage space would run out.

The LM had stayed on course, but odd things were happening with the DSKY, including a ten second blackout. That added up too. Evidently SERVICER was running normally through the point where it issued throttle and attitude commands, but was being cut off during the last of its functions, updating the DSKY display.

We also understood what happened inside the computer when an alarm occurred. All activity other than interrupts dedicated to a particular purpose was flushed and then reconstructed from information stored in the tables maintained by the restart system. Only essential jobs were restart protected. That is why Aldrin's Verb 16 Noun 68 disappeared after each of the alarms in P63. The software restart had shed load, and in P63 that was enough. In P64 alarms occurred even without Verb 16 and that made sense too, because guidance itself took more time in P64.

Fine and dandy. But there was no satisfaction in it. Yes we had coped. Yes, but why? Why did it happen at all? There was still a bogeyman hiding in the thickets.

We listened in to the activities right after landing, which consisted of getting ready to leave again in case something awful happened suddenly. Finally Houston said Stay*. It was estimated that the LM had landed about 4 miles downrange of the intended site. The crew decided to get out of the spacecraft before sleeping and began their preparations for their "surface EVA." Finally I biked home across the Longfellow Bridge, and marveled at the crude pictures from the Moon on my television, and the chatter of the humans who were there—and finally slept for a while, still wondering why?

Only one man had looked the beast in the eye—only one, at least, who knew what he had to do at that moment. That was call mission control. He got through but never got the callback. Blamed himself for not leaving a crisper message.

George Silver worked for MIT but was stationed at Cape Canaveral, where his job was to check out the primary guidance system as installed in the spacecraft. Silver was a genial, bluff, burly, blond guy who looked like he could rassle the alligators that abounded in the bayous around the Cape. He had more hands-on experience than anyone with the fully assembled systems that were soon to be launched.

Silver had returned to Massachusetts to help monitor the mission. He watched the landing on television in his living room and followed the same train of reasoning as we had in Cambridge. Something was stealing execution time. Then he remembered LM-3, the lander that had flown on Apollo 9.

On June 14, 1968 the ascent stage of LM-3, containing the guidance system, was delivered to the Kennedy Space Center by Super Guppy—a strange bulbous aircraft, operated by Aero Spaceline Industries, that we had seen on Grumman's runway in Bethpage. On arrival the LM was moved to a high bay area in the sprawling Manned Spacecraft Operations Building (MSOB) where it immediately began undergoing tests.

---

* The word Go was normally used to indicate that the mission could proceed as planned but when the LM was on the Moon the word Stay was substituted.

Silver noticed that occasionally, when the guidance system was powered up, a flood of pulses began flowing into the computer from the rendezvous radar interface.

The rendezvous radar had nothing to do with landing on the Moon. It was for finding the Command Module when the LM returned to orbit, whether after aborting the descent or ascending normally after a stay on the surface. The radar used a steerable antenna whose pointing direction had to be known to the computer. Two devices called resolvers received information from sensors attached to the shaft and trunnion of the antenna and derived angles that were passed to the computer in the form of increment and decrement pulses. Silver traced the spurious pulses flowing into the computer to these resolvers.

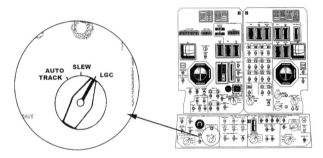

Rendezvous Radar mode switch.

The rendezvous radar had a mode switch with three positions: LGC, AUTO, and SLEW. When the switch was in LGC, the resolver used as its reference signal an 800-hertz signal from the PGNCS, and therefore its data made sense to our computer. When the switch was in SLEW or AUTO the 800-hertz reference signal came from the Grumman system. The trouble was, Silver discovered, when the mode switch was in AUTO or SLEW, data still flowed to the LGC—only it was nonsensical non-data because the wrong reference signal was being used.

How much non-data was generated depended on the phase relationship between the two 800-hertz signals. That relationship was established when Aldrin and Armstrong floated into the LM and first activated its systems. The Grumman system was always powered up first, followed by the PGNCS. The relationship between the 800-hertz power supplies in the two systems was completely random, determined by where Grumman power was in its cycle when the PGNCS sprang to life. In about one hundred tests Silver saw the pulse storm only twice. It occurred only when the phase mismatch was at its worst. Evidently Apollo 11 had hit the sweet spot.

Silver called the phenomenon "cycle stealing." Each spurious pulse from the RR resolvers was handled by the computer with an involuntary increment or decrement operation that consumed one memory cycle of 11.72 microseconds. In the worst case—as the resolvers went crazy trying to find an impossible angle—enough pulses would go to the computer to consume more than 13 percent of its execution time. Even 13 percent might not be noticed in flight, Silver realized, except during the most complex phase of the mission, the lunar descent.

Back in 1968 Silver had written up the problem and proposed a simple hardware fix that would synchronize the two 800-hertz signals so neither system would receive meaningless data in any switch position. The change was not made, apparently on grounds of cost and schedule impact.

I was back in the SCAMA room the next morning. There were no new theories until Silver walked into the room about an hour before noon (my guess). In his hand was his 1968 memo. Lunar ascent was scheduled for about 2:00 PM, Boston time. George explained his theory. It added up. He had already been on the phone with Russ Larson in Mission Control.

We can trace Silver's information in the conversations between the LM and Houston as preparations were being made for the ascent to lunar orbit. At 161 minutes before lunar liftoff, this exchange occurred:

Houston: ... a couple of minor changes in the checklist. The main one being that we do not want the rendezvous radar on during the ascent, and we think that this will take care of some of the overflow of program alarms that you were getting during descent.

Aldrin: Okay. We had the rendezvous radar in SLEW during descent, though.

Houston: Say again.

Aldrin: We had the rendezvous radar switch in the SLEW
            position, not the LGC position.

Houston: We copy that. But there's a greater duty cycle
            on—there's a good 15-percent duty cycle on the ascent
            program there, so just go ahead and leave it off.

Silver's information had gotten through, but not fully. Mission control now knew the problem had to do with the rendezvous radar, but they made the same mistake that has been made by almost everyone ever since—that the problem had to do with the radar being on. Silver knew that the problem could occur even with the radar off because the resolvers would still be powered up and sending spurious data.

Aldrin's comment that the radar was in SLEW, not LGC, exposes another misunderstanding that has lingered. He wants to connect the problem to the computational load on the LGC, as opposed to the dumb burden of counting meaningless pulses. He thinks having the rendezvous radar in AUTO or SLEW should have lowered the burden on the computer not increased it.

Nine minutes later a red herring pops up, based on a theory whose origins are unknown to me.

Houston: ...and then you might add a little note down there at the
            bottom of the page: Do not use tape meter in PGNCS, do
            not place MODE SELECT switch to PGNCS.

Aldrin: Okay. We'll put it in AGS.

Houston: Fair enough. That's some more of that computer load
            business.

In other words the tape meters that displayed altitude and altitude-rate would be driven by the abort guidance system. The primary system would still be in control of the spacecraft.

More than two hours pass. The crew still has not been vouchsafed the key fact, until, about 19 minutes before liftoff, almost as an afterthought:

Houston: Roger. Just a reminder here, we want to make sure you
            leave the rendezvous radar circuit breakers pulled to
            avoid a computer overload. However, we want the
            rendezvous radar mode switch in LGC.

For the ascent to lunar orbit the guidance equation was simple, radar data did not have to be incorporated into navigation, and the engine on the ascent stage was not throttleable. The computational load on the computer was lighter than during any part of the powered descent. The problem that made the landing so exciting would not have been noticed during the ascent anyway.

That does not detract from what George Silver accomplished. He was a hero on July 20 and 21 because he was the difference between flying with a problem that was not fully understood, and thus hugely disquieting, and a problem that had been understood and avoided.

DEBRIEFING

The ascent was normal and with Doctor Rendezvous onboard the LM easily found and docked with the CSM. The return to Earth was uneventful and the Command Module splashed down southwest of Hawaii. Aboard USS *Hornet* the crew and their moon rocks were hustled into a shiny, wheel-less Airstream trailer, which was airlifted to Houston and disgorged into the Lunar Receiving Lab, where the astronauts would live for 15 days in the company of lab mice of whose health they were quite solicitous — all this in case they had, against expectation, brought home some otherworldly microbe or other lunacy. For the doomsday case bulldozers were standing by to bury the laboratory under a mound of dirt, astronauts, staff and all.

While the crew was in quarantine a series of debriefings were held. Allan Klumpp and I attended the guidance and navigation session on August 4. Russ Larson sat in a room separated from the astronauts by a glass partition. Allan and I were in another room in the same building. A few rows of chairs faced a big television screen where Neil Armstrong, in a white shirt, was flanked by Buzz Aldrin and Mike Collins wearing NASA overalls. Larson would speak for MIT and ask a series of questions that we had all helped compile. Allan and I would be free to ask additional questions later.

The debriefing followed the mission timeline. The crew seemed tired and a little bored until they got to the lunar descent, when everyone seemed to perk up. By then Allan and I had moved into empty front row seats. I took notes for the report I would write when I got back to Cambridge.

Armstrong understood that the alarms had been caused by having the rendezvous radar mode switch in the wrong position but was uninformed about the underlying mechanism. Aldrin asked whether the ground sees program alarms when they happen. Yes. Then they should read them aloud. Jack Garman commented that Apollo 12 was making a placard explaining computer alarms. Apollo 11 had one too but it did not include 1201 and 1202. Laughter. What was your reaction to the DSKY going blank for ten seconds during P64?

"Seemed like a long time," Armstrong chuckled, "I never expected it to come back."

The lunar surface began to be visible earlier than expected in the braking phase. Would Armstrong give up the visibility in P63 to have more visibility in P64? Yes, because he already was not counting on it. He did not look at the LPD until about 2000 feet because he was concerned with understanding the alarm problem and keeping the machine flying. "On roughly four peeks roughly ten seconds apart the spot indicated by the LPD moved downrange about one crater diameter, one quarter mile." If he had redesignated he would have redesignated short because the near edge of the rock-strewn crater looked like an "interesting" spot.

Armstrong described how he eventually flew past that crater in P66, apologizing for his "mind-changing exercises." Attitude response in P66 was "as anticipated, crisp and responsive." Control of rate of descent felt "smooth not jumpy" although his meters showed fluctuations in chamber pressure as the throttle responded — a comment we should have paid more attention to. "Around 300-500 feet is an important place to have time." No kidding. Armstrong had used almost 150 seconds. But would he accept a lower High Gate and shorter visibility phase in return for more fuel for final maneuvering in P66? "Not willingly."

Distance judgment? "Good enough." Now Allan asked, could you distinguish a five or ten degree slope? "No, but a big area couldn't slope that much without its being noticeable." Below 100 feet it was tricky to judge lateral translation because of dust kicked up by the engine. "It's not hard, but one has to be mentally prepared to be distracted by the moving dust."

During the final landing phase the DSKY had displayed horizontal velocity, the composite of forward and lateral movement. Armstrong commented that this was not useful. Here I asked my only question, "Would either forward or lateral velocity be more useful than what's there now?"

"Forward velocity, Don," replied Armstrong.

I had not realized that the crew could see us. Did Armstrong really know who I was, from our brief conversation in the hallway during crew training when I urged him to use the redesignator if he saw an "interesting" spot? As possibly the most "alternative" person they saw around the space center had I become a topic of special notice? Well, there must have been a degree of respect in it because they had just flown my software to the lunar surface. Needless to say I changed the velocity display as recommended.

As the debriefing moved on to the ascent and rendezvous phases Allan left to catch the Metro Airlines shuttle that flew the route from nearby Clear Lake airport to Houston International. I cut it closer but we ended up on the same plane sitting forward with a good view into the cockpit as we flew over the city. Allan was worrying about the downrange LPD creep mentioned by Armstrong. As we descended, watching the altimeter through the open cockpit door and the ground out the window, we tried to imagine how the Moon had looked to Armstrong at 700 feet, 500 feet, 300 feet, never mind that we were in a De Havilland Twin Otter not the LM and it was parched Texas scrub not lunar regolith.

We narrowly made the flight to Chicago and the connection to Boston. A few others were onboard and someone had engineered an upgrade to first class for us all. First class liquor flowed and Allan and Jim Nevins flirted with the stewardesses by showing them Apollo documents from their briefcases.

In Boston the ceiling was low and visibility short and we did a hair-raising wave-off on the first try at landing. This quieted everyone down, especially Allan, but we landed smoothly on the second try. I sped home in the Alfa. It was late but not too late to call Christy and we met at the playground on Myrtle Street.

We had met in the spring. "Do you ever play on the swings?" she had asked. She meant the swings at the playground near the summit of Beacon Hill. I had not been on a swing since DeSoto Park in Memphis, near the Indian mounds. There the view at the top of the arc was the mighty Mississippi, in some seasons so broad that you could hardly make out the other side.

Christy was lanky, ash blond, pale and a little fey, a spirit in the mist. She committed herself to the swing totally and attained amazing heights. Across the street from the playground was a stone building with a big door, and nearer still a fence and a few benches. You could judge the height of your arc by what you could see over the crossbar at the top of your backswing. When I asked Christy, "Can you see the doorknob?" she did not even answer she was so far above me, her loose dress snapping in the slipstream. Other times we flew a lazy arc through heavy summer air electric with the threat of lightning, synchronized, seemingly motionless together while the universe swirled around us. Christy and I were more buddies than lovers. We went to the movies with provolone cheese in our pockets to munch on, and shared a bed fairly chastely.

It was late summer when I met Amy in a shop in the Back Bay, a porcelain beauty with hourglass figure and thick auburn hair down to the small of her back, perfectly turned out in art-student style in miniskirt and black tights and good shoes—and cheeks that flushed deliciously pink when she was provoked or aroused. She was a survivor, she said, of Music and Art High School, but she was a graduate of the school of New York, with so much urban sophistication, self-acquired in defiance of the outer borough where she grew up, that sometimes I felt like a yokel. That warm day in August or September we started with an ice cream cone, but as summer turned into fall we left Norman Rockwell behind and became worthier subject matter for Titian or another late Renaissance master.

WHAT JUST HAPPENED? PART 2

The problem of the alarms on Apollo 11 ran deeper than what happened during the mission on July 20 and 21. The story has become a sort of palimpsest on which is written, in layers, the flight software, the hardware in which it was embedded, the procedures to operate it, and the decision-making in mission control—but like an artifact it retains certain mysteries. The mysteries may even deepen as the documents that might solve them are discarded or decay and human memories fade; but even if every veil were lifted and we knew everything about who did and wrote and coded what, when and where, assigning causality might still baffle Aristotle.

It was a checklist error. The relevant checklist was titled the *Apollo 11 LM Timeline Book*, and it is on page 8, just before the selection of P63, that the rendezvous radar (RR) mode is set to AUTO TRACK. It was natural to assume that the machine would operate properly with the radar in that mode—it would have except for an obscure, unmarked booby-trap in the hardware—but it was an assumption.

Two weeks after the crew returned, Apollo Program Manager George Low complained that "675 checklist changes were processed in the 30 days prior to launch." In that number there were bound to be a few stinkers. Low demanded that in future enough time be allowed for checklist changes to be reviewed by all the relevant organizations. Low did not explicitly link his complaint to the alarms on Apollo 11, but indeed such a review might have caught the problem. Low's memo was addressed specifically to Deke Slayton and it is hard not to read it as a rebuke of the astronaut corps for playing fast and loose with the checklists. For Low, that may have been answer enough. For me, I am loath to find a root cause so amenable to bureaucratic fiat. At most it was another lost opportunity to prevent.

Buzz did it. Aldrin himself is the primary protagonist for this theory. He takes responsibility for having the rendezvous radar turned on — probably one of those 675 checklist changes deplored by Low — but he also feels aggrieved, asking Hugh Blair-Smith in 2009, "Why would you not think that Doctor Rendezvous would want the radar on?" That way it would be ready in the event of an abort.

Blair-Smith conjectures that Aldrin's role was as follows: (1) the baseline circa 1965 was to have **RR** on, mode in **LGC**, and tracking the **CSM** during the descent, (2) at some point tracking during descent was scrubbed to reduce processor load, so the plan became **RR** off, mode in **LGC**, (3) Aldrin in June 1969 said "If the **LGC** hasn't got time to do that, the **AGS** has," and the plan became **RR** on with mode in **AUTO** or **SLEW**. That would explain why Aldrin feels guilty about the change — but he is wrong about which part of the change caused the problem. It was not having the **RR** on, it was having the **RR** mode in **AUTO** or **SLEW**.

But the system *should* still have worked properly with those settings. All that's left is to chide Aldrin for fiddling with procedures too close to launch for the relevant experts to hear about it and flag the pitfalls. Maybe one other thing: karma. Was "Doctor Rendezvous" a little too focused on abort scenarios for someone who was about to be the *second* person to step on the Moon?

It was an ICD problem. The purpose of an Interface Control Document (ICD) is to define the relationship between two systems, in this case the relationship between the **MIT** primary guidance system and the enclosing system provided by Grumman. The **ICD** failed to require that the 800 hertz signals on each side of the interface be in phase with each other. The document itself has not come to light and its exact wording is not known to me. Perhaps it was ambiguous or did not address the issue at all. As a scapegoat the best thing going for the **ICD** is that it happened first in time, probably in 1964, but that is actually an exoneration. The role of the **ICD** is only to set the ground rules according to which systems on each side of the interface will be developed. An **ICD** cannot be *wrong* any more than the rules of backgammon can be wrong.

It was Grumman's fault. The case against Grumman rests on the fact that Grumman actually discovered the rendezvous radar interface problem on LM-3, before George Silver did, as proved by a Grumman report describing tests run in May 1968, when the spacecraft was still in a clean room in Bethpage, New York.

The report correctly diagnosed the problem but then, instead of proposing a fix, dismissed the issue with the breathtaking rationalization that the rendezvous radar mode switch would only ever be in SLEW or AUTO if the PGNCS had failed—oblivious to the fact that this unguarded switch had the potential to *cause* the PGNCS to fail, as it almost did on Apollo 11.

The Grumman engineers probably did not understand that the condition they diagnosed could have the effect of squeezing the guidance computer during a critical phase of the mission. The report's distribution list included about 40 Grumman personnel, starting with Tom Kelly, but unfortunately not our Grumman liaison Clint Tillman—who would have understood the implications.

It was the design. The design of the rendezvous radar interface was faulty in that its results made sense only to the system (MIT or Grumman) that supplied the reference signal, while nonsense information would flow to the other system. The hardware design must have been based on one of two wrong assumptions: that the 800 hertz reference signals were in phase with each other, or that the nonsense data could do no harm to the system that received it.

Testing missed it. No complex design is perfect from inception. Testing exists to detect faults so they can be fixed. The rendezvous radar interface problem only cropped up in a noticeable way occasionally, and it could only be observed on the flight systems because no simulator modeled the electrical relationship between the two systems to sufficient detail. Yet the problem *was* discovered. In fact it was discovered twice. To that extent the system worked, yet the spacecraft flew with the problem uncorrected.

It was us. No, we saved the day. Yes we did, but the battle we won in the software, by the skin of our teeth, was a battle we had lost in the hardware.

George Silver identified the rendezvous radar interface problem at Cape Canaveral a month or two after Grumman discovered it in Bethpage. He wrote up the problem—the memo I saw in his hand on July 21—and devised a solution that involved a small hardware change. The change was not approved, as Silver remembers it, because of the cost and schedule impact. We can only fault Silver for not making a bigger stink. He might not have gained approval for his fix, but a larger group would have known about the problem and been in a position to suggest other ways of working around it. In fact there *was* a simple fix, one which would have had no impact on cost or schedule. Our software could simply send a signal that would zero the rendezvous radar CDUs any time that the rendezvous radar mode switch was not in LGC. That is the fix that we put in place after the mission.

When the problem occurred in flight, our software coped with it. After the mission, software provided a definitive fix at the cost of six words of code. The case for blaming MIT is in the fact that in the summer of 1968, when George Silver was testing the hardware at the Cape, and Allan Klumpp and Bob Covelli and I were worrying about duty cycle in Cambridge, and we all were members of the same organization and knew each other—at that time the problem and the solution were closer to joining hands than at any other point in the story.

In his famous memo "Exegesis of the 1201 and 1202 Alarms Which Occurred During the Mission G Lunar Landing," dated August 4, 1969, the same day that Allan Klumpp and I were in Houston for the debriefing with the crew, George Cherry wrote:

> There were folks who knew about the RR resolver/ECDU/LGC interface mechanization. There were also a great many people who knew the effect which a 15% TLOSS would have on the landing program's operation. These folks never got together on the subject.

If George Cherry was willing to accept the blame for MIT then so am I. Our software had functioned perfectly, but in some way we had failed to take a fuller responsibility.

PINPOINT LANDING

I was promoted to Principal Engineer. I thought that sounded very nice. My salary was up to almost $900 a month. My rent in Lime Street was $180. I picked up a hitchhiker near Harvard Square who told me she planned to go to a rock festival in Woodstock, New York.

Less than a week after Apollo 11 splashed down in the Pacific Ocean, George Cherry, Allan Klumpp, Nick Pippenger and I travelled to Houston for a meeting of the Data Priority Panel. For Apollo 12 Pete Conrad and his crew had been given an ambitious goal, a pinpoint landing at a predetermined spot. We were there to help figure out how to accomplish that. The mission was slated for the middle of November. We had to release the new version of LUMINARY in August. If software changes were needed, as they surely were, we would have to work fast.

The Data Priority Panel was chaired by Bill Tindall. The name, inherited from a panel Tindall had led during the Gemini program, was misinformational, like the dingy doorway that leads to the hippest downtown club. The panel's real business was mission techniques: to determine, once a goal was set, how each mission would be flown. Tindall's network gained more and more influence as missions began to be flown, almost eclipsing Chris Kraft's Software Control Board as the place where software changes were hatched and, for all practical purposes, approved. Tindall sat below Kraft in the hierarchy, but he also had a direct connection to the Apollo Program Manager, George Low.

The other key to Tindall's effectiveness was his personality: lucid, affable, unselfish. Astronauts and flight controllers did not necessarily make it to every meeting they were invited to, but they came to the Data Priority Panel, along with the engineers, and so it became the natural place to discuss and decide operational issues. People came because it was fun—or rather, people who thought operational planning was fun, came. The right people were in the room and they could see progress being made.

Malcolm Johnston found his calling as our regular representative at these meetings. "Carrying Bill Tindall's bags was the best thing I ever did," Johnston says. Johnston was the perfect kibitzer, technically savvy, with a masculine old-school manner that inspired confidence in the astronauts with whom he developed relationships. He was careful not to give off-the-cuff answers. His method was to bring questions back to Cambridge, consult around, and return with answers that everybody trusted. Sometimes the answer might be, "No, you can't do that." But we hated to say no, so very likely, at the same time Johnston was reporting back, we were bubbling with ideas about how to add the capability.

Tindall's meetings were important — something like them had to exist if we were to be successful — but his memos were famous. We dubbed them "Tindallgrams" and they even had a distinctive look, using stationery that included an exhortation to

Buy U.S. Savings Bonds Regularly on the Payroll Savings Plan

running along the bottom of the page, accompanied by a drawing that resembled the Minuteman statue in Concord, Massachusetts.

In these memos Tindall summarized his meetings, his musings, and his hallway conversations; he raised issues that needed to be considered by the wider community, shared his hopes and misgivings, stroked the enterprising, cajoled the reluctant, reported the status of long-running deliberations; and when conclusions were reached, disseminated them, perhaps to reopen the case later on new evidence. If the mission phase under discussion was yours, you saw it from a new angle. If it was an issue normally outside your interest you were drawn in by the pungency and hooked by the surprise turns.

For us, focused on our own pieces of the puzzle but hungry for context, Tindallgrams were pure candy. There was a whiff of the epic, an odor of lightning, the curtain raised on the breadth and intricacy, the enormous clockwork of the thing we were attempting. As Tindallgrams were copied and passed round, circulation became very wide. Tindall gained enormous leverage simply by writing (or rather dictating) a readable memo.

Tindall titled his memo about the meeting we attended, "How to land next to a Surveyor—a short novel for do-it-yourselfers." The Surveyor in question was an unmanned spacecraft that had soft-landed on the Moon in April 1967. Never one to bury the lede, Tindall announced the goal in his first sentence:

> As you know the decision has been made for the H mission to land next to Surveyor III... Obviously the techniques used on G are not adequate for that purpose...

Apollo 11 (the G Mission) had touched down four miles downrange of its planned landing spot. That was an absolute millennial triumph. It was the Moon! Four miles made no difference. NASA had tried to pick a broad, flat zone, but for all that was known before the mission, the boulders Neil Armstrong maneuvered to avoid could just as easily have been at the target spot. As he had said to me in the hallway, any spot would be "interesting" on the first visit.

But future trips, it seemed, would not be wasted on landing sites targeted with safety as the *only* priority, and every mission would have to achieve more than the last. The sites of greatest geological interest were in rougher terrain. Before the LM could go there Pete Conrad had to prove that it was possible to land within walking distance of a preselected spot. Tindall did not sound hopeful:

> If you would like my guess as to how well we will actually do prior to getting any analysis results for the techniques proposed or even much understanding of what happened on the last mission, I would guess that we will probably be able to land within about one mile of where we aim. If we land within walking distance, it is my feeling we have to give most of the credit to "lady luck."

The first question was, where was the Surveyor anyway? The "mapping people" had compared photographs returned by the Surveyor itself with photographs taken from orbit and they were "virtually certain" they knew. They had created relief maps of the surrounding terrain for Conrad to study.

Precision landing on the Moon required the human touch. When the spacecraft pitched forward at High Gate it was essential that Conrad's eyes and brain recognize the terrain ahead, and then, with

Al Bean operating the computer and stealing at most a quick glance out the window, translate that recognition into signals to the computer, and at the end into old-fashioned helicopter-like flying, to reach the goal.

The Surveyor itself would be in shadow and that was intentional. Landings were timed for when the Sun was behind the LM and near the horizon], so that the astronauts, approaching at a steeper angle, would see enough shadow to distinguish the craters that would serve as their signposts. The Surveyor was in one of those craters.

It was the job of our guidance system, and of the mission techniques being developed by Tindall's panel, to put the LM within a few hundred feet of the Surveyor so Conrad could do the rest. Some errors were unavoidable. Nothing could be done about the Moon's lumpy gravitational field except try to improve the gravity models used by orbital navigation. Other sources of error were amenable to Tindall's exhortations. The key was not to do anything that resembled thrusting during coasting flight because navigation had no good way to correct for that and small perturbations could propagate into big errors. Attitude control should be performed with balanced jets so that translational effects would be minimized. RCS testing should be reduced. Undocking from the CSM should be managed in such a way as to reduce the effect on the LM's orbit. All station-keeping should be performed by the CSM. The LM should forego its show-off pirouette for inspection by the other spacecraft. And...

> Absolutely no venting or dumping is allowed!! For heaven's sake, will all spacecraft system people please take note of this. What seems insignificant to you is a nightmare to orbit determination people.

But Apollo 12 had an important asset that Apollo 11 did not have—sixteen minutes. Conrad and Bean's landing site was sixteen minutes in flying time further to the west. That provided just enough time to measure the LM's orbital parameters by independent means, and to use that data to correct the onboard navigation.

That, in fact, expressed the limitations of the autonomous system that Doc Draper's Lab had created. The spacecraft could travel to the vicinity of the Moon and back by themselves (as Apollo 8 proved), and the LM could land safely within a general area using only its own human and electronic resources (as Apollo 11, leaving aside the alarms, showed). But, without the help of some exterior source of navigational information, the LM could not land accurately at a predetermined location on the Moon.

That exterior information would come from the Manned Space Flight Network. MSFN had antennas on Earth that could track the LM as it orbited the Moon. When the LM came around the edge of the Moon the spacecraft was moving directly toward the MSFN antennas. That was the ideal setup for measuring the spacecraft's position and velocity. The last reading would be taken as the LM emerged for the final time, and because of the extra minutes there would be time to update the LM's navigation with the fresh data before the landing began. On Apollo 11 the tracking data had been almost two hours older. The window of time was still small. Tindall wrote:

> It must be done within the period of five minutes or so between availability of the correction and the crew call-up of P63.

The normal procedure for updating the LM's state vector was too cumbersome to do quickly. A simpler way was needed and at the meeting Allan and I proposed one. We would devise a way for the crew to update the landing site vector through the DSKY. Instead of correcting the navigation in one direction we would move the landing site the other way. The end result would be the same. If the correction was big, we preferred that it go in before P63 was selected and guidance computed the time of ignition. If it was smaller, it could be keyed in later, even after the burn began. Tindall added:

> It is to be noted that the crew can use this new extended verb even after PDI... If they have the guts!

What was needed was not actually an extended verb (a verb with special processing attached), but merely a new noun to give access to a vector that would be understood by guidance as a correction to the landing site position. We called it Noun 69, not for the raunchy reference, although that was hardly lost on the Apollo 12 crew, but because it was the last available number in the 60s.

And at last, after five lively pages, Tindall signed off with, "Good luck... and good night, Suzy, wherever you are."

Jimmy Durante aside, that was hardly the end of the story. Seven weeks after he wrote the "short novel for do-it-yourselfers" Tindall was beside himself:

> Analysis based on a typical spacecraft attitude time history shows that an estimated 0.16-lb. thrust from the LM water boiler will result in a 6,000-ft. miss. Grumman is now reporting that it may actually be more like a 0.25-lb. thrust. If this data is right, we are in deep trouble with a capital "S."

The water boiler was used for cooling. It expelled a steady stream of vapor and Bill Tindall was fuming:

> This basic spacecraft design deficiency, along with other unknown per-turbative effects, have forced us to accept a proposal which worries a lot of us. Namely, it is now felt necessary that a final correction to the descent targeting be carried out during powered descent through use of the new program capability [Noun 69] that we requested at our last meeting. Furthermore, this manual input will only be done at that time, never before entering P63 as we had previously planned.

The crew would need guts after all. Then Tindall got worried about another problem:

> Pressurization causes the LM to become bloated and that in turn moves the LPD window markings. Since this can't be corrected in the Apollo 13 LM, we propose to add some biases in the LPD program. (Conrad will have to do this in his head I guess.)

The LM was delicate, her pressure vessel so finely milled in places that it was said you could puncture it with a pencil. Now it had been tested in a vacuum chamber and the LM changed shape—bloated a bit to become more like a balloon. That meant that the markings on the left window that would show the astronaut where he was going during the visibility phase might be shifted. There were actually two scales, one on the outside of the window, the other on the inside. When matched up they were meant to define the plane that contained the landing site, but now we knew the plane defined by the markings might be offset by as much as a few degrees.

Allan introduced biases in azimuth and elevation into the window-pointing calculations. He compensated for the azimuth distortion by yawing the spacecraft by an equivalent angle. Correcting elevation was as simple as tweaking the LPD angle that we displayed on the DSKY. It was too late for these changes to be part of the Apollo 12 rope, but a procedure was worked out for measuring the actual biases in flight by maneuvering the LM to put a bright star at the 40 degree point on the LPD scale. Whatever the distortion turned out to be, Conrad would have to apply it, as Tindall said, in his head.

THE LM SIMULATOR AT THE CAPE

Noun 69 was approved verbally by Chris Kraft on July 31 and the paperwork caught up four days later. By that time the new noun was in the code and tested for basic function. Then we started making runs to understand the effect on the trajectory of various corrections at various times.

In short order Pete Conrad invited Allan Klumpp and me down to Cape Canaveral to show him the new capability on the LM Mission Simulator and to talk about how the software could help him achieve an accurate landing. Equally, I think, as when he invited George Cherry and me to watch him fly the LLTV, Conrad wanted us to see what our programs looked like in operation from his point of view. This was the best place to do that. The LMS at the Cape, like the similar one in Houston, had a cockpit that was realistic to the last detail and superb out-the-window displays that were far superior to anything we could afford in Cambridge.

Allan and I flew to Orlando, grabbed a car and hopped on the aptly named Bee Line (now Beachline) Expressway that led straight to Cocoa, crossed the causeway to Cocoa Beach and checked in at the Islander Motel, an unassuming hostelry of about twenty rooms, right on the beach, at the same latitude as the famous Ron Jon Surf Shop a block away out on Highway A1A. Allan had discovered the place on a previous trip. The Islander had two advantages: friendly owners in the persons of Doug Melvin and his family; and it was built parallel to the beach, not perpendicular like the newer motels.

In every room you could hear the surf and smell the sea and the subtropical vegetation. You had a balcony and an ocean view if you were upstairs, and a back door that led straight to the pool and the beach if you were below.

Back in the car, we drove north on A1A, and entered the government reservation near the dredged inlet of Port Canaveral, where a large white tracking ship, bulbous with antennas, was tied up. We drove north five miles more, vestiges of the historic Mercury and Gemini launch pads looming up to the right along the shore, then left across the causeway to Merritt Island, another four miles, watching the distant cube of the Vertical Assembly Building and the new Apollo launch pads float across the palmetto scrub off to the right. Both pads were empty; the Apollo 12 stack was still in the VAB. When we pulled into the parking lot at the Flight Crew Support Building we noticed three Corvette Stingrays, painted identically in a combination of gold and black.

Inside we met Bob Pearson, who would be our contact at the LMS. I never knew Pearson's title but to us he soon became Mr. LMS. Knowledgeable and cooperative, he had to deal with managers, crews, and engineers like us, and had to understand the huge operating console and what lay behind its switches and indicators. During tests it was Pearson's job to introduce simulated malfunctions to test the crew, working from a big notebook that sat on his console. His biggest trials, in common with his counterparts at other simulators, were the arguments about whether a given problem was in the simulator or the flight system.

Pearson led us into a long room with desks along the sides that felt like a high school study hall except it was littered with checklists and data books and the walls were papered with lunar maps and photographs — where we found the owners of the Corvettes. I knew Pete Conrad already, had watched him fly the bedstead at Ellington, but it was my first encounter with Dick Gordon, swarthy and intense, and practically my last because his assignment was Command Module Pilot.

It was also my first meeting with Al Bean but he was the LM pilot so I would see more of him. At the moment he was talking to a fidgety

NASA artist who had the task of designing the Apollo 12 mission patch. The patch showed a clipper ship under full sail rounding the pockmarked orb. "That crater looks like it's on the Moon not in it," Bean was saying. If you look at the finished patch you can see his point. (Bean himself now paints Moon scenes on canvas.)

It was a classic cast of characters: the charismatic leader, the wing man who would wade through hell for you and relish it, and the brash kid. Today it was just introductions. Allan and I would meet Conrad early the next morning to talk lunar landings.

Pearson offered to show us around and led us through the door at the other end of the crew office into the high-bay area that ran the length of the building. The space seemed bigger than it looked from outside. It was populated by odd structures that towered over rows of tall metal cabinets. Everything was painted either green or tan: green if it related to the LM simulator, tan if it pertained to either of the Command Module simulators that flanked the LM. Pearson pointed out the visitor's gallery above us, running the length of the building, populated by wide-eyed tourists who got off buses, used a separate entrance, and paraded through. At the far end of the room there was what appeared to be a full-sized LM.

The metal cabinets contained electronics and optical devices. The LMS did not have a real AGC, but in these cabinets the operation of the onboard computer was simulated in line-by-line detail, along with the spacecraft dynamics and the physical environment. The full-sized LM was a mock-up for practicing exiting and entering the LM while wearing bulky suits.

The most imposing structures were the simulators themselves. Each was a two-story jumble of metal boxes the size of dishwashers and large deep freezers (but less rectilinear) thrown together at odd angles, with a carpeted stairway leading up into the middle of it. The first time I saw a rendering of Frank Gehry's Guggenheim Museum in Bilbao I thought of the LM simulator. Astronaut John Young called it "the great train wreck." It looked haphazard from the outside because the focus of all the apparatus was the spacecraft cockpit that was somewhere deep inside the heap.

Where the designers of these simulators had really extended themselves was in the visual displays they provided for the windows and optical devices of the simulated spacecraft. A canned movie would not do at all. The simulator had to be interactive. When the pilot maneuvered the spacecraft the lunar horizon must tilt and he must see different stars, and beneath him an accurate moonscape.

In one of the cabinets was a black globe studded with polished ball-bearings, in various sizes, to represent stars down to magnitude +3. A light shone on the bearings and the reflections were picked up by a vidicon tube and channeled to the LM's windows and the alignment telescope. Views of the other spacecraft, the CSM, originated in a long cabinet, painted flat black on the inside, where a maneuverable model of the CSM faced a TV camera that could go forward and backward on tracks. When a joint simulation took place, with astronauts in both spacecraft, the model CSM responded to the CSM simulator controls. A corresponding LM model in another cabinet, visible in the CSM's windows, responded to the LM controls.

What interested Allan and me the most was the view of the lunar surface that was provided for the LM's triangular windows. That view originated in a large structure known as the L&A, for landing and ascent, the two phases of the mission when it was used. The lunar surface that the astronauts would see out the windows had to be accurate enough for training to land at a specific spot among the jumble of craters. For each mission the Army Map Service constructed a three-dimensional model corresponding to a five by eight mile area of lunar terrain, at 1:2000 scale, with the intended touchdown point near one end. The model, the size of a large carpet, was mounted horizontally, but upside down, inside a canopy that could move up and down under control of the computers running the simulation. At the lunar-eastern end of the model was a bank of powerful lights that moved along with the canopy to simulate the oblique sun. Underneath, on tracks, was a long platform that could move (lunar) east and west; on top of that was another, smaller platform that could move north and south, and on top of that a tiny television camera that could rotate about a vertical axis — all under computer control.

With changes in altitude represented by up and down movement of the canopy containing the terrain model, horizontal flight simulated by the north-south-east-west motion of the TV camera, and the spacecraft's yaw represented by the rotation of the camera, an image resembling the view from the LM was captured by the television camera. The image was processed, a LM shaped shadow was provided because the Sun was always behind the spacecraft during a landing, mountains were added along the horizon as a sort of theatrical backdrop, blowing dust was faked by defocusing when the LM was below 100 feet (if the engine was on), and the result was projected on screens outside the LM's forward windows. When the LM landed the camera nearly touched the terrain.

You could reach the terrain model by climbing up on the platform that carried the video camera. When the West German Premier Willy Brandt visited, someone attached a toy Volkswagen repair garage to the terrain near the landing site. Another day someone found a dead frog in a flower bed outside the building and stuck it on just before John Young and Charlie Duke were due to fly lunar landings. Duke was in on the joke. When the LM pitched over at High Gate, Young started jumping up and down, yelling, "Hey. What's that?"

"I don't see anything," replied Duke.

"There's something down there!"

Young landed next to it. It was not a big frog but at one inch to 160 feet it loomed over the LM.

The LMS was a multi-media interactive theatre, Plato's cave for a sophisticated audience. To deceive a computer you need only feed information into the cables. With a human it is not so easy. You cannot tap the optic nerve; you must fool his senses. On the other hand a man can help you out with his imagination. *There's something down there*, Young had exclaimed. In his excitement he forgot he was on Earth.

So far we had only seen the reverse of the theatrical machinery but now at last the LM cockpit was free. We left our shoes at the bottom of the stairs. (There was a cushioned bench with compartments for the shoes of the CDR and LMP, and a shoehorn on a chain.) We entered the cockpit through a low door that opened into the rear of the cabin, corresponding to the bulkhead where the guidance computer was mounted in an actual LM. The cockpit was as perfect as it could be made, with one small compromise. The simulated ascent engine cover, similar to an upside-down washtub, was usually not in place because it would unnecessarily obstruct the path from the entrance door to the front of the cabin.

The cockpit was dimly lit, by overhead floodlights turned low, by bulbs in the larger instruments, by the green-blinking computer display, and eerily, by the back-lighted labels on scores of switches and dials. The effect was cool and rather serene. Maybe there was a slight new-spacecraft smell.

In front of us were two triangular windows with sun-shades and crash bars, each window measuring about two feet on each side. Above the commander's position on the left was another small, rectangular window for use when docking with the CSM.

The guidance computer's keyboard and display unit, the DSKY, formed a sort of console between the commander and the LM pilot on the right. Either astronaut could reach it but during the landing the job of operating the computer fell to the LM pilot.

Near the left handhold, each position had a translational hand controller (THC), which doubled as a manual throttle for the descent engine. During a normal landing the manual throttle was never used because the computer controlled thrust. Near the THC was the engine stop button. You hit it when the probes attached to the landing gear touched the surface and the two blue lunar contact lights came on. You did not trust the automatic system to recognize the moment of touchdown. What if it was premature? On the other hand you did not want to grind the descent engine bell into the ground while it was still firing.

Near the engine-stop button on the commander's left was the *rate-of-descent* (ROD) switch, used to control the LM's descent rate during the final descent. It was a two-way toggle with a spring return to the middle position. It worked like the faster/slower switch on a car's cruise control. Each click, up or down, changed the descent rate by one foot per second.

To his right each crewmen had another joystick, called the rotational hand controllers (RHC), normally used to control attitude. You gripped the stick with your right hand, twisted it to yaw the spacecraft, leaned it left or right to roll, or bent it forward or backward to pitch. How it worked depended on the setting of the PGNCS attitude mode switch. During most of the landing the mode was set to AUTO. For manual maneuvering at low altitude the most useful mode was called ATT HOLD, in which moving the stick out of detent made the spacecraft rotate, releasing it stopped the rotation and held attitude. The joystick was a very intuitive way to control a flying machine, especially if you were accustomed to flying helicopters and jets. The commander's stick was given a different function during the visibility phase of the landing: it was used to signal the computer to redesignate, or move, the targeted landing site.

At eye level, each man had an *eight-ball*, much like the ones found in airplane cockpits, which indicated the spacecraft's attitude. The instrument contained a sphere of ingenious mechanical design that seemed to remain fixed as the LM rotated around it, so that at any moment you could read your attitude from the latitudes and longitudes inscribed on it. The instrument also had *error needles* that the computer could use to indicate desired attitude changes.

Above each eight-ball was a *cross-pointer* instrument that indicated the spacecraft's two-dimensional horizontal velocity across the lunar surface, and nearby an altimeter and an altitude-rate meter. These were called the *landing analog displays* and they were mechanical devices that may have looked analog, but they were driven by the computer. There was a thrust meter (truly analog), gauges for the RCS and the propulsion systems, and at the top of the panel several clocks and timers. There were abort and abort stage buttons, protected by a little door, that could be used to terminate the landing in an emergency. The difference was that abort stage dropped the descent stage before blasting back to orbit.

Along both sides of the cabin, from waist level up, were rows of push-pull circuit breakers, the on-off switches for the scores of systems that made up the LM. Below the circuit breakers on both sides, and behind the commander's position on the left, were white fabric pouches of various sizes, each with a label saying TOWELS, FACIAL WET WIPES, URINE RCPT, and so on. Behind the LM pilot's position on the right was the system that could supply breathing gas if you plugged in your spacesuit.

Pearson left us in the cockpit and went back to the console. Allan and I put on headsets. Allan took the commander's position on the left. I was in the LM pilot's position. Pearson started us at 15,000 feet, late in the breaking phase, and in an instant we were inside a very busy, living machine that we already perceived as a space-craft not a simulator — however firmly our feet were planted in Earth gravity.

And then, less than a minute into the run, we reached High Gate. The display changed to Noun 64 and over the simulated sound of the descent engine we heard the simulated sounds of maneuvering jets as the spacecraft pitched forward and we stared in wonder as the wide lunar surface came into view. Allan put in a few redesignations and then let the LM land automatically in P65.

Then we swapped positions and began again at 15,000 feet. We entered P64 and the LM pitched forward. I had lived the lunar land-ing, night and day, for three years. I knew its logic inside out. I had flown numerous instrument-reliant landings from commander's posi-tion in our plywood LM in Cambridge. But surrounding me now was something quite different, something very like a real spacecraft, and out the window, stretching for miles, was a pockmarked monochrome moon-puzzle that contained a specific target.

Allan read off LPD angles from the DSKY. I tweaked the RHC to designate a site closer in, and the piped-in sound of the descent engine increased as guidance tried to pull up short. I entered redesignations left and right and the spacecraft rolled in response.

At about 300 feet I entered P66, the rate of descent mode. Now, with my eyes out the window, my left hand on the ROD switch and my right hand on the joystick, I set the LM down survivably, if not gracefully — and experienced all that could be experienced on Earth of landing on the Moon.

LANDING ON THE MOON WITH PETE

We woke in darkness, ate quickly, and headed back up the beach. In the parking lot of the Flight Crew Support Building this time were several Corvettes but only one of the black and gold jobs.

Pete Conrad appeared wearing a beat up baseball cap and got us coffee—terrible coffee to my taste as a non-coffee drinker who had not yet located the Coke machine—and we walked through the back door of the crew office into the high bay area that contained the simulators.

Bob Pearson was at the operator's console starting the process of loading the latest version of LUMINARY. Pete and Allan and I sat down at the console and Allan explained Noun 69. To modify the landing site the astronaut would key

Verb 25 Noun 69 Enter ±ΔZ Enter ±ΔY Enter ±ΔX Enter

where Verb 25 meant "load" and ΔX, ΔY and ΔZ represented the downrange, crossrange and elevation corrections, or "deltas." There was no reasonability check in the software, so you had to be careful when you punched in the data—but when did you not? If the correction was large it was best to put it in before starting P63 so the ignition algorithm could calculate the ignition time and attitude based on the new information.

Finally the new LUMINARY was loaded and Pete was ready to fly. What is more, with Al Bean absent and conceivably still asleep I was offered the role of LM pilot. I put my shoes in the LMP cubby and followed Conrad up the carpeted ladder and into the cockpit. I took the right hand position and put on my headset. My job was to operate the DSKY and read out information as appropriate, especially during the visibility and final landing phases.

Conrad said "Okey-dokey." Down on the console, Pearson said "Okey-dokey" and pushed the RESET button, held it down until it lit up (a signal that the computers were ready) then released it and said "You're running." (I learned that procedure later.) We knew that already because the eight-balls had just whipped around and now indicated the simulated attitude of the simulated LM.

For the first run we started at the beginning with the selection of P63. Then we introduced a landing site "correction" via Noun 69. Actually, there was no point in using Noun 69 as it would be used in flight: to put in a correction based on Earth-based radar tracking. In a simulation that would simply be adding an error in one place and subtracting it in another. Instead we used Noun 69 to introduce an error that would point the LM toward one of the less hospitable areas in the vicinity. That way we would come at the landing site from an unusual direction and Conrad could have fun with the redesignator in P64, and fun scuttling around in P66, as he tried to get back to the vicinity of the crater where the Surveyor was thought to be hiding. This added value as a training tool we had not anticipated.

We started out windows-up and since Earth was not simulated there was nothing to see. (Earth was the crudest part of the window displays, simply a patch affixed to the star globe, when they bothered.) Pearson threw a few malfunctions at us, which Conrad batted away in a flash each time with colorful commentary. "Aha the old Main Bus A undervolt trick, heh heh heh," he said, as he quickly switched to Main Bus B.

To my regret I did not make notes afterward so I am unable to document the verbal dimension of being shoulder to shoulder with Pete Conrad in the LM cockpit. Fortunately there are hours of voice recordings from Apollo 12 (and Skylab 1) that capture Conrad's pungent flavor — but perhaps not exactly as I experienced it in the simulator. In flight he was liberated to radiate the joy of being there and doing that. In the simulator there was more focus, a sense of responsibly preparing for a mission on which a great deal, not to mention his reputation as a pilot and his own Ivy League derrière, was riding. As for me I was both thrilled and tongue-tied in our intimacy in the small cockpit. I did not know that the future held many more hours of flight time for me in this fantastical toy, more often than not from the position now occupied by Conrad.

The braking phase ended and P64 started. Over the course of a few seconds we pitched forward and now the lunar terrain lay spread out in front of us. Pitchover was a crucial juncture and a lonely one for the mission commander, whose job it was to recognize the intended landing site among the jumble of craters that lay ahead. Despite the Noun 69 *un-correction*, Conrad quickly recognized the Snowman, the formation of craters that bracketed the one that hid Surveyor. He set to work with the redesignator to bend the trajectory in that direction.

I was fascinated with how the lunar terrain out my window wheeled as the LM responded to Conrad's commands. It was hard to keep my eyes inside the cockpit. Once or twice Conrad, squinting at the redesignation scale in the left window, had to remind me to continue reading LPD angles from the DSKY. He would have to remind Al Bean in flight too.

Conrad took over semi-manual control in P66 at about 300 feet. When I flew P66 on the hybrid simulator in Cambridge, with its billiard-ball Moon and no window display, all I had to do was work pitch and roll to null the cross-pointers—the cockpit instrument that indicated forward and lateral velocity. On the hybrid the cross-pointers were jittery, and the tape meters for altitude and altitude rate made a chugging sound. We had blamed it on the simulator. Now I saw that they behaved the same way on the LMS. Conrad remarked on it. Maybe it was our problem, I thought.

But now, with a realistic Moon out the window, Conrad was flying the terrain not the instruments. His stick inputs were decisive and quick. To create horizontal velocity in the direction he wanted to go he would rapidly pitch or roll the spacecraft, or both at the same time, count "One potato, two potato..." and just as quickly maneuver back to upright to maintain the velocity he had accumulated. As he approached the target he would make the reverse maneuvers, with the same timing, to bleed off velocity, and finally touch down without skidding. Conrad called the LM a "sporty" vehicle. It was when he flew it, at least.

We flew several more runs. At one point Allan came into the cabin and crouched behind us. When he opened the door he said, "Take this LM to Havana." These were the days of the Cuban airplane hijackings and that was a joke that never seemed to get old.

———

It was on this trip, or the next, that Allan uncharacteristically suggested that we have dinner at a restaurant some miles down the beach — but he was vague about it. As we drove along, the ocean on our left, Allan kept checking his watch. Finally we pulled into a gas station, just in time to see a fast streak rise quietly from the horizon, leaving behind, high in the sky, a perfect spiral pattern of blue and green. Allan never admitted it but he must have been tipped off that there would be an offshore launch of a Polaris or Poseidon missile from a submarine. The Lab had also designed the guidance system for those missiles. The computer bore no resemblance to ours but the inertial sensor was a close relative of the Apollo inertial measurement unit.

That was probably not the Polaris launch I heard about later. Two Lab engineers were up late on the eve of a test, trying to solve a problem in the guidance system electronics. They figured out that an isolation transformer added to the circuit would fix the bug, but there was none on hand. Finally they realized that there was a suitable component right in front of them. The missile flew, successfully, with a transformer borrowed from a soldering iron.

TRAINING APOLLO 12

Two weeks after our sunrise tête-à-tête with Pete Conrad, Allan and I returned to the Cape with a larger group for the Apollo 12 crew training meeting. Conrad wanted less formal sessions than the ones laid on for Apollo 11 in Houston. He chose the Cape, in other words, to discourage attendance by managers.

Conrad and his crewmen Alan Bean and Dick Gordon were in attendance, along with the backup crew of Dave Scott, Al Worden, and Jim Irwin. Scott and his crew, whose Corvettes were painted blue, white and red (respectively) would fly on Apollo 15. We sat in a small conference room with a long table and a few rows of chairs. The room was just inside the entrance to the building so no one could go in or out without passing our open door, which occasioned a certain amount of peeking, waving, and ogling.

It was a three-day meeting, starting with Command Module operations, followed by rendezvous. We would not get to descent and ascent until the third day.

The only reason to sit through the CM presentations was to be entertained by the crew. They were entertaining, but Bob Schlundt, describing the thrust vector control autopilot, and Bob Bairnsfather on Entry operations, were not. During a break I tried out the ladder on the LM mock-up at the far end of the high-bay area. With the bottom rung of the ladder almost three feet above the floor it took some agility to mount. On the Moon, for astronauts wearing suits that tripled their mass and restricted movement, which in lunar gravity netted out at half their naked Earth weight, it did not seem to present any difficulty at all.

The afternoon of the first day was open. Professor Wallace VanderVelde from the Aero-Astro Department at MIT, a friend of Allan's, was at the Cape for the first time so we took him to the VAB, where I acted as guide. We worked our way up to the roof of the building, a blinding expanse in the hot sun, giving way, at a distinct straight edge, to a mist-softened landscape extending flat in all directions. Stretching towards the Saturn V launch pads, and the sea beyond, was the perfect crushed stone track along which the mighty rocket would creep to its launch point.

On the second day the morning topic was Command Module navigation, followed by a presentation of several hours by Peter Kachmar and Gene Muller on the subject of rendezvous. Normally the LM was the active vehicle for the rendezvous, following ascent from the Moon, but under some circumstances the CSM might have to come to the LM instead. For some reason Al Bean kept catching my eye and grinning. I took a long lunch break and sped back to Cocoa Beach for forty-five minutes in sun and surf before racing back.

Thursday morning, with the Command Module pilots no longer in the room, we came to what I thought of as real LM operations—Descent and Ascent. I led off with a presentation covering the interactions between astronaut and computer during the landing. Conrad and Bean knew most of this already. I was followed by Bernie Kriegsman on navigation, Allan Klumpp on guidance, and George Kalan on the digital autopilot.

In the afternoon Larry Berman discussed Ascent and Aborts, and that occasioned the most serious moment of the day when Conrad reeled off the procedures he would use if the ascent engine, the only hope of getting off the surface, failed to fire, concluding, "And if that didn't work it would spoil our whole day."

As I rounded the big curve near Port Canaveral, on my way back to the Islander, two of the Apollo 12 astronauts, in matching gold and black Corvettes, blew past me in tight formation.

For me the Cape contained two pleasures, separated by a security fence. There was warm and disreputable Cocoa Beach with its broad sands and girls and dependable surf and the funky comforts of the Islander Motel — and to the north, wide expanses of tropical scrubland punctuated by enigmatic buildings and distant towers, where the wind blew salty and you sensed in the ragged interface of alligator swamp and oceanic sweep a parallel to this place's other distinction as the point where our planet reached out to limitless space.

From Cocoa Beach you entered the government reservation from the south. If you drove straight north by the shortest route you passed the runway called the skid strip and the buildings of the Air Force station, and in about five miles you reached an intersection where a left turn took you to a long causeway that led to Merritt Island and the Kennedy Space Center itself. One of the first buildings on the left was the Flight Crew Support Building, which was becoming my usual work headquarters at the Cape. After that came the Manned Spacecraft Operations Building, which housed, among other things, astronaut living quarters, and then the headquarters building. A bit further along a right turn led to the Vertical Assembly Building and the launch Saturn V launch pads.

That was the direct route. If you had time you could follow a series of roads that hugged the coast of Cape Canaveral itself, that promontory named by the Spanish in the 16th century, also called the Cape of Currents, which the Air Force selected in 1948 as a suitable site for missile tests.

The shore route was a rough history of the space program, although not chronological. First you passed the Navy complex, situated the furthest south to be near Port Canaveral, where Polaris and Poseidon missiles were launched from dry land or loaded onto submarines to be fired offshore. Next came Launch Complexes 5 and 6. Here in 1961 Alan Shepard and then Gus Grissom were thrown into space in tiny Mercury capsules on Redstone boosters. Then Complex 26, where Wernher von Braun launched the Explorer satellite to answer Sputnik, and a little further along, Complex 18, where the unlucky Vanguard belatedly took flight. These pads were obsolete—Complex 26 was the centerpiece of the Air Force Space Museum—but close by was the still active Complex 17 from which unmanned spacecraft were sent aloft on Delta rockets.

Near the black-and-white banded lighthouse at the very tip of the Cape was the site of the first launch attempted here: a modified V-2 called Bumper 8 that was successfully launched in July 1950.

From there you could either turn left onto Central Control Road, which led west to meet the causeway that crossed to Merritt Island, or take ICBM Road, a two and a half mile straightaway that passed the launch pads, some still active, from which Earth-orbital Mercury and Gemini missions were launched on Atlas and Titan boosters.

Some of the older launch areas were open and deserted. At some only concrete remained, aprons and mysterious ramps, bulky plinths, flame trenches, a blockhouse like a shallow igloo with small armored windows, all of it invaded and colonized by the surrounding wildlife and vegetation. On other pads the steel towers still stood. At a deserted pad from the Mercury era I left my car near the blockhouse and climbed the abandoned gantry. The white paint in the area where astronauts were helped into their spacecraft was blotched with rust. Tattered tarpaulins flapped in the breeze and to seaward the surf was booming. The seagulls that had taken over the structure squawked angrily at my intrusion. I must have watched this exact spot on television in 1962 or 1963.

Still further north, along the beach, were complexes where Saturn 1 and Saturn 1B rockets were launched, and beyond that the mysterious assembly areas and launch pads for the powerful Titan 3—a liquid-fueled rocket with two solid-fuel motors strapped on the side, capable of launching very large "classified payloads."

Doc Draper in the navigation simulator on the roof of Building IL-7 at 75 Cambridge Parkway. [CSDL 51483BW]

Installation of the SPIRE inertial measurement unit in MIT's B-29 bomber at Hanscom Field in March, 1953, prior to the first cross-country flight guided by an inertial navigation system. The man in an overcoat at lower left is Roger Woodbury who, under Doc Draper, led the SPIRE project. [CSDL 8312]

* Photos marked "CSDL" provided courtesy of the Charles Stark Draper Lab., Inc

The Apollo Inertial Measurement Unit (IMU). The assembly at center contains three gyroscopes and three accelerometers. Three sets of pivot points are visible: the inner and outer gimbals are at left and right (coinciding, in a non-operational condition known as "gimbal lock"), the middle gimbal is at top and bottom. [author's photo of CSDL exhibit]

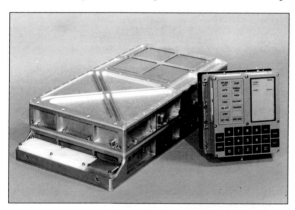

The Apollo Guidance Computer (AGC) and its Display and Keyboard Unit (DSKY). The white panel covers the connector that links the computer electronically with other spacecraft systems. (DSKY markings were different on flight units.) [CSDL 40266]

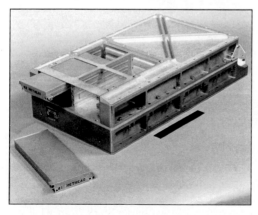

Rear view of the AGC, showing two of the six core-rope modules and how they were inserted. The black ruler is 6 inches long. The modules in the picture contain a very early version of the Apollo flight software titled RETREAD. [CSDL 40265]

Listing of LUMINARY. Also shown is a copy of Hugh Blair-Smith's Memo #9, the bible of AGC programmers, and a form used for writing down code before transferring it to punched cards. The button is from the April 15, 1967 Mobilization to End the War. The Coca-Cola was the author's usual beverage when working. [author's photo]

The hybrid lab, showing the core-rope simulator (right) and cabinet with front-mounted DSKY and AGC (not visible). Sims could be run from here if the cockpit controls were not needed [CSDL 54173]

Another view of the hybrid lab, showing Beckman analog computer with its plug-boards and (left) strip-chart machine. [CSDL 54172]

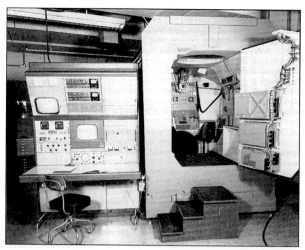

The author's KSC badge. The numbers correspond to buildings to which I was allowed access. [author's photo]

The LM simulator at MIT, located on the third floor and linked to the hybrid lab directly below. Console at left controls the unsuccessful visual display. [CSDL]

The LM Mission Simulator (LMS) in the Flight Crew Support Building at the Kennedy Space Center. The LM cockpit is inside the irregular cluster of boxes in the foreground, reached by a stairway on the far side. The canopy-like structure behind the LMS is the L&A, which contains a model of the lunar terrain that provides out-the-window views when lunar landings are simulated. The operator's console is at left. The structure in the background is a Command Module Mission Simulator (CMS). The visitors' gallery is at upper left. [NASA KSC-68C-1097]

*Apollo 14 astronauts Ed Mitchell (left)
and Alan Shepard [NASA]*

*Sam Drake (left) and the author
[in reenactment for NASA FILM]*

*The Lab was at pains
to identify in two tiers
the people responsible
for the Apollo 14 fix.
At right the most-
involved group:
(from left) Larry
Berman, Sam Drake,
Peter Volante, Bruce
McCoy, and the*
author. On the table are listings of the LM and Command Module ropes.
The men in the upper photograph are (first row) Vince Megna, Doc Draper,
the author, Dave Moore, Tony Cook; and (second row) Phil Felleman, Larry
Berman, Allan Klumpp, Bob Werner, Robert Lones, Sam Drake. Bruce McCoy
and Peter Volante were travelling and missed this photo. [both CSDL]

Doc Draper in conversation with the reporter Mary Bubb in the press grandstand at the launch of Apollo 15, July 26, 1971. [author's photo]

Hugh Blair-Smith [his photo]

Dana Densmore [author's photo]

George Cherry [CSDL]

Allan Klumpp [author's photo]

Marjorie Shepatin, Musée Picasso, Antibes, December 1969. [author's photo, artwork © 2018 Estate of Pablo Picasso / Artists Rights Society (ARS), New York]

Peter Adler, aboard MS Jugoslavija near Dubrovnik, September 1971 [author's photo]

Dick Battin [CSDL 63170]

Hal Laning [CSDL 63152]

Norm Sears [CSDL 63084]

Jimmy the Flea at the Block Island Inn: from left, Lenny Kaye, Tim White, Ed Finney, Patrick O'Connor, Robert Palmer, Steve Krevsky, and the author [author's photo on self-timer]

Television image from the camera mounted on the lunar rover, from late in the third surface EVA conducted by the Apollo 17 crew [author's photo from NASA video]

The hugest of the shapes on the horizon, and the newest, were on Merritt Island — not so much an island as another lobe of the marshy sand dunes that ran along the east coast of central Florida. The grandest of these structures, worth a visit on every trip, was the Vertical Assembly Building, the VAB, a huge cube within which Saturn rockets were stacked and prepared before being moved to the launch pad, three miles away, to be fueled and launched.

The VAB was perfect in its straightforwardness, from its low wing through which the incoming rocket stages, delivered by barge or Super Guppy aircraft, moved horizontally; to its 450-foot doors that opened, when assembly was complete, to release a tall vertical object that resembled, next to the huge cube, a slender, white wand. Yet the building was not ponderous. It seemed to be, from the outside, just what it was, a thin skin draped around a complex skeleton.

Inside, extending the path of the low wing, was the great central nave, called the transfer aisle, as tall as the building, where two 250-ton cranes could lift massive rocket stages to a vertical posture and add them to the stacks taking shape in the four tall bays that adjoined the nave like chapels, two on each side. From catwalks that hugged the ceiling, almost 500 feet above the floor, I could look down the entire height of the transfer aisle and the side bays — then by far the vastest interior space on the globe.

Surrounding the nave and the bays was a dense fabric of steel trusses and scaffolding, anchored to permanent towerlike structures. At different levels movable platforms with cut-out circles fit tight around the stack, giving access to every part of the rocket's anatomy.

Some areas were tightly controlled — I never came within touching distance of an engine — but nothing prevented a curious person from visiting most of the structure's thirty levels. Always there was the great white shaft, from these angles not slender at all, its white paint slightly pebbly to the touch. You might come across a circular hatch open in the skin of the vehicle, and peering inside see the rounded bulkhead of a fuel or oxidizer tank and a technician with a work light working on the plumbing.

Once I signed my name in purple felt-tip pen on the side of a Saturn third stage. That is the closest my hand has been to the

Moon, where that stage ended up. My mind went there more abundantly in the code aboard the Lunar Modules that landed. It exists there still, like fossil DNA, if the information we encoded in core-rope memory, and protected with a stout case, survived the used-up spacecraft's inevitable return to the surface—that information now perhaps safer over geologic time than here on our tectonic Earth, where we dwell on a thin crust floating on convection currents of molten iron and stone.

DELTA GUIDANCE

Testing of the Apollo 11 rope, LUMINARY 99, had continued and even intensified after it was released for manufacture. No serious problems were found but several dozen small anomalies were uncovered. New revisions of LUMINARY were made to correct them even before Apollo 11 flew.

One of the changes we made before Apollo 11 looked good afterwards. We changed the procedure for approving the incorporation of landing radar data to avoid the need to use Verb 16 Noun 68. The monitor verb consumed an extra 5 percent of the computer's time, enough to cause the two alarms that occurred during the braking phase on Apollo 11.

The Apollo 12 rope, LUMINARY 116, would be released just 22 days after the first lunar landing. There was not much time to incorporate changes based on the Apollo 11 experience but two of those changes were important: the new Noun 69 designed to put Pete Conrad down next to the Surveyor, and the software fix for the rendezvous radar interface problem that caused the alarms.

Meanwhile, of course, NASA had revised the crew checklists so the switch would never again *not* be in the LGC position during the powered descent. The specific problem that caused the overload on Apollo 11 was fixed twice over.

We had not yet absorbed all the lessons that Apollo 11 had to teach us. All the same, its success freed us to focus further ahead. From here on our heads were occupied with improvements intended for the mission after next or the one after that. When a mission was flown we would have to refer back to a version of LUMINARY that might already seem antique.

Two guidance guys in Houston named Tom Moore and Jay Montgomery came up with something called Delta Guidance that could fly on Apollo 14 if it panned out. Bill Tindall got excited

> The pay off could be impressive compared to things like trying to de-crease LM weight. Specifically, a delta-V improvement on the nominal mission of as much as 100 FPS might be realized, which is equivalent to 18 seconds of hover or 300 lbs. increase in descent payload.

Delta Guidance had other advantages. It always put the LM at the same spot relative to the landing site at the start of the visibility phase, no matter what (within bounds) had happened before then. That was an advantage for astronauts who needed to recognize the terrain the moment it became visible. Delta Guidance also prevented the trajec-tory from drooping in the event that a huge downrange correction was required.

The idea behind Delta Guidance was that instead of computing a whole new trajectory to the landing site following some perturbation such as a redesignation, a Noun 69, or a landing radar update, the guidance equation would seek to return to its ideal trajectory — but the way it worked was weird. Instead of throttling down once, late in the braking phase, Delta Guidance lowered the throttle for brief peri-ods throughout the phase. In my simulations there were eight of these *pulse-downs* during the braking phase. There were also cases where the engine would *pulse-out*, return to full throttle for a brief period, during the visibility phase. The thought of operating the throttle in that way made everyone queasy. The "engine people" would have to give their blessing.

> In order to reap one of the greatest benefits, it is necessary that the DPS be qualified to operate in a new way and so that must be vigorously pursued. Why are you still sitting here reading this stupid thing when there is all that important work to be done?

Tindall did not mean us because by the time he wrote that Allan Klumpp had whipped up the new equations and I had created an off-line assembly based on LUMINARY, programmed the new equation, and written a memo about it. A version to be tried out in the simulators, which Tindall had requested in the same memo, already existed. Naming an off-line version was its creator's privilege so I called it AMELIA.

By revision 11 of AMELIA, Delta Guidance was running smoothly. When a big lateral redesignation was put in, instead of following a sweeping curve, guidance turned the LM quickly and took a straight line route to the new landing site. When I tried putting in a large up-range Noun 69 correction at the start of the visibility phase the spacecraft pitched back sharply and the engine, as expected, pulsed out, but visibility was quickly restored. Oddly, a big redesignation downrange also caused a pulse-out. The runs I made were hardly enough to qualify Delta Guidance for flight, but I made AMELIA 11 available for others to experiment with.

In early November I flew back to the Cape to try out Delta Guidance on the LMS using AMELIA. Back in Boston, with the delightfully flesh-and-blood Amy, I heard The Who perform the rock opera *Tommy* in the big space on Lansdowne Street that was the new home of the Boston Tea Party, the fine old room on Berkeley Street lost to rock-and-roll forever.

APOLLO 12

Three days after *Tommy*, Apollo 12 took flight, and joystick wizard Pete Conrad lost no time in creating a stir. President Nixon was in the control room. Phil Felleman, who was there, had no doubt that it was Tricky Dick's impatience that made NASA decide to launch despite the thunderclouds over the pad. The result reproduced, on a larger scale, Benjamin Franklin's experiment with the kite and the key.

Conrad: Okay, we just lost the platform, gang. I don't know what happened here; we had everything in the world drop out.

Houston: Roger.

Conrad: I got three fuel cell lights, an AC bus light; a fuel cell disconnect, AC bus overload 1 and 2, main bus A and B out.

When Conrad said he had "lost the platform," he meant that the IMU had tumbled, had lost its alignment. This had no immediate effect because the rocket was being steered by the Saturn's instrument unit, located lower in the stack.

Then 24 seconds went by. In a back room in Houston John Aaron, the ECOM or electrical system expert, stared at gibberish on his console. Telemetry data was no longer being received from the spacecraft. Aaron, however, remembered seeing the same pattern once before.

Aaron: Flight, ECOM, try SCE to AUX.

No one in mission control knew what that switch was, and Aaron himself was grasping at the slenderest of straws. SCE meant Signal Conditioning Equipment. AUX was pronounced "auks."

Houston: Apollo 12, Houston. Try SCE to AUX. Over.

Conrad: Try FCE to AUXILIARY. What the hell is that?

Gordon: Fuel cell...

Houston: SCE—SCE to AUXILIARY

The only man on the spacecraft who knew that switch was Al Bean, in the right-hand couch: the Lunar Module Pilot. The switch was right in front of him. He reached up and flipped the toggle down to the AUX position. It worked. Downlink data was recovered and Houston began to understand the problem. Staging happened on time and the second stage stayed on course.

Conrad: Okay, now we'll straighten out our problems here. I don't
            know what happened. I'm not sure we didn't get hit by
            lightning.

Lightning had indeed struck the rocket just after Tower Clear. One of the funniest things in the whole Apollo program is to hear Pete Conrad, riding an enormous bomb without a REFSMMAT, chortling his way into orbit. One thinks of Slim Pickens in Kubrick's *Dr. Strangelove*, riding his bomb in the opposite direction.

Conrad: Well, I'll tell you one thing. This is a first-class ride,
            Houston.

Houston: Kind of a rough start.

Conrad: Yes, I always like to start out behind the eight-ball and catch up.

Once in Earth orbit everything went smoothly. The spacecraft was intact. The IMU was turned off for a few minutes, turned on, coarse-aligned to a rough orientation using P51, fine-aligned using P52, and later fine-aligned again, showing that during the interval the platform had held its alignment perfectly. So it was off to the Moon and into lunar orbit.

Ten days before the liftoff, and three months after the "short novel for do-it-yourselfers," Bill Tindall had written:

> I would like to take this opportunity to modify a prediction I made in writing early in August. At that time I thought our chances of landing near the Surveyor were very low. That if we landed within about a half mile, we would have to credit Lady Luck. Based on things that have happened since then, including the addition of the [Noun 69] update during powered descent, and particularly the confidence the crew has developed in the LPD since the visual capability of their LMS is working so well—and for whatever it's worth—my feeling now is that as long as the systems work as well as they have in the past, we have a pretty good chance of landing near the Surveyor.

Now it was up to Conrad and Bean to make good on Tindall's highly qualified optimism. Bean selected P63 and the countdown began. The engine sprang to life on time. About one minute after ignition Noun 69 was used to move the landing site 4200 feet in the down-range direction to compensate for navigation errors measured by Earth-based radar. The LM's landing radar acquired the surface on time. Throttle down was as expected. High Gate and pitchover were on time. Orienting himself using the LPD scale on the left window Conrad immediately recognized the Snowman, the formation of craters that marked the target.

Conrad: Hey, there it is! There it is! Son of a gun, right down the middle of the road!!!

Conrad was already miles ahead of Neil Armstrong in exclamation points.

The decision had been made to target the mission exactly on the location of the Surveyor spacecraft, which sat near the middle of a crater about 300 feet in diameter. It would have been hubris to think there was any risk of literally landing on top of it, but

Conrad: Hey, it's targeted right for the center of the crater. Look out there. I can't believe it!

Conrad was surely itching to use the redesignator but so far the trajectory looked perfect. In fact, as post flight analysis would show, the LM was headed to a spot just beyond and to the left of the Surveyor crater, about 400 feet from the theoretical target. That was the spot indicated by the LPD angle displayed on the DSKY. Compare that error of 400 feet to the 20,000 foot miss on Apollo 11. Navigation, with a little help from the ground, had done its part.

In the right-hand position, LM pilot Al Bean kept his eyes on the computer display, reading out altitude, altitude-rate, LPD angles, and the time remaining for redesignations. On the left side Conrad peered at the surface through the LPD scale. While in lunar orbit Conrad had maneuvered the LM to place the bright star Aldebaran at the 40-degree mark on the scale and had found the star no more than half a degree from where it should have been. Evidently spacecraft bloat was not as bad as Tindall feared.

In simulations, Conrad had grown fond of a spot on the near side of Surveyor crater, and a bit to the right, that he called the "parking lot." As the spacecraft approached 2300 feet Conrad still thought the LM was headed straight for the center of the crater so he tweaked the joystick to put in a single redesignation to the right. More puzzling is what Conrad did about 15 seconds later.

With the LM headed to a spot 300 feet beyond the Surveyor crater, and about 500 feet beyond his favorite touchdown point, Conrad put in two redesignations that moved the landing point about 800 feet further *downrange*—that is, in the wrong direction. Conrad's comments in the post flight debriefing deepen the mystery:

I didn't LPD for quite a while until we got down around, as I remember, 2300 feet or so. I LPD'd one right to move it off the crater and headed for the landing area short of the crater. At that point, I listened to some more LPD angles from Al and I had the feeling that I was a little high; so I LPD'd two clicks short, and I let it go for a while.

That corresponds exactly to what happened, and is exactly what he should have done if he thought he was high, except that he *actually* LPD'd two clicks *long*, not short. I hesitate to say so, but I believe the explanation that best fits the facts and statements is that Conrad meant to redesignate short, but he pushed the stick in the wrong direction.

Whether it was a mistake or not, and whether Conrad realized it or not, he set about correcting it. About 25 seconds later he clicked the hand controller twice in the uprange or short direction. Since he was closer now, each redesignation was worth less distance on the ground, so these actions recovered only half of the earlier downrange shift.

At about 400 feet, Conrad switched attitude control to ATT HOLD and clicked the ROD switch to enter P66. Now the guidance system would control rate of descent in response to the ROD switch while Conrad controlled the LM's attitude to maneuver horizontally. For about 20 seconds Conrad avoided changing the spacecraft's pitch—angled back about 27 degrees—in order to brake harder. He also began maneuvering to the right. Bean reads off altitudes and altitude rates from the DSKY—and steals an occasional look out the window.

Bean: 300 feet, coming down at 5... Hey, look at that crater, right where it's supposed to be! Hey, you're beautiful!

They were approaching Surveyor crater and Bean's "you're beautiful" was meant for Pete not the crater—but, audible under the LM pilot's remarks (in a statement not in the official transcript but teased out of the voice recording by Eric Jones) Conrad says, "Gosh, I went by it."

Bean: 10 percent, 257 feet, coming down at 5. 240, coming down at 5. Hey, you're really maneuvering around.

Conrad: Yes.

Bean: Come on down, Pete.

Conrad: Okay.

Bean: 10-percent fuel. 200 feet, coming down at 3; need to come on down.

Conrad: Okay.

At the end, Conrad's subdued responses betray his level of concentration — but you have to chuckle at Al Bean's tone of concern — and so they landed, just beyond the crater that contained the Surveyor.

As Conrad said after the lightning strike, "I always like to start out behind the eight-ball and catch up." Or in this case, after his erroneous downrange redesignations, start out beyond the eight-ball and pull back.

FRANCE, VENICE

Apollo 12 was on the way home when Marjorie called. Two years earlier her sister Paula had met a man named Tim and they fell in love. When Tim moved to New York to get a graduate degree in American history at New York University, Paula and then Marjorie had moved too, Paula to live with Tim on 14th Street in an apartment with a direct view of the Empire State Building, Marjorie to her own small apartment near the Museum of Natural History, where she worked as an illustrator.

Sometimes I broke my return from Houston with a few hours in New York — depending as usual on the efficient travel office at the Manned Spacecraft Center to make the arrangements. A late dinner, a pipe, music, talk, and I was off in a cab to JFK to catch the 2:30 AM flight to Boston.

Tim's cousin Jeff was often around, and Tim's fellow history student Lenny Kaye. One day Tim and Lenny had sat down next to each other in a seminar and become friends. Lenny's thesis was "Communism in America." Tim's was "Socialism in America." Lenny's other education, the one that counted, was his job at Village Oldies, a record store in Greenwich Village. One day he said to Tim, "I met this chick who wants me to play guitar behind her poetry." That was the beginning of the Patti Smith Group.

On those nights in New York, returning from Houston with my head buzzing with the Moon, my work was always part of the conversation. In the friendliest way I was probed. Many of the same organizations that were central to Apollo were also building missiles armed with nuclear warheads. That included my own employer, the MIT

Instrumentation Lab. It was not surprising that some of my friends found it hard to distinguish between the civilian space program and the military. The way I saw it, the space program tended to pump technology, and talent, away from weapons to exploration; because, if there were an opportunity to work on the Moon landing, would not the best engineers prefer to do that than design for nuclear war? No matter how geopolitics had figured in its genesis, Apollo was about exploration, I thought, something I counted as one of humankind's more noble qualities.

Paula married Tim and they embarked on an extended honeymoon in southern France. Now Marjorie brought me up to date. They were living in a resort on the Mediterranean called Palavas-les-Flots, a ghost town at this time of year. They were not getting along and Marjorie wanted to conduct a reconnaissance — or maybe it was a rescue mission. I enlisted.

For a week we sat at a table overlooking a wide, deserted beach and a wintry sea, eating French bread and French butter, never more delicious, while a gas heater labored against the cold. Somehow grey, bone-chilling days coexisted with hard starry nights, Orion at center stage to seaward. On an outing we clambered around the fortress of Saint Jacques across the Rhone from Avignon, our clothes flapping in the mistral. One day Tim and I hiked along the Marseilles-Sett Canal, ending up at Maguelone, the seaside summer home of the pope during the period in the 14th Century known as the Babylonian Captivity — now a decayed and vandalized Romanesque pile, not lacking an alert sacristan to show us the gloomy interior and the glass-fronted bins of accumulated monkish skulls that his own head already resembled.

But Palavas was making Marjorie and me crazy. We decided to drive to Venice and take Paula with us. Indeed it was her car, and, distracted and depressed or not, she insisted on driving.

We spent a night in Marseilles, disappointed to find the sea too rough for an excursion to Chateau d'If, where Alexandre Dumas imprisoned his hero in *The Count of Monte Cristo*. In Cannes there was a small traffic accident. The next day, after a stop in Antibes to visit the Picasso Museum, we made it to an awful hotel in Monaco. From

Nice, Paula took the Haute Corniche, from which we could look down a thousand feet to the azure sea.

At the rate we were going we might never make Venice, even if we failed to plunge off the cliff. In Menton, after a fine meal in a sea front restaurant where we were the only customers, we parted company. The sisters continued in the car as far as Genoa, then turned around and made for Paris. I would meet them there a week later. I found my way back to Nice and caught a late flight to Venice.

And so began a magical night. I checked into a tiny room at the Europa & Britannia, on the Grand Canal, and gave myself the luxury of a room-service Coca-Cola and a long shower in my own bathroom. Then I ventured out. The hotel gave me a tourist map that proved exceptionally accurate—there had been centuries to get it right.

I struck out along the wide pedestrian way that runs between the Campo San Stefano and the Piazza San Marco. The city was very quiet. My judgment of distance was uncalibrated so it was sudden—and the architectural experience of my life—when I emerged into the Piazza: the great Basilica San Marco directly ahead, its seven arches topped by five and above that three domes, like a game of Nim, made toylike by the false perspective of the unrectangular piazza; to the left the Torre dell'Orologio with its intricate clock (started February 1, 1497); to the right the too tall Campanile, and beyond a pink slice of the Doge's Palace beckoning me around the corner into the Piazzetta, where the broad sea entrance to Venice opened up, and across the fairway loomed up the great Renaissance church of San Georgio Maggiore.

I kept going, towards the Arsenale and beyond, into damp and shadowy mazes of rough buildings; an unexpected square with its church; an arched bridge over a narrow waterway with a mysterious light flickering on the stonework to either side and a door with its threshold a few inches above the water; a gothic palace with its upper windows softly lit; all of it suffused with fog and sea salt and wet stone, and occasionally the stink of canal water where it did not flow enough to be entirely wholesome. In my memory I stopped at several small cafés for hot chocolate, surprised to find them open so late, warm refuges for someone unsuitably shod for the damp in flimsy loafers. The next day I bought superior shoes for about 8000 lira ($12), amazing shoes that I wore for years, and moved to less pricey quarters.

It was December and darkness came early. One night I heard Puccini's *Turandot* from a perch in the gods at La Fenice—afterwards watching as the elegant crowd from the good seats departed in sleek mahogany motorboats. Another evening I wandered into one of the glassware shops on the Piazza San Marco. It must have been obvious that I had nothing to spend, but there was no one else for the salesman to entertain and he was proud of what he had to show me. We walked through a series of ornate chambers, each dark until my guide threw a switch, whereupon the space exploded in color as tables crammed with fantastic plates and goblets and vases and flasks and chalices and candlesticks and candelabra and a thousand other fanciful shapes took the light and gave it back transformed; and then on to the next palatial chamber where another still brighter galaxy of swirls and whorls and curlicues and sprays and arabesques delighted us both.

I settled on a routine that included one good meal a day—a late breakfast of an omelet, bread, and a half bottle of Soave—for which it pleased me to choose Caffé Florian, established 1720, on the south side of the Piazza San Marco. I was usually the only person seated in a small room of marble topped tables, occupying who knows whose customary chair—Proust's, Henry James's, Stravinsky's, Casanova's? It was from here on Europa & Britannia stationary that I wrote to Amy back in Boston, eight pages, wishing she were there to share my delight, and my bed.

Then it was back to Paris to rejoin the Shepatin sisters and eat *crêpes au sucre*, then Boston, and then Atlanta for Christmas with my mother and siblings. 1969 ended, a year in which we had twice done what Jack Kennedy had dared us to do. At MIT we shared the glory with thousands of others who were just as excited and who had worked just as hard, but we thought we were luckier because as creators of the flight software we were connected to almost every aspect of development and operations, and the programs we wrote were the precious distillate of pure logic that flowed in the LM's wiry veins.

Delta Guidance never flew. I never heard what the "engine people" said about pulsing the DPS up and down, but after Pete Conrad made landing accurately look easy on Apollo 12 the issue of hover time lost some urgency. It was not worth making extensive changes to the guidance and throttle control programs for only 20 seconds of additional hover. But, Bill Tindall wrote:

> [T]here is one survivor from this delta guidance program change "package." There appears to be unanimous agreement that we should add the terrain model of the specific landing site we're going to in place of the present "billiard ball" moon. This will eliminate some objectionable pitch excursions and will make the LPD work better.

And more importantly, make it safe to land in interesting places even if that involved approaching over a mountain or a deep valley.

The purpose of the "a priori terrain model" (as we called it) was to tell navigation about the shape of the terrain the LM was passing over. Consider landing on the far slope of a wide valley. As the valley drops away under the radar beam, navigation senses that altitude is increasing, or at least not decreasing fast enough, so the guidance equation closes the throttle and the LM drops faster. Then, as the terrain suddenly rises near the landing site, the spacecraft may find itself dangerously low. There was a similar problem if the LM had to pass over mountains.

As Tindall indicated, I had already coded the terrain model in the Delta Guidance text-bed AMELIA. Bernie Kriegsman did the analysis — using as a test case the Taurus-Littrow region that Apollo 17 would later visit — and authored the Program Change Request (PCR) to add it to LUMINARY in time for Apollo 14.

Hover time was passé, but another matter had *gained* urgency since Apollo 12: moondust, the fine particles of lunar soil kicked up by the descent engine during the last hundred feet of the lunar descent.

As expected, both Neil Armstrong on Apollo 11 and Pete Conrad on Apollo 12 had taken over semi-manual control at around 400 feet using P66. From that point they had flicked the ROD switch up or down to decrease or increase the descent rate in increments of one foot per second, while they controlled the LM's attitude to move across the surface and finally slow to a hover, before descending vertically.

We had no way to know in advance how much dust would be kicked up, or how it would affect the pilot—but we knew now. Armstrong told it this way:

> [T]he thing that was confusing to me was that it was hard to pick out what your lateral and downrange velocities were, because you were seeing a lot of moving dust that you had to look through to pick up the stationary rocks and base your translational velocity decisions on that. I found that to be quite difficult.

Pete Conrad described it a little differently:

> I got her down around 100 feet.... At that point, the dust was bad enough and I could obtain absolutely no attitude reference by looking at the horizon and the LM. I had to use the 8-ball. I had attitude excursions in pitch of plus 10 and minus 10 [degrees], which happened while I was looking out the window making sure that the lateral and horizontal velocities were still nulled.

The alternatives to P66 were P65 and P67. P65 was fully automatic. If there was no action by the astronaut, P65 would take over at about 100 feet, maneuver to null out horizontal velocity, and bring the LM down at three feet per second. P65 was useful for simulations but not flight because it landed blind. P67 was a challenging, fully-manual mode in which the astronaut flew with one hand on the throttle and the other on the joystick.

You entered P66 from P64 or P65 by switching to ATT HOLD and clicking the ROD switch. You could enter P67 from P65 or P66 by switching the throttle control mode, a switch labeled THR CONT that was below the eight-ball on the commander's side, from AUTO to MAN. Once you selected P66 you could not return to P65. Once you selected P67 you could not return to P66. The astronaut could not switch backwards from a less automatic to a more automatic mode.

This was an example of how formal "requirements" can lead design astray. The GSOP described three alternatives for the final descent, so we programmed three separate modes. The GSOP also described a manual-modes monitor (R13, known as GUILDENSTERN), that envisaged transitions only from more automatic to less automatic modes, and so we allowed *only* those transitions. It is all too easy for the implementer of a system to abdicate the responsibility to design — to build a harmonious whole — instead of dumbly banging out the requirements. You can still have a requirements document, but do not be limited by it. Sometimes more capability is cheaper than less.

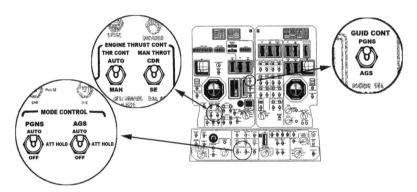

From left, the switches that set the attitude mode for the primary system (PGNCS) and the abort guidance system (AGS); the switches that control the operation of the throttle; and the switch that determines whether PGNCS or AGS is responsible for controlling the spacecraft.

The first step in shaping the final-landing modes into a harmonious whole was the elimination of P67, which occurred when we realized that P66 with the throttle switch in MAN was identical to P67, with the advantage that you could return to ROD-switch control by switching the throttle back to AUTO. In fact, this philosophy became general. The throttle could be switched to manual, and back, even during P63 or P64. This was a backup in case the computer's interface with the throttle were broken. To give the astronaut something to go on if manual throttle operation were necessary we created a new noun that could be called up to display the throttle setting desired by guidance.

Now the decisive step was taken by Allan Klumpp, and it resulted in the elimination of P65. Now there would only be P66, but P66 could be operated in a range of configurations that included all the required modes, with full flexibility to switch among them.

Allan in his memo introducing the new capability provided this interesting background:

> My first knowledge of the P65 guidance equation was in August 1965 when I produced it for the sole purpose of making simulations work. It was the simplest conceivable stopgap measure to allow deferment of the minor problem of vertical descent until some of the major problems were solved. I never would have believed at the time that this inadequate algorithm would survive to be coded in the guidance computer of the first two lunar landing missions.

Inadequate? First I heard about that. But even before Apollo 11 Allan had asked a young engineer named Nick Pippenger to look into improving the equation to make it both quicker and better behaved. Nick's ideas had not made it into the code. But that was before there had been lunar landings in which dust made it difficult to judge horizontal velocity (Apollo 11) or control attitude (Apollo 12).

Allan's idea was to give the astronauts a way to call on the computer to null horizontal velocity, but with full freedom to switch back to semi-manual operation. Allan and I first talked about it as we returned from the crew debriefing after Apollo 11. Allan credited me with producing "the germ of the idea when [I] suggested the capability to return to P65 from P66."

Allan called it P66 Auto. You entered P66 from P64, as before, by switching attitude mode to **ATT HOLD** and clicking the **ROD** switch. You could maneuver as before. But now, if you switched attitude mode back to **AUTO**, Pippinger's new equation would come into play to null horizontal velocity. The astronaut could maneuver toward a desired touchdown point, high enough to avoid the dust, and then switch back to **AUTO** to let the computer bring the LM to a (horizontal) stop, before descending vertically. If necessary he could switch back to **ATT HOLD** and repeat the process.

Meanwhile in the vertical dimension the descent rate would be under the control of the astronaut by means of the **ROD** switch — unless, by switching THR CONT to MAN, he took over using the manual throttle. In that case he could switch the throttle back to AUTO and ROD operation would resume from the starting point of the vertical velocity at the time of the switch.

All the modes envisioned by the GSOP were there, but now the unnecessary limitations implied by the requirements were erased. The modes could be employed in a unified way with full flexibility to switch among them as expedient. Deleting P65 and P67 made room for the new code.

It was such an attractive idea that we rushed its development. It was provisionally approved by Chris Kraft's Software Control Board on December 18, pending the results of simulations to be run just before Christmas. When the sims proved favorable the Apollo 13 flight rope was rereleased in early February, under the name LM131, and the fine ladies at Raytheon got busy weaving core rope memory all over again.

TLOSS

As 1970 dawned, with P66 Auto finished and onboard for the upcoming mission, Allan and I found time to reconsider the problem that so nearly ruined the Apollo 11 landing — deprivation of processor time, which we called TLOSS — but we went about it in different ways.

Allan kept the IBM 360 humming as he ran simulations on the Apollo 13 rope to see how it behaved under varying amounts of TLOSS. We already knew that if the amount of TLOSS was just right, then during a period of high activity incomplete SERVICER jobs could accumulate in the Executive queue. The last thing the SERVICER did on each pass was send information to the DSKY for display. Just before it did that it issued attitude commands, and before that, throttle commands. What concerned Allan was what would happen if a SERVICER job was cut off before the throttle or attitude command was sent out. If enough of these suspended jobs accumulated, a software restart would occur, as it did on Apollo 11, and the suspended jobs would disappear. But what if the computational burden eased before they were flushed?

What could happen, Allan found, was that the suspended jobs (Allan dubbed them "lurkers") could come back to life, unaware that they had been in hibernation, and proceed to issue an attitude or throttle command applicable to an earlier point in the trajectory. Suddenly the LM might maneuver to the wrong attitude. The worst cases were when suspended jobs that accumulated during P64 were executed after the transition to P66.

On March 4 Allan put out a carefully written memo describing "a collection of known manifestations of time loss." Allan described eight separate modes of bad behavior, starting at a TLOSS of about 8 percent. In an unusual precaution Allan signed the memo, and asked Gerry Levine to sign as having approved it.

The demons Allan had stirred up did not surprise me. On the other hand, the anomaly that caused the Apollo 11 alarms had been understood and fixed, and flight experience had given no indication that vibration was a real problem. No other sources of TLOSS were known to us.

On the other, other hand, the success of Pete Conrad's pinpoint landing had emboldened NASA to fly to more rugged sites, and that would require new software—starting with the a priori terrain model. For my part, I was less focused on the possibility that TLOSS on the scale of Apollo 11 would crop up again than on the desirable new capabilities that we could add if we increased our margin of safety.

We were vulnerable to TLOSS because SERVICER's rigid two-second period made it brittle. It did not degrade gracefully under time-stress. One of Allan's lurkers might pop up unpredictably and do something inappropriate. On Apollo 11 the system in which SERVICER was embedded reacted adaptively, saving the mission, but SERVICER had stepped on its own tail.

The two-second guidance period was set before I arrived and it was a reasonable choice. One second was clearly too short and three seconds sounded awkward. For every other powered-flight phase—orbital maneuvers, mid-course corrections, lunar ascent—a two-second period provided an ample margin. The landing was another story. It needed radar measurements, a more complicated guidance equation, landing site redesignation, and throttle control. But why must SERVICER have a fixed period at all? What if SERVICER could extend its period if there were excessive TLOSS? Lurkers would become impossible. The accuracy of navigation and guidance would barely be affected.

Conventional wisdom held that the two-second period was built into the navigation and guidance software so deeply that it would be hazardous to change, but Peter Adler and I had already built a version of a variable-period SERVICER in an "underground" version of LUMINARY called DIANA, so we already had the measure of that very slight problem. Now I created a new off-line program called ZERLINA, starting from the latest version of LUMINARY, and began to construct a new version of the variable guidance period SERVICER, designed to bend but not break.

On March 3, the day before Allan's memo but aware of what was in it, I wrote in a memo that "LM powered flight is approaching a sort of asteroid belt of TLOSS difficulties as its time margin slips away." I proposed the variable guidance-period Servicer as the solution, and announced that it was running successfully in ZERLINA. The code changes could be described in a few pages. The two-second guidance period was implicit in only a few calculations, such as the average-G equation, and the measured period could easily be used instead. Subsequent tests showed good performance with TLOSS as high as 30 percent. The imperviousness to time-stress translated into time made available for added capability. Still, a great deal of testing would be required. Variable Servicer could not be ready before Apollo 14.

Allan kept his focus on Apollo 13. He had written a Program Change Request to discard any guidance command that was out of date, and the change had been approved — but only for Apollo 14. The Apollo 13 rope had already been released, and rereleased, for manufacture. The change would fly on Apollo 13 only if there was a decision to release the program yet again. That was not good enough for Allan. Early one morning, probably also March 3, he placed a direct call to the Kennedy Space Center office of the Apollo 13 commander, Jim Lovell. He requested an opportunity to brief him about the problems he had found.

It was a big gaffe. "Your political savoir faire has reached a new low," Dick Battin told him—a line Allan likes to quote in mock modesty. There would be a briefing but Allan was invited not to attend. Restless George Cherry had departed to find new challenges and Russ Larson, struggling to fill Cherry's well-polished shoes as the LM software project manager, would fly to Cape Canaveral instead. I would be in Houston when I heard about it.

AGC program names, as printed across the top of each page, included a "by" field. For example, the full name of SUNBURST had been "SUNBURST BY NASA 2021106-031," that being the contract number under which it was produced. For off-line assemblies there was no official mandate for this field so we used it imaginatively. DIANA had been "DIANA BY MOONLIGHT" and for ZERLINA I chose "ZERLINA BY ZOROASTER."

Zerlina was a servant girl seduced by Don Giovanni in the opera by Mozart—a name from fiction since I had already named a program after Amy.

Zoroaster (or Zarathustra) was a Persian prophet from 600 BCE. I picked the name for the alliteration and the incongruity but it touched a nerve with another engineer a few offices away, who recognized in me a fellow initiate in a mystical sphere related to numerology. The license plate on my Alfa (W95-125) clinched his conviction that I was "one of us." I played along at first but it got out of hand. He also made himself obnoxious to Dana Densmore. Then one day he was gone. Another engineer whose name I never knew wore shorts to work in the summer. So did many of us. But the shorts got shorter and shorter and the shirt became optional. The last time I saw him in the building he was working in a bathing suit.

BRIEFING IN CREW QUARTERS

ZERLINA was anytime work and I was in a high production jag that cut the week into six cycles. If I was awake and absorbed in what I was doing it seemed unnecessary to go to sleep at the same time as the day before—but I still liked to sleep when I slept. When the cycle precessed to the point that I was ready for bed late in the afternoon of the next day, I would usually just stay up until evening. That averaged out to a week of six 28-hour days, 20 awake, 8 asleep. I never popped uppers or downers but the use of marijuana may have helped me laugh at the so-called circadian rhythms.

Not that I did not come up for aria. In February Amy and I sat in the second row for Sarah Caldwell's production of Donizetti's *Daughter of the Regiment*, staged in a gym at Tufts University. Grayson Hirst pinged out Tonio's famous barrage of tenor high Cs but Beverly Sills as Marie stole the show, wielding her stratospheric instrument with exuberance and utter confidence, launching dazzling coloratura embellishments well above her own brilliant high C.

And then, mid-afternoon on a Tuesday (again March 3) Bruce McCoy asked me to stand in for him at a meeting of the Software Control Board the next day. I barely had time to rush home and pack and dash to Logan Airport. American to Dallas, Braniff to Houston Hobby. Over Texas I watched a huge electrical storm to starboard. Every second, extravagant cumulus clouds were lit up blue-white from within in awesome patterns that rippled across the whole towering formation. From Hobby an AMC Javelin that honked when you squeezed the steering wheel took me through a petroleum-scented fog to a bed at the Ramada Inn on NASA Road 1.

The next day, Bill Tindall was in Chris Kraft's chair at the SCB. Neil Armstrong was in attendance. I sat down in the back and listened as Command Module PCRs were "dispositioned." After lunch I moved up to the table, sitting between Ken Greene, our standing representative on the board, and Bob Covelli, our landing radar expert.

Covelli was also in the TLOSS business and what he did about it, it turned out, was more useful than anything Allan or I came up with. Incorporating landing radar data in the state vector, which had to be done every two seconds, was complicated by the fact that their times did not match. The state vector had to be extrapolated to the time of the radar reading before the two could be compared or combined. Covelli got rid of the extrapolation by scheduling the reading of the landing radar so that it was centered on PIPTIME, the moment when the accelerometers were read. The SCB had approved this change the previous October, and it became relevant today when Bernie Kriegsman's PCR, titled "A Priori Terrain Model," came up for discussion. His idea was to equip navigation with a simple model of the terrain under the LM so that mountains and valleys would not be misinterpreted as altitude errors. Tindall had already embraced the idea and I had long since coded it in the Delta Guidance test bed AMELIA.

But was there enough duty cycle, fretted Bill Tindall, when the terrain-model PCR came up. Covelli's change had saved several percent. I said I was sure I could code the terrain model in less than that. I already knew it would take about one percent. The model was a gross approximation, consisting of only five line segments, so high precision was not required in the calculations. Now Tindall approved the change for Apollo 14.

But also on the docket were two change requests related to the TLOSS problem. One was Allan's PCR 1013 to drop stale commands, which had already been verbally approved. Today it was approved again, but it was still contingent on the decision to rebuild the Apollo 13 rope. But the next PCR Tindall drew from his stack should not have been there. It proposed more extensive TLOSS modifications for later missions, beginning with Apollo 14. We had intended to withdraw it for the time being because we thought it needed further study—it had an impact on navigation—but now it seemed Bill Tindall was about to approve it.

"But we don't want you to approve PCR 1012," I said.

"Oh, okay," said Tindall and let it drop, but he was still worried about the impact of the terrain model on the duty-cycle margin and picked it up again. The PCR had four parts. Why not approve parts one and two, someone suggested. On the spot, I could see no strong objection, and so it was approved. At the next SCB it was finally disapproved in its entirety at our request.

It was then that I heard about the big brouhaha Allan Klumpp had started with his phone call—he probably expected Lovell to act on it more discreetly—and about Russ Larson's briefing for the Apollo 13 crew. I realized the flap was probably the reason McCoy had missed the SCB and asked me at the last minute to go instead.

The briefing would be the next day at the Cape, at a time not yet determined. I was not necessarily invited, but I was interested in the scene and reluctant to leave it to Larson and McCoy alone, neither a landing specialist. I booked a late flight to Daytona, 50 miles north of Cape Canaveral.

I was in the habit of asking Avis for "something sporty." Tonight it was a Dodge Challenger convertible. My first cop that night caught me doing 50 in a 35 in New Smyrna, but on an empty I-95 I put my foot down and the Challenger topped out at 110.

If you had a badge the best route to Cocoa Beach from Daytona ran through the space center. The roads were straight, perfectly maintained, and empty except at shift changes—but I was beckoned off the direct route by the Vertical Assembly Building looming up off to my left, and beyond it the brilliantly lit launch pad. Near the VAB I turned onto the road that led toward the pad, then took the gravel cut-through to the paved road that ran between the pad and the beach.

I pulled over at the point closest to launch Pad 39A and cut the engine. To my right was the ocean. Once on a windy day I had scrambled across the ditch and an embankment to look at the narrow beach, deeply scalloped by the booming surf. Tonight the Atlantic was quiet. The Moon had set. The stars were brilliant. The Florida air seemed as clear as no atmosphere at all, but at the same time warm and salt-scented, fecund to the deprived senses of a refugee from monochrome March Massachusetts.

And 2000 feet away the gleaming shaft stood quietly in a fan of spotlights, poised tonight not yet in the steaming quiver of fully-fueled expectation, but in the calm of careful preparation. It already harbored the flaw that would ruin the Apollo 13 mission.

The cop who pulled up five minutes later was gray-haired and courtly. My credentials checked out but he asked me to move on. I drove south, out the Cocoa Beach gate, and roused Doug Melvin at the Islander Motel to give me a room. I put on a bathing suit and waded into the Atlantic until my toes barely touched. The unseen waves hissed toward me with perfect regularity and I let them rock me as I watched the stars.

The Islander had a comfortable seediness. One night I surprised a wolf spider and a palmetto bug wrestling on the balcony. Maybe that is why Russ Larson preferred the Hilton, or maybe it was the Hilton's reputation as the scene of astronaut high jinks. I reached him there the next morning and he seemed happy enough that I was at the Cape. The briefing would be that evening in the astronaut living quarters in the Manned Spacecraft Operations Building—and we were invited for dinner. I spent the day at the simulator.

We were ushered in the back door and through the kitchen and offered beers by Jim Lovell and his LM pilot, Fred Haise. Tom Price and Floyd Bennett—young guys from the mission planning and analysis division—were already there. Rocco Petrone arrived, the Falstaffian long-time manager of Apollo launch operations who had just been promoted to Apollo Program Director. In the conference room Petrone sat in front of a relief map of the lunar surface, legs apart and hands on his knees, as Lovell described the route he planned to walk as he explored the landing site. Then we crossed the hall to the dining room to enjoy steak, potatoes, asparagus, salad and iced tea. I was with McCoy and Price and Bennett at the overflow table so we did not share in the conversation at the grown-up's table, where Deke Slayton, Jim McDivitt and several other people I did not recognize had swelled the number.

We moved back to the conference room for the briefing. Larson described the sort of behavior that was possible if there was a large TLOSS, but minimized the likelihood of that happening. There was no reason for the crew to be especially concerned. Lovell rejected complicated workarounds such as the one Allan had devised for use if his software change did not fly on Apollo 13. He would land manually if he could, or else abort on the abort guidance system. I kept my mouth shut but I could not help feeling that the whole affair had spring-loaded Lovell to take control away from our system at the slightest sign of trouble.

—

I caught a late flight to Atlanta, where my mother had returned to her former profession as a high school science teacher, and my sister Mary Anne, a chemist, did research at the Yerkes Primate Research Center. Yerkes was said to have the largest collection of great apes in the world. Mary Anne had arranged to get me in for a tour the next day.

After we viewed my sister's experiment her boss offered me a clean lab coat and we went to see the apes in their outdoor cages. A female orangutan of about 200 pounds with a beautiful auburn coat clung to the front of her cage with four hands, her triple-chinned face pressed between the bars so you could reach in and stroke her upper lip—but I was warned not to try it with the male orang next door. A slapping sound came from around the corner and we moved on to see a sleek, black adolescent gorilla beating his chest while lying down, macho and languid at the same time. In another cage a younger gorilla and a young orangutan (dubbed Romeo and Juliet) lived together in an experiment to see if they would mate. Cautiously we peeked around to observe the adult chimpanzees. They were at the far end of the long row for the same reason we wore lab coats. The chimps were infamous for their accuracy with a handful of their own shit.

Back inside, three happy chimpanzee toddlers welcomed us as new playmates—I introduced the game of drumming on a cardboard box and they took it up with enthusiasm—but through a window we glimpsed another experiment: a little chimp who sat, rocking back and forth, fed alcohol with his milk, drunk from birth.

TRAINING APOLLO 14

I was burning up the computer running tests of the ZERLINA under different conditions and there were complaints about the amount of computer time I was using. On April 1, 1970 I fired off a snippy note to Dick Battin and Bob Millard (a higher-up on the business side) with copies to Russ Larson and Margaret Hamilton:

> Besides preparing the variable servicer, for example, I am testing the a priori terrain model.... It may be true that people have to wait a week

for long runs these days. I often do. But anyone who comes in at the right times over the weekend can get good turnaround time. I hate to be bugged for adopting this solution. I hope these observations will moderate your zeal in complaining about my computer usage.

In my own insubordinate mind I wanted my bosses to feel like they had touched a live wire. However bratty I must have seemed, no one complained about my computer usage after that.

The reason Margaret Hamilton got the memo was that she was now my boss too. The Lab had been renamed. We were now the Charles Stark Draper Laboratory. Organization charts were coming out into the open. The structure (or lack of structure) that had enabled us to do what everyone said was a great accomplishment was now to be "improved." That such things were being thought about was probably a sign of Doc Draper's loosening grip, as signaled by the name change.

The immediate effect was that Hamilton took over the position occupied by Dan Lickly — who had left to work at a new company called Intermetrics and help develop the language to be used by the Space Shuttle computers — so the LM team was now part of her group. However, that group was now defined as the "software" group, which in principle made us available to work on software in all business areas, potentially including military projects.

The Lab had been less an organization than an organism. Authority was earned but mostly unwritten, and grew along lines related to the job at hand. Now we would start to be an organization whose structure was imposed from above. Fortunately our culture was too well entrenched for it to be more than a nuisance so far. On the LM side, everything we were doing was connected to operations and mission goals, and in that we were taking direction from our project manager — Russ Larson, who had taken over from George Cherry — and working directly with NASA engineers and astronauts. My relationship with Allan Klumpp was unchanged, even though we had become, in organizational terms, cousins of greater degree. In these respects the reorganization had no effect whatsoever.

Hamilton was a star at the Laboratory, one of only a few senior female engineers and a very attractive woman as well. Her specialty was what we would now call the "system" software, which was the same in the LM and CM computers. She played a leading role in refining the software-restart logic — pioneered by Charley Muntz — that had come into play on Apollo 11.

Hamilton came from the more straitlaced Command Module side and may have thought that the LM group needed to be domesticated. Not long after Apollo 13 Hamilton put out a memo in which I was listed as part of a "landing group" headed by Bob Covelli. Since I had software responsibility for all the lunar landing phases, that felt like a snub. Was my new boss not acquainted with who did what on the LM side, or might it have something to do with my recent note about computer usage? And why did our hierarchy need an additional tier anyway? I threw another small tantrum and the decision was rescinded — but I felt dirtied by having been drawn into a way of thinking that I disdained.

Meanwhile, Allan Klumpp and I found ourselves again in the little room near the entrance to the crew training building at Cape Canaveral. We were there to brief the crew that was scheduled to fly the mission *after* next, Apollo 14, commanded, to the surprise of many, by Alan Shepard.

Shepard had been sidelined by an inner ear condition called Ménière's disease shortly after his suborbital Mercury mission, and returned to flight status eight years later after undergoing a then-novel surgical procedure. His flight assignment caused some resentment — but the will of the two men who did the deciding was implacable, as Pete Conrad found out when Shepard and Deke Slayton came to inform him that Neil Armstrong would fly Apollo 11 — all the more so if one of the deciders was the beneficiary.

I did not begrudge it. You wanted lucky astronauts and Alan Shepard had luck written all over him, now that it had changed, even if in this case it was a self-fulfilling chicanery. Maybe it suited Shepard to avoid those overnight flights in stinky little Mercury and Gemini "capsules" and then travel in style on the through train to Fra Mauro. When his original assignment to Apollo 13 was changed to Apollo 14, to provide more time to prepare, his luck continued to hold.

Malcolm Johnston was one of the people who minded that Shepard had jumped over better-prepared astronauts. As it happened, Johnston wore the same size gym shoes as Shepard (elevens) and, since Shepard almost never showed up at the Manned Spacecraft Center gym, Johnston got in the habit of using his shoes when he played squash with Bill Tindall or one of the other astronauts. After the decision he took special pleasure in wearing down Shepard's soles.

This ended badly for Steve Copps, who also wore elevens. Johnston told him, "Just use Shepard's," but by then Shepard was trying to get back in shape for his flight. He walked in just as Copps was lacing them up.

"So you're the bastard who's been wearing out my shoes!"

It was odd, but it wasn't, that we held the training session for Apollo 14 before Apollo 13 flew. Alan Shepard had not flown a rocket since his fifteen-minute mission in 1961, and now he had a Moon-landing only a few months away (or so he thought). He knew he needed extra work — and not just in the gym.

The agenda was a comprehensive survey of LM topics in three days, but this time I was not a presenter. Russ Larson gave an overview. George Kalan described the LM digital autopilot. Allan Klumpp explained the descent guidance. Steve Schroeder covered descent navigation and procedures. I was there to answer questions that might come up. When the meeting moved on to ascent and rendezvous I was more or less off duty and free to enjoy the show.

Shepard was a big golden man with a big gold watch and a disposition that was not just sunny, it was sun-like. I knew Shepard had a dark side but I never saw it. Easy to explain. For eight years he was the flawed prince, haunting the battlements, the brilliant pilot not allowed to fly solo, the original astronaut, grounded by an obscure condition that hardly affected his everyday life, sticking with NASA, rising in responsibility, watching other men fly missions he would have eaten up.... It would have been crazy not to be moody. It was my pleasure to see the man reborn.

Fifty-six hours into the Apollo 13 mission, while the spacecraft was coasting towards the Moon, an oxygen tank in the Service Module, which had been damaged during fabrication and testing, overheated and exploded. In the Command Module mission commander Jim Lovell felt "a dull but definite bang." The spacecraft was surrounded by so much debris he could not see the stars. All sources of power except emergency batteries dwindled and failed.

It happened just after ten in the evening, Boston time. I was in bed with Amy. If it was a typical night we had smoked a pipe and the Rolling Stones' *Beggar's Banquet* might have been on the stereo in the other room. A friend called to tell me what had happened. I pulled on clothes and drove to the Lab.

Bob Covelli, in the AGC support room at Mission Control, was the first person on Earth to see the problem, when the restart light on his console lit up. The indication could occur erroneously because of a transmission problem so Covelli checked an onboard register where hardware restarts were counted. The counter read one. The restart must have occurred at the moment of the explosion when power switched from fuel cells to batteries. Covelli was on the phone to the flight controller when CM pilot Jack Swigert uttered his chilling understatement "Okay Houston, we've had a problem here."

It would have been hopeless except for one fact: the LM Aquarius was still attached. Just maybe, by using its resources, there was a way to get the crew home alive. But was there enough oxygen to last four days? Enough electrical power? Enough gas for the maneuvering jets?

At least they had a REFSMMAT. Lovell and Fred Haise had hurried to activate the LM and transfer a rough IMU alignment from the CM before it died. Lovell said later, "One of the big turning points in the flight was the fact that we got the LM platform up."

At MIT the main implications were for the control system. The LM would be called on to control the entire stack— the LM, the CM and the SM, all fully fueled—during several engine firings. The autopilot depended on knowing the mass properties of the vehicle it was controlling, but the Service Module, the heaviest component in the stack, had been scrambled by an explosion. If a rocket's thrust is not aligned with the spacecraft's center-of-mass it will spin like a pinwheel. Another problem was that the coupling between the top of the lightly built LM and the pointed end of the CM was not completely rigid. Simulations were being pushed through our computers as never before.

As a lunar landing specialist I had no part in it, however dramatic it was for Amy when I rushed off to the Lab. I did what I could to be useful: brought coffee, fetched printouts from the computer room.

Five and a half hours after the explosion the LM fired its descent engine for about 35 seconds, using Peter Adler's P40, to place the combined spacecraft on a course that would lead back toward Earth if no further action were taken. Dead or alive, the astronauts would return to their home planet, but only after looping around the Moon first.

Eighteen hours later, behind the Moon, the DPS fired again for over four minutes. Further corrections would be required to make a safe reentry. Power was so tight that the LM's attitude indicators were turned off. For each of the burns Lovell had to maneuver to angles displayed numerically on the DSKY, something he had not practiced and found difficult.

The Command Module, its batteries depleted, would be required again for the reentry. A way was found to transfer power from the LM, but would the guidance system work when it was called on? The heaters in the CM's inertial measurement unit would be turned off for more than three days. In Cambridge, gyro wizard Jerry Gilmore put an Apollo IMU in the trunk of his car and left it there during a bitterly cold night. When he brought it inside the next day the unit functioned perfectly.

The LM stayed with the Command Module until the blown-out Service Module was jettisoned and the CM woke up on batteries to control the reentry. No contingency checklist existed for activating the CM in flight. No procedures had been written for outlandish maneuvers such as jettisoning the Service Module while the LM was still docked with the CM. The complete electrical death of the CM had not been planned for. The intellectual struggle, as teams in Houston labored to stretch the onboard resources and plan operations that had never before been contemplated, has been captured in book and film.

The human struggle of the Apollo 13 astronauts has, of dramatic necessity, been misrepresented. The engine firings, and the explosion itself, were much less violent than they have been portrayed, but imagine those long hours—87 from explosion to splashdown—as three men who might already be dead huddled together for warmth in an inert spacecraft damp with condensation, weakening physically but with plenty of time to think; then executing a complex checklist and plunging into the Earth's atmosphere, watching the first flames sweep by the windows in full awareness that their heat shield may have been damaged when the tank blew up; not knowing until the very last minute whether they would ever breathe Earth-air and feel Earth-gravity again.

The usual radio silence during reentry extended past the point when it should have ended. In Cambridge, our first sign that the crew had made it home was the sight of the three big-bellied parachutes on the color television in the classroom.

BOOKS

During a break in the pre-mission briefing in crew quarters, in a spirit of mischief, I had asked Jim Lovell if Norman Mailer had had anything to do with his choice of the name Aquarius for his Lunar Module. Mailer had adopted the persona "Aquarius" in his just-published book about the space program, *Of a Fire on the Moon*. Lovell said he had picked the name before he read the "Mailer piece."

Two days after Apollo 13 splashed down in the South Pacific, Mailer read from his book in Harvard University's Sanders Theatre before an audience estimated at 500 by the *Harvard Crimson*. During the Q&A I poked at the question from the other side, asking Mailer if he claimed any psychic credit for the heroic role as lifeboat played by the LM Aquarius. He did not rise to the bait either.

Mailer's book contained a wonderfully poetic and as far as it goes accurate account of the alarms that occurred as Neil Armstrong and Buzz Aldrin, in the LM Eagle, descended "toward the gray wife of the earth's ages." Mailer blamed the alarms on a "sneak circuit" and an "undetectable" error in the checklist. That was rather good shorthand for what occurred. He continued:

> No one, however, could be certain—to anticipate every whim of a computer was equal to foreseeing the steps of a virgin whose heart was nymphomaniac—electricity could not run through a multiplicity of circuits without creating a wake of electromagnetisms and interferences whose results were occasionally so bizarre a flight controller could be known to give assent, with unhappy expressions on his face, to the possibility that a computer operator charged with psychic tension on an extraordinary day could also have his effect on the malfunction of the computer.

If anyone's psychic tension was bothering the electronics it was Aldrin's, no malfunction of the computer occurred at any time, and Mailer may have misinterpreted the flight controller's expressions—but goodness, who has ever written such malarkey so magisterially.

Around the same time, Little, Brown came out with *First on the Moon*, an account of their mission by the Apollo 11 astronauts, "written with" Gene Farmer and Dora Jane Hamblin. (The title was borrowed from Jeff Sutton's 1958 science fiction classic, which I reread immediately after, as seemed appropriate.)

When it came to the alarms during the descent, the book rightly emphasized the leadership of Gene Kranz, who had "brilliantly" demanded the review of alarm conditions that established the back room expertise, in the person of Jack Garman, that was able to say go instead of abort.

But, before I got to that part of the book, I found myself reading something that sounded very familiar. The introduction was in Armstrong's voice:

> The computer people are reaching the absolute epitome of short-cut technical English. Of course they must speak in machine language when they are talking with the machines, but they carry over that kind of phraseology into their daily conversation. And into their writing. In 1968 I received a copy of a memorandum which said in part...

The memo in question was Colossus Memo No. 58, Luminary Memo No. 26, titled "RTB," one page long. Now, since Neil did, I will quote the passage, just as it is quoted in the book, except I will correct the outright errors in the quotation:

> A small (but interesting) change in the interpreter makes it possible to call from interpretive, using RTB, in general any basic subroutine which may be called using BANKCALL: in particular any basic subroutine which (1) ends with a TC Q, or a TC K if it stores Q in K, (2) does not clobber BUF2 or BUF2+1, (3) does not clobber interpreter temporaries LOC, BANKSET, EDOP, and of course such erasables as FIXLOC and PUSHLOC and PRIORITY with which no one should trifle. A TC Q from such a routine leads through SWRETURN to DANZIG.
>
> This amounts to a quantum jump in the sexiness of the RTB op-code; this change merges the RTB op-code with the larger set of basic subroutines callable using BANKCALL. This immediately opens a large virgin territory to interpreter users; and as TCF DANZIG routines are converted to TC Q subroutines a significant area may be opened to users of Basic... [Some] subroutines which have required interpretive interface routines can now do without; for instance the SGNAGREE interface for TPAGREE can be dispensed with.
>
> Note that... Q points to SWRETURN: BUF2 to a TCF DANZIG.

The passage's evasive punctuation conceals whether it is Armstrong or one of the with-writers who then adds, "Understand?"

I did not know whether to sputter or die laughing. I not only remembered the memo in question, I had written it! Written it for people who were writing code for the AGC, a select audience that would understand every well-considered word. It was not meant for astronauts, and certainly not meant for the general public to whom it was now being peddled as a cheap-shot example of obscure jargon.

Those words in upper case may look exotic, but most of them were not acronyms. They were in all-caps in obedience to our practice when writing references to precise program locations. That made sense because the program listings were completely in upper case.

The real marvel was that such a memo would reach an Apollo mission commander. Did all our LUMINARY Memos get routed to astronauts? Or did someone pass this one in particular to Armstrong, and if so why? Was it evident that despite my serious purpose I had been trying to have some fun with my "sexiness" and "virgin territory" and semicolons?

The innovation described in the memo was simply to set the return address to point to **DANZIG** (the finishing point for all Interpretive instructions) whenever any Basic-language subroutine was invoked from Interpretive using the return to Basic (**RTB**) instruction. Thus the identical subroutine could be called both from Basic and from Interpretive.

You did not need that information. Neither did Neil Armstrong, yet my memo had somehow crossed his desk and had come to mind when he was interviewed by Farmer and Hamblin. Was this astronaut-think again, a survival instinct for seeking unfiltered information from the lower depths of the intricate apparatus to which they were trusting their lives? Could they sense trouble, some evasion or lack of confidence, even without understanding the subject matter? Was it reassuring or unnerving if the "computer people" were talking in incantations, or joking around?

TEAR-GASSED

May 4, 1970 — bad vibrations. Shooting of 4 (2 coeds) in Ohio by National Guard. Stock market dips 19 points, worst since Kennedy assassination. Cambodia. North Vietnam. Gassed Saturday in New Haven. The car is missing fire. The Red Sox lost Saturday. Amy leaves in a week.

That is from a notebook I was sporadically keeping. I do not know why I was interested in the stock market, having no stake in it. The Red Sox would end the season 21 games behind the Baltimore Orioles. Amy was going to spend the summer in New York.

I was just back from New Haven where I had gone, with Marjorie and Paula, on the weekend of the May Day demonstrations to protest the prosecution of Bobby Seale, Ericka Huggins and other Black Panthers. Nixon had just invaded Cambodia. A rumor said he had commissioned the Rand Corporation to study what would happen if he canceled the 1972 election. The mechanic who worked on my Alfa passed on another rumor, that a National Guard truck carrying 300 machine guns had been hijacked in Connecticut.

On Saturday in springtime weather the mood was calm. As an airplane drew a peace symbol against the blue sky we sat on New Haven Green with 15,000 others. Abbie Hoffmann suggested painting the White House black (later a song by George Clinton). Tom Hayden said there had been enough rallies, it was time for action. John Froines, David Dellinger, Ralph Abernathy, Benjamin Spock, and Jean Genet also spoke. "Free Kim Agnew. Free Bobby Seale," we chanted. I was not entirely comfortable with repeatedly thrusting my fist in the air in the black power salute. Jerry Rubin thought it would be a good idea to put the courthouse on the Moon.

New Haven was in ferment. Yale students were on strike. Yale President Kingman Brewster had opened the campus to demonstrators, famously saying "I am appalled and ashamed that things should have come to such a pass in this country that I am skeptical of the ability of black revolutionaries to achieve a fair trial anywhere in the United States."

With evening we roamed. The Yale courtyards were gypsy camps, spiced with the tang of food cooked over open fires. Flickering flame-light painted desperados and wild-haired Aphrodites. We ate rice and beans and iced tea in the courtyard of Calhoun College. Later we were having french fries and listening to the jukebox in a joint called Hungry Charlie's when we saw people streaming past outside holding handkerchiefs to their faces.

Leaving Paula locked in dialectic with a Yale student I went outside, followed by Marjorie and her cousin Carol, and we smelled tear gas for the first time in our young lives. Marjorie retreated but Carol and I pressed on against the flow as far as the Art and Architecture Building. An elevator took us up to the third floor but a window that was stuck open let in a fierce gust of gas and we hurriedly descended to the basement where in a room full of graphics presses we found a sink to bathe our eyes and rewet the bandanas we had been holding over our noses. Ascending again we found a vantage point that looked obliquely down on the corner of York and Chapel Streets where in the glare of floodlights a line of National Guardsmen in gas masks confronted demonstrators, some seated, seemingly meditating, others standing and shouting into the faces of the troops. Marshals ran around trying to calm both sides. Again an order to disperse was given Again the Guardsmen fired gas.

I showered when we got back and went to bed, gradually digging into the blankets. Paula cleaned up the kitchen beyond a burlap curtain. My head ached—though surprisingly little after a drive, sunny time on the Green, Hungry Charlie's, excitement & tear gas. At last off the light and Paula joined me. We talked for a while and failed to do anything but confirm the impossibility of optimism.

For the authorities, the surprise was how little violence occurred. The novelist John Hersey, master of Pierson College, who had been unnerved by the same rumor about the machine guns, later claimed for Yale a "historic triumph" over the "head-fever" of "confrontational hysteria." The rhetoric on the Green had been invigorating but not, in the result, incendiary. At least no live ammunition was fired. At least in New Haven. I was back in Boston when news broke of the killings at Kent State University. Had the struggle against arbitrary authority now become a shooting war?

I think I am most angered by the fact that even by the most conventional standards Nixon has gone wild. He practically condoned the shootings in Ohio by calling the demonstrators bums, setting an example of violence by invading Cambodia, and saying there "might" be an investigation. Angry! Amy expected.

Amy took refuge with me when her dormitory was emptied by a bomb scare in the middle of the night.

CASTELLATIONS

Before Apollo 11 we were just getting the basics down. Between Apollo 11 and Apollo 12 we rushed to develop the new capabilities needed for the pinpoint landing. Between Apollo 12 and Apollo 13, we created P66 Auto and worked on the TLOSS problem—Allan Klumpp nailing his "manifestations" to the door, me building Variable Servicer in my off-line assembly ZERLINA, Bob Covelli squeezing the last drop of time out of his landing radar logic.

There would be a longer delay before Apollo 14 would fly. The Apollo 13 problem had to be understood and fixed—but not by us.

For once the software was in the clear. On the other hand we did not want to waste a disaster. There would be forty-seven revisions of LUMINARY and three separate releases before the rope that would fly Apollo 14 was finished.

It may have been our busiest and happiest period. With two successful landings to learn from and an extraordinary recovery from extreme peril written into history, the whole Apollo program was flying high with its capability at a peak. At MIT we were bubbling with ideas for ironing out the last few wrinkles we knew about — those jittery cross-pointers and tape meters for example — and for adding new capabilities to facilitate missions that could only become more and more ambitious because we were not the only ones with ideas.

Variable Servicer had come up before Chris Kraft's Software Control Board just before Apollo 13 — the meeting made me miss the launch — and was disapproved for Apollo 14. It was perceived as an unnecessary major change to the software. It still had a chance for Apollo 15 and beyond but I saw that the TLOSS argument was obsolete. Variable Servicer would become attractive only if it was necessary to support new capabilities that would have a significant impact on how missions would be flown and what they would be able to accomplish.

I kept ZERLINA alive as a test bed for new capabilities. In ZERLINA something new could be made to work without concern for time margins, which only came into play if and when the new capability made the jump to LUMINARY, as the a priori terrain model had done.

The tedious part of maintaining ZERLINA was that I had to track any changes that were being put into LUMINARY that affected the new code I was writing. I wanted to be able to make a clean transplant if the new capability was approved for LUMINARY. The task was made easier by detailed memos describing each set of changes written by Dana Densmore, who as Assembly Control Supervisor was expertly nurturing the LUMINARY rope at this time. The attraction between us had hardly gone away but we were no longer acting on it.

—

The period following Apollo 13 was also a season of bafflement, encompassing a great mystery that would not be resolved until four months after it was first noticed, and more than a year after it could have been.

Since things were now being done a little more la-di-dah, it was by means of a form labeled "Action Item" routed by Bruce McCoy to Dave Moore, Allan Klumpp, and me, dated five days after Apollo 13 splashed down, that I learned that the book was not closed on Apollo 11 and Apollo 12. Clint Tillman, our Grumman liaison, had observed strange throttle behavior in simulations on the Full Mission Engineering Simulator.

The FMES was Grumman's contribution to the mix of simulators that in aggregate gave us confidence in the LM's systems before they flew. It was located in a partitioned area inside a large hangar in Bethpage, Long Island. To get there you walked through a cavernous space populated by enormous sculptural objects painted acid green that you could approach and caress — airframes for F-14 fighters.

Action Item

No. M - 143
Date 4/22/70
Program LUMINARY 1D

From: R. LARSON
To: D. MOORE / D. EYLES / A. KLUMPP
Due by: 5/1/70

Action Requested:
GAEC has noticed that in P66, the GTC has a "castling" effect. The MV people have also seen this on the hybrid. Please evaluate as to cause and magnitude (   ) and prepare a report.
Comments:

Authorized by Bruce McCoy

The action item that instigated the investigation of erratic throttle behavior during the Apollo 11 and Apollo 12 lunar descent.

The forte of the FMES was its use of real spacecraft hardware — not just a real computer as in our hybrid, but also, when possible, the peripheral electronics, and even some of the sensors and actuators. In particular, the hardware that controlled the descent engine throttle in response to the signals from throttle control was real.

Tillman noticed that during P66, when the throttle was very active as it responded to attitude maneuvers commanded by the pilot and to inputs from the ROD switch, the throttle fluctuated through a wide range as it settled on a new thrust level. It could have been a simulator problem, but then Tillman examined the telemetry data from Apollo 12 and saw the same pattern.

On a graph the throttle level had the irregular blocky shape of castle walls so Tillman dubbed the problem "throttle castellations." Those castles, for Allan Klumpp and me, represented our closest brush with disaster, and our luckiest escape.

The story goes back to the throttle control routine that I had coded for SUNBURST three years previously. Throttle control worked by subtracting the current measured acceleration from the acceleration desired by the guidance equation, multiplying by mass to determine the thrust change required, and then issuing the corresponding up or down pulses. What made it tricky was that our accelerometers were not really measuring acceleration, they were measuring the velocity change over a two-second interval—and the previous throttle command had occurred at some time during that interval.

To compensate, Allan had derived, and I had programmed, an equation that accounted for when the previous throttle command was issued, the rate at which throttle pulses went out, and the interval by which the engine's thrust lagged the throttle pulses. That last number, the engine response time, was 0.3 seconds. Allan found it in an official document signed by NASA, Grumman, and the engine manufacturer. The builders of our hybrid and environmental simulators incorporated the same number into their mathematical models of the descent engine. Now I examined my code carefully and could see no flaw, except for one small thing: I had used the value of 0.2 seconds for the engine response time.

I had approached the problem empirically. I wanted to be perfectly sure that Allan's messy compensation terms were necessary before I let them clutter up my equation. The right tool was at hand. I could make runs on the environmental simulator and obtain a plot of the simulated engine behavior in response to a throttle change.

I tried a run in which I did not compensate for the engine lag at all. The throttle change was followed by a wiggle that converged on the new setting — analogous to the ringing of a bell after it has been struck. The wiggle was not caused by the engine. It was being commanded by the software because of the error in estimating acceleration. In my next run I compensated for 0.1 second of throttle lag. The ringing effect was much reduced but it was still evident. Then I tried 0.2 seconds. No ringing could be seen in our fine-grain plots. I quit there. Allan tells it this way:

> I derived an equation to compensate for the engine delay, and Don tried it in the simulator. "The performance certainly is superior to what it was, and I had to compensate for only 0.2 seconds of the delay," beamed Don. I agreed with his assessment, but wondered why he had chosen less than the optimum value for the compensation. "It's just like medicine," he said, "don't give it more compensation than it needs." I knew it wasn't just like medicine; it would be optimum to model the engine exactly. But there was a nontechnical consideration also.
>
> Don was a new hire, fresh out of Boston University. I felt it was important to nurture self-reliance, to let coworkers' decisions on small matters prevail, even when not optimum. So I withheld my thoughts and let Don's decision stand, at least until he might reconsider it independently.

I did not. I thought I was right. I thought it was better to undercompensate than to overcompensate. At least, I was more comfortable on the low side of the "optimum" value. We landed on the Moon with it that way on Apollo 11 and Apollo 12.

But that was not the answer. That could not have been the source of the throttle behavior. If the engine-lag mismatch had caused the throttle oscillations we would have seen the effect in our simulations and fixed it before flying..

Meanwhile, Allan found a source of error that we had not considered, which he called "IMU bob." The Inertial Measurement Unit, containing the accelerometers, was mounted in a location that was above and forward of the spacecraft's center of mass — the point about which the LM necessarily rotated when it maneuvered. Usually this fact was insignificant but when there were rapid maneuvers, as there were during the final descent as the astronaut maneuvered to find a safe landing spot with fuel running low, the IMU was flung back and forth and up and down. The accelerometers registered this motion as a velocity change affecting the vehicle as a whole. The throttle was commanded to compensate for it. It was simple physics. We should have thought of it. Allan easily added logic to correct for the effect.

The trouble was, that did not fix the castellations either. Allan, assisted by a smart control-system expert named George Kalan, racked his brains trying to understand why were we unable to duplicate in our simulations the throttle behavior observed in flight. Two months passed. Then, probably on June 17, as Allan relates it,

> Jim Alphin from MSC called with a bombshell. Telemetry showed that the engine was four times as fast as specified. He measured a delay of 0.075 seconds, not the 0.3 second value still appearing in the Interface Control Document.

It turned out that the engine response had been "improved" by the manufacturer, but the documentation had not been updated. Allan plugged the correct engine time constant into the simulation and the results matched what was observed in flight and on the Grumman simulator. That was not all.

> Months later an outside simulation showed that a 0.075 second engine with 0.3 second throttle compensation was unstable. I verified that conclusion with our simulator and analytically as well. It became clear that had I insisted on Don coding the optimum 0.3 second compensation, Neil Armstrong and Buzz Aldrin, about a minute before touchdown, would have been propelled like a yo-yo by a throttle oscillating between full thrust and idle. They probably would have aborted the first lunar landing.

Would it really have ruined the mission? Was my passive-aggressive response to Allan's messy compensation terms—or was it my brilliant synthesis of Occam's Razor and the Hippocratic Oath?—really one of the knife edges on which the success of Apollo 11 was balanced, along with the review of alarm codes ordered by Gene Kranz, and Charley Muntz's inspiration to trigger a restart if the Executive was overloaded?

That is not for me to say, but I frame the question as follows:

The throttle behavior was independent of the condition that caused the alarms earlier in the landing — but no one knew that at the time. It would have been natural to connect the two problems. The ruling on the alarms had been to continue the landing as long as there was no additional indication of trouble.

So. Armstrong enters P66. Throttle goes wild. The behavior is associated with the mysterious problem that caused the alarms. Our entire primary guidance system has fallen under deep suspicion.

With the LM so close to the Moon, Houston will not call for an abort. It is up to Armstrong.

Faced with computer alarms, throttle instability, low fuel, and an unexpected boulder field, does Armstrong abort the landing and fly back to orbit using the independent abort guidance system? Or does he in a split second switch to manual throttle and attitude control and land, knowing that if he succeeds he may find himself sitting on the Moon with a failed primary guidance system?

THE SUMMER OF 1970

In memory, it was a golden summer, work satisfying, the hours long but flexible. Amy away. Adventure followed misadventure.

One might happen, on a hot day, to meet a woman while bicycling, or at the laundromat, and soon be skinny-dipping in a suburban pond — then sitting together hip to hip on a rock, air-drying, in Edenic innocence, bound by etiquette not to seek to seduce. But after that, bona fides established.... I remember one fortnight's idyll of talking about architecture (her field of study), and soft skin, and sleeping on top of the sheets in the thick summer nights.

As my web of friendships had propagated, Marjorie had led to Tim, and Tim to Emily, his cousin, who had moved with several other women into a house in Cambridgeport that they styled a commune. Emily was compact, nut-brown in her summer tan, quick as a terrier and dangerously spontaneous. We swam at night in Sandy Pond in Lincoln, and found private hollows among the dunes on Plum Island, near Newburyport. Friday night was party night at the commune and we danced freestyle in the cramped living room to records by Van Morrison and Janice Joplin.

It was just weeks since the killings at Kent State and the Mayday events in New Haven. The previous spring, students had seized University Hall and state troopers had entered Harvard Yard. Maybe it was to appease the rabble, as Harvard President Nathan Pusey might have put it, that a series of concerts was arranged for Harvard Stadium. I saw The Band in June, B.B. King and the James Cotton Band a week later, and on an already steamy day in mid-July — with Cambridge Police in Harvard Square looking for after-concert trouble that they eventually created — Ike and Tina Turner. I think I was with Emily, in mid-August, for Janice Joplin. The set was delayed for hours because the amplifiers had been stolen and when she came on stage Joplin calmed the crowd in her own way: "My music isn't supposed to make you want to riot. My music's supposed to make you want to fuck." No one suspected that it was her last concert.

I read *The Black Cloud* — astronomer Fred Hoyle's imagining of an enormous life-form that gobbles stars for sustenance, but is persuaded to spare our solar system when communication is established and the *Hammerklavier*, Beethoven's mightiest piano sonata, is played to it — and *Intelligent Life in the Universe*, a thick paperback authored jointly, in a strange interleaved fashion, by Carl Sagan and the Russian astrophysicist I.S. Shklovskii. The book first considered astronomy, then life's origins and how it may have arisen, and reached finally to speculations about alien civilizations.

Something had been on my mind ever since I flew landings with Pete Conrad at the Cape before Apollo 12. It had to do with what we called the *landing analog displays* — steampunk-style cockpit instruments that provided a backup for the digital displays on the DSKY.

For the vital numbers, altitude and rate of descent, there were devices called *tape meters* located just to the right of the commander's eight-ball. On both sides there was another instrument called the *cross-pointers*, used during the landing to indicate the LM's horizontal velocity during the last minute or two before lunar touchdown. It had two crosshairs, one that moved right or left to indicate lateral velocity, another that moved up and down to indicate forward or backward motion. The cross-pointers were mounted vertically but were understood to indicate the spacecraft's velocity in the horizontal plane—a topic that had vexed Neil Armstrong at the Pussycat Team meeting in November 1967.

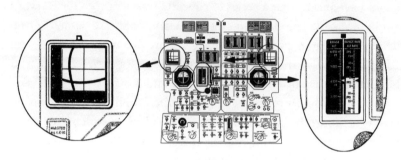

Location of the cross-pointers and tape meters.

These instruments may have looked analog but they were driven by our digital computer. Unfortunately they did not work very well. The altitude-rate display was jittery, with a chugging sound like a speedometer with a cable that needs to be lubricated. The cross-pointers jiggled and could be off by as much as three feet per second. I knew by now that the problem was in the software, but the code was an orphan. Its maker had departed—and a good thing too, as I realized when I took a good look at his legacy.

On the NASA side the problem had become much bigger for the same reason Allan's P66 modifications had been so attractive: the lunar dust kicked up by the LM's engine, which had made it difficult for Armstrong and Pete Conrad to judge and correct their horizontal velocity by eye.

Inertial navigation could do it better—but we had to present the information accurately. The errors came from the fact that the instruments had to be updated at least twice each second, whereas accurate navigation was performed only every two seconds as part of the SERVICER job. The SERVICER values had to be extrapolated forward and the extrapolation had been programmed with no understanding of how to preserve precision when doing fixed-point arithmetic. I

recoded it in a judicious mix of single-precision and double-precision*
and installed it in ZERLINA.

One advantage of developing something first in an offline version
was that you could make your decisions without interference and
when the time came to seek approval, your decisions, especially if
they involved additional capability, would probably be accepted in
the package. (And if you were also sending the offline programs to the
simulators, there was the possibility of building up a constituency.) In
that spirit I added several features that were actually simplifications.
The analog displays previously started at ignition. It was simpler to
let them start at TIG minus 30, when seeing the displays come alive
would be an additional indication that powered flight navigation had
started. I also removed what seemed to be an unnecessary restriction
that prevented the displays from operating during ascent.

I wrote a Program Change Request to put the new code in
LUMINARY for the Apollo 15 mission, and followed up with a
memo describing the changes in detail and presenting test results.
Meanwhile Tom Price called Russ Larson from Houston to say, "Crew
won't accept anything but zero error." They had probably gotten wind
that there was a new version in the works.

THE ERSATZ SCB

On July 22, 1970 I was in Bill Tindall's office at the Manned Spacecraft
Center in Houston with Russ Larson and Bob Covelli, Clint Tillman
from Grumman, two engineers from BellComm, Jack Garman and
Tom Price from MSC, and the astronauts Fred Haise and Gene Cernan.
Cernan had not yet been selected to command what we now knew
would be the final Apollo mission, Apollo 17, and he was said to be in
competition with Dick Gordon, Pete Conrad's command module pilot
on Apollo 12, for that slot.

---

* The multiply operation in Basic took as input two single-precision numbers and produced a double-precision number. How else could the product
of one-times-one and of POSMAX-times-POSMAX both be accommodated?
Conversely, the divide operation took a double-precision dividend. The way
to preserve accuracy was to do the multiplications before the divisions.

First on the agenda was a sheaf of change requests intended to eliminate tiny holes in our restart protection. To be a problem the restart had to occur at precisely the wrong point in the code. "It's like a swarm of mosquitoes. They're not too annoying unless the bite gets infected or they're carrying malaria," said Tindall. (I wrote it down.) Restarts were uncommon enough already—apart from the five software restarts on Apollo 11 there had been only two, caused by lightning on Apollo 12 and an explosion on Apollo 13—yet still we aspired to perfection. Disapproved.

My PCR to fix the landing analog displays got a warmer welcome. I described the new software and announced that it was running in ZERLINA and that a copy was already at the Cape. When I got to the part about allowing the displays to operate during the lunar ascent, Cernan perked up. It was something the astronauts had wanted because it provided another way to monitor their out-of-plane velocity as they flew to orbit. But Cernan pointed out a problem. The lateral velocity on the cross-pointers was referenced to the LM, so it would correspond to out-of-plane velocity only when the LM was facing ahead, and the LM was often cocked left or right during ascent to improve communications.

To be useful during ascent, the lateral velocity displayed on the cross-pointers would have to be computed differently. It was simple—I had already coded it in my head—but Larson did not commit to the change despite Cernan's urging. Finally we were given the option: either turn off the cross-pointers during ascent and aborts, or provide the correct calculation, our choice. I enjoyed this because it was in my hands and it was as good as done.

The other funny thing was that Larson learned right before the meeting that ZERLINA was being run on the LMS that morning and the new displays were not working. He suggested we keep quiet about it "so we don't look like assholes." I called Bob Pearson at the Cape, who felt sure it was a simulator problem so he was keeping quiet too. It *was* a simulator problem—it would have worked perfectly in flight—but that was still a problem. We had to make a small change to the software for no other reason than to make it run right in the simulator.

Tindall's summary of what he called an "ersatz Software Control Board Meeting" was the only time that I was mentioned by name in a Tindallgram:

> The approach MIT prefers for fixing the cross-pointer problem is essentially to relocate the Landing Analog Display Routine (R10) from Don Eyles variable servicer offline assembly into the previously released Luminary.... In the package, whether we like it or not, a number of other improvements are accrued....

Not only were the new displays approved, they were approved for Apollo 14. LUMINARY was going to be rereleased and the new landing analog displays would be included. But Tindall's tone of grievance, that in return for fixing the displays he was forced, *forced* to accept several other benefits, brought another smile.

The new displays were not the only reason LUMINARY was going to be rereleased, nor the only interesting topic on Tindall's agenda. This was the point where the notorious issue of the marginally-stable throttle finally bubbled up to the level of management where a fix, preferably the right fix, would be approved for flight.

Allan Klumpp's "theory" that the erroneous engine time constant had caused the castellations was not universally accepted. Months had passed since Clint Tillman's discovery and other theories had sprung up. In particular, engineers from the Guidance and Control Division in Houston maintained that the autopilot gains were not optimum and claimed that Allan's IMU-bob compensation, plus changing the gains, would fix the problem. Allan and George Kalan thought these changes would actually make it worse, but they had no other theory to offer. In a memo dated June 10, Bill Tindall accepted the Houston theory and asked MIT to fall into line. So it was just in the nick of time, a week later, when Jim Alphin called Allan with his "bombshell" about the engine.

The problem was solved, but the competing theory had run too far to shuffle away quietly. The discussion at the meeting was inconclusive, and when Tindall came to the topic in the Tindallgram he dictated after the meeting, he played it both ways:

The final correction to the program deals with the throttle instability during descent you've heard so much about. We are all convinced the changes made previously, i.e., IMU offset c.g. compensation and erasable memory control system gain changes, are more than adequate.

But then he seemed to embrace the MIT position, again using the word "all":

On the other hand, it is recognized that a fixed constant describing the throttle hardware lags is clearly wrong. All of the control system experts insist that there is no danger but only good things and joy if we change this constant....

The two positions were not really compatible. Klumpp and Kalan realized that going through proper channels was not working. "Something drastic had to be done quickly," recalls Kalan. With Allan still under a cloud because of his maladroit call to Jim Lovell before Apollo 13, it was Kalan who made the call to Gene Cernan to explain the situation. Gene promised to keep quiet about his source of information, and immediately acted to set up a showdown between the rival engineers. Kalan was there:

On August 4, 1970, Allan and I faced a room at MSC packed with guidance and control "experts" ready to tear us to pieces. We presented our case with two parallel viewgraph projectors... Russ Larson introduced us and we proceeded to tell our story with me projecting the predictions of the model for each set of conditions and Allan reinforcing the result by showing the consistent simulation results, using the correct engine time constant, for the same set of conditions. By the time we finished, you could have heard a pin drop and it was clear that our audience was quite shaken up by what they heard.

I had dashed to the airport after Tindall's meeting — hopping across town on the Metro Airlines Twin Otter, then to New Orleans, then Eastern to Boston, the Alfa, the tunnel and home. I walked into my apartment, switched on the stereo and started the disc that Marjorie, who had keys, had left on the turntable — Side 2 of *Tommy*.

The next day I made the change to make the cross-pointers useful during ascent and aborts. After I tested the new wrinkle in ZERLINA I installed the new display package in LUMINARY.

With the addition of the new landing analog displays I had written somewhat more than 2200 of the approximately 36,000 lines of code in the final LUMINARY.

JOHN YOUNG'S EXCELLENT IDEA

We always wanted to comply with astronaut requests. We wanted to comply with every request that made sense, but if it was from an astronaut it probably made sense — and as Russ Larson said, they were our best advertisers.

On Apollo the coders and the fliers dealt with each other directly. We even kept secrets. It was a wonder. With ideas flowing in both directions we worked together to perfect our techniques for landing on an airless planet. An astronaut with an idea could find a cooperative software guy and see the idea turned in a few days or weeks into working software that he could fly in the simulator, whether or not it was ever approved for flight — such was the agility of our medium and the freedom of our working conditions. For us the astronauts were more than a focus group, they were the focus itself, the absolute tip of the huge pyramid.

More than that, we felt a kinship. At only one remove our minds were onboard alongside the two astronauts with their fragile brains of flesh and blood. However safe our bodies were on Earth, when our software flew we were fully identified with it. If a mistake in our software cost even a mission, much less a life, our suffering would be much like a death. Had we not seen what that looked like, in the spectre of John Norton, stalking the corridors in Houston?

Six days after the "ersatz SCB" I flew to the Cape with tapes of the new version of LUMINARY containing the new landing analog displays.

There was still one loose end: the vexatious question of whether the cockpit instruments, in particular the cross-pointers, should be *fly-to* or *fly-from*. The urgency was that I wanted to set the polarity right from the beginning, and that meant as soon as LUMINARY 174 was loaded, later the same day.

I had first heard the concepts of fly-to and fly-from when Neil Armstrong had discussed the cross-pointers at the Pussycat Team meeting back in November 1967. It had to do with the direction of the control input that is required in relation to the error being corrected. The best everyday example, if your computer has a track pad, is which way you set the swipe. If you swipe upwards to reach the top of a document — as though you were piloting a hovercraft above the document — then your track pad is fly-to. Translated to the cross-pointer instrument in the LM cockpit, the terms referred to whether the movement of the stick to correct the indicated horizontal velocity would be toward the indication, or away from it.

What bothered me today was that the out-of-plane velocity that we were now going to display during ascent had the opposite sense from the same quantity if the information came from the Abort Guidance System, which was independently computing it. This mattered because one reason the display could be switched between the two systems was so the AGS could provide a crosscheck on the PGNCS. We did not simulate the AGS in Cambridge so we had not noticed the inconsistency.

Seeking opinions, Pearson and I walked into the crew office and found Alan Shepard (America's first space hero); his steady LM pilot, Edgar Mitchell (who planned to perform mental telepathy en route); and Stuart Roosa, the Command Module Pilot — all bent over their desks studying like schoolboys, or in Shepard's case autographing photographs of himself.

As for the cross-pointers, Shepard did not give a hoot, "I'm for throwing the thing out." He thought its usefulness during ascent had been oversold — he might have meant by Gene Cernan in his striving to earn a flight assignment — and he had better ways to know the "pings" was healthy than rely on the "aggs." He had a point. Mitchell opined that PGNCS should be consistent unto itself. That meant the ascent display would be fly-from like the descent displays, even though that was contrary to the AGS display and violated the default rule that all displays be fly-to.

The comments from the Apollo 14 crew did not seem to settle the question, so Pearson and I got on the phone to Dave Scott, the handsome and capable Air Force Colonel who was Pete Conrad's backup on Apollo 12 and would command the *next* mission, Apollo 15. Scott's first answer was that the display should be fly-to like the AGS, but when I pointed out that this was inconsistent with the lateral velocity display during the landing, and repeated what Mitchell had said, Scott reserved his opinion—for the moment.

The next morning I overslept and tore up the road drinking a quart of milk and eating a chocolate bar on the way. I need not have rushed. LUMINARY 174 still had not been processed. Bruce McCoy and Russ Larson had shown up, along with Tom Price, who was on his way back to Houston from Boston. I found them sitting around the console with Bob Pearson, while Shepard and Mitchell, in the cockpit, flew landings using an older version of LUMINARY.

Then a guy about my size (five-nine), with a mustache and a retro look that made me think of a Spitfire pilot from the Battle of Britain, walked over and introduced himself—the astronaut John Young.

Young had come up with a very clever idea, which had been relayed to me the week before. It concerned the final descent, beyond the point where landing site redesignations were possible. If it worked you could land the LM in a hatbox.

On both Apollo 11 and Apollo 12, once the guidance equation had brought the LM to within a few hundred feet of the lunar surface, the mission commander chose to fly the spacecraft the rest of the way in a semi-manual mode called P66. Our software controlled the rate of descent in response to the ROD switch. The astronaut controlled the spacecraft's attitude (in rate-command attitude-hold mode), vectoring the thrust of the descent engine to move around in the horizontal dimensions. With two minutes of fuel remaining when he entered P66, Armstrong (using all of it), and then Conrad, brought the LM to a stop above his chosen spot, then descended vertically to touchdown.

It was important to land level without much horizontal velocity but that was hard to judge because of the dust kicked up by the engine at low altitude. Allan Klumpp's P66 Auto fixed that by giving the astronaut a way to hand attitude control back to the computer—by switching the autopilot mode from ATT HOLD to AUTO—whereupon the new equation derived by Allan and Nick Pippenger would maneuver the **LM** to null out horizontal velocity. Naturally the spacecraft would travel some further distance horizontally while it slowed to a perfect hover.

Now Young wanted to take it a step further. Could the computer, he wondered, display an angle, referenced to the same **LPD** scale on the left window that was used during **P64**, which would indicate the spot above which the **LM** would come to a stop if at that instant attitude control were returned to the computer?

Picture it this way: The **LM** skims over the surface at a more or less constant altitude of perhaps 150 feet. The **LM** pilot reads off the **LPD** angle from the **DSKY**. The commander, his eye in position to sight along the scale on the window and his hand on the **PGNCS** attitude mode switch, watches the spot indicated by the computer move across the lunar terrain. Then, at the moment when it reaches a desirable touchdown spot, he pushes the switch upwards to **AUTO**. The **LM** pitches back to slow up, and then returns to upright, with zero forward or lateral velocity, directly above that very spot. All that remains is to descend like an elevator.

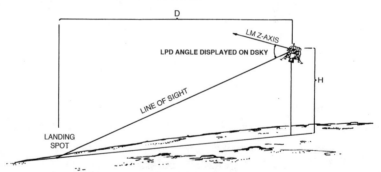

Geometry of the P66 LPD system. H is the LM's altitude, D is the distance the LM will travel between the switching of attitude mode to AUTO, and reaching zero groundspeed.

To compute the **LPD** angle I needed to know the altitude, and how far the **LM** would travel in the process of slowing to a stop. Altitude was known. I thought it would not be hard to predict the travel distance.

The real problem, as usual, was not the math, it was the timing. The part of **P66** Auto whose job was to null horizontal velocity ran only every two seconds. At any time during that period the switch might be flipped. Thus the accuracy with which P66 LPD could hit its target could be no better than the distance the LM would travel during two seconds. That did not seem acceptable. I knew I would need to find a way to speed up the reaction time.

That is how it stood when I met the author of the idea. We walked over toward the L&A (the lunar surface model) to discuss it. Young was effusive about how smart the computer was. That was endearing but — the other shoe dropping — he thought there was a lot more capability there to be brought out. He showed me a handwritten chart he had devised that mapped lines of constant LPD angle on a graph of altitude versus forward velocity. Even without the computer's help Young had a pretty good feel for what the angle would be.

I had a few questions. How fast would he be going? 40 feet per second, Young guessed, which is a bit over 25 miles per hour. What accuracy did he expect? To get into a 100 foot slot. Young was conscious of the error inherent in the two-second guidance loop. I explained that having to put the decision logic on a faster basis made it a bigger project, and for that reason it probably could not be done without the variable guidance period servicer. He had already assumed that.

When the "big boys" finished with the simulator and LUMINARY 174 was finally loaded Young and I climbed up to the cockpit and flew half a dozen landings. As usual, Pearson threw in a few curve balls.

"Aha, the old burned out motor in the eight-ball trick eh?"

Unfortunately, as I soon realized, this version of LUMINARY had a new bug that made the throttle oscillate wildly in P66. Distracted by that I was not a great LM pilot, sometimes forgetting to read out LPD angles. Young implied that the actress and dancer Joey Heatherton, with whom he had flown a landing several days before in Houston, had more to offer.

Young had no trouble landing, with perfect nonchalance, despite the wild throttle. It was embarrassing that he kept on about how smart the computer was when it was actually having a dim moment. I phoned Bob Covelli in Cambridge to tell him about the throttle bug, and I was awake until two in the morning, looking for the erasable memory conflict that I thought might be responsible.

Maybe my mind worked on it while I slept. The next morning in two quick steps Pearson and I got to the bottom of it. We set the simulator to display the memory location where the throttle compensation term FWEIGHT was saved for use next pass. It was zero. The only place it was set to zero was in a bit of code that was supposed to run just once when we entered P66. A flag called RODFLAG prevented it from happening every pass. I compared the entry for RODFLAG in the symbol tables of LUMINARY 173 and LUMINARY 174, and found one fewer reference in the later version. The setting of RODFLAG had through a pure clerical error been deleted. Good to get that settled. Back in Cambridge Covelli independently found the problem at about the same time.

Sharon Albert, who was helping me prepare for an upcoming Variable Servicer design review, was at the Cape on her first visit, so Bruce McCoy and I took her to see the VAB, that great cathedral that you wanted to visit every time you were in town.

In August, Sharon and I presented the variable guidance period SERVICER to a design review panel in Houston. One worry dominated the discussion. Two seconds. The two-second period of the old SERVICER had been built in at various points in the program. There were only a few such cases, and I had changed them to adjust to a flexible period. But what if I had missed one? It was almost a superstition. Two seconds was more ingrained in NASA's mind than it had ever been in the code.

Sharon had planned and run an extensive series of tests using the environmental simulation. John Norton had reviewed the code and we had satisfied his concerns. Admittedly it was a major change. In the end the advantages were not persuasive. The existing programs had shown themselves adequate. No one was worried about TLOSS any more. There would be only four more lunar landing missions anyway because Apollo 18, Apollo 19 and Apollo 20 had just been cancelled. At the Software Control Board, two weeks after the design review, ZERLINA was praised as an advance in the state of the art but disapproved for flight.

That did not mean I stopped work on P66 LPD. That was personal between me and John Young. I entered a Holmesian trance as I tried to figure out how to speed up the response time, smoking a lot, sleeping eclectically. I had to reorganize P66 completely. The concentration was in keeping track of the parts spread out, as it were, all over the floor of the garage. I removed both the throttle control and the attitude maneuver logic from SERVICER and added it to the job that operated the landing analog displays, which ran four times a second—a speedboat compared to the container ship SERVICER. The error due to switch timing was reduced by a factor of eight and throttle response became exceptionally crisp.

One day I spoke to Apollo 15 commander Dave Scott about some changes that were in the works to simplify the procedures for accepting landing radar data during the landing, then spent the night working on P66 LPD. When I returned to the Lab the next day in the middle of the afternoon I found my office plastered with pink slips saying "call Col. Scott"—not an everyday occurrence. It was not the radar. It was the fly-to-fly-from issue again and Scott was on the warpath. Was changing the sign on the cross-pointer display a big change? No. Good, because he wanted all the displays consistent, across the board, both spacecraft, all the instruments, PGNCS and AGS, all fly-to. Astronauts needed to know instinctively which way to move the stick. He would not recommend it for Apollo 14, Shepard's mission, but it would probably be a year before Scott flew, so now was the time to do it.

NASA came to Cambridge in force for what was called a FACI—first article configuration inspection—a formal meeting to consider the readiness of the software for Apollo 14, now six months away. I sat in selectively. In the hall I had a rambling conversation with Clint Tillman, our friend from Grumman. He expressed wry outrage about the state of the documentation. "You come to absolutely believe some things and completely disregard others. One paragraph gospel truth, the next a lie. It's like folklore."

By the middle of September P66 LPD was ready. Plots showed rapid, precise reaction to crew inputs. I flew back to the Cape with a tape of ZERLINA 50. That night I sat on the beach, contemplating the brilliant Moon over the water, just past full—and set the clock for 5:00

AM. But in vain. It was a few days, including a weekend, before John Young and I got a solid block of time on the simulator. Alan Shepard and the Apollo 14 crew were training heavily and they had priority. One night Pearson and I set up his reflector telescope and peered at Jupiter, fuzzy in the Florida haze.

Charlie Duke's German measles had led to some changes. Duke was the backup LM pilot on Apollo 13 and when he got sick he exposed the prime crew to the disease. Command Module Pilot Tom Mattingly lacked immunity and had to be replaced by his backup, Jack Swigert. It was an experience no one wanted to repeat. Now crews were to be isolated for several weeks before launch. No one else would use the simulator during that time. The Flight Crew Support Building now had a new entrance just for next-mission crews, and the room near the entrance where we had met with the Apollo 12 and Apollo 14 crews now had a glass partition at one end behind which astronauts could be briefed in microbiological safety. Needless to say the new procedures occasioned some merriment. "They'll need bars to keep the crew in or else turn crew quarters into a whorehouse," joked Young, "and Shepard will come down with the clap anyway three weeks before the mission."

Finally on Monday the "big boys" were somewhere else and John Young took over the LM, with me in the right-hand position as LM pilot. We flew twenty landings, starting at the beginning of the visibility phase. Pearson threw ever-increasing navigation errors at us, up to 4000 feet uprange or downrange, combined with 3000 feet crossrange. Every time, using the new P66 LPD capability, Young put the spacecraft exactly where he wanted. "It's the slickest thing I ever saw," said Young.

Apollo 13 was still an unhealed wound. I would not have brought it up but somehow, in the intimacy of the LM cockpit, it did come up. "I went home and cried. I didn't think the guys were coming back," said Young. It was enough to make me tear up on the spot. Soon enough, of course, he had gone back to work.

As for P66 LPD, we both knew by now that it would never fly. The new code reduced the time margin during P66 to almost zero. It could only be added to LUMINARY in conjunction with Variable Servicer, and Variable Servicer was dead beyond the capability of John Young or me to revive it.

ZERLINA would never fly, but I could at least write it up for the record. There was a symposium one year away, in Dubrovnik, Yugoslavia, that would be the perfect occasion.

I read Buckminster Fuller's *Operating Manual for Spaceship Earth*, and *The Greening of America*, by Charles Reich. With Reich, I wanted to believe that a new consciousness was ascendant and that what we were doing was part of it. Bucky has stood up better.

APOLLO 14

Apollo 14 launched on the last day of January 1971, Alan Shepard commanding. The landing would be attempted at about 4:00 AM, Boston time, on February 5, a Friday. I spent Thursday afternoon and evening at home in Lime Street and walked across the river to the Lab about 11:30 PM. For the record, I smoked a joint with a neighbor in the late afternoon. I have what follows in detail because I had the presence of mind, the next day, to type it out on my Remington electric at home, four pages.

I talked to Allan Klumpp for a while about some simulations we had run with a modified version of the terrain profile that NASA had given us. Our modification prevented a crash in the event of a huge, short position error, but we decided not to bring it up because there was no chance of having such a big error without knowing it.

Allan lay down for a nap on the only couch available, located in the women's restroom on the second floor. I promised to call him in time for the landing. I walked upstairs to the computer room to work on a program for making plots. When I returned to my office about 1:00 AM I was intercepted by Bruce McCoy, who told me that onboard the spacecraft the abort discrete had appeared. Bruce did not seem too concerned and I responded more to his manner than his words. I said "That's interesting," and went back to what I was doing.

The abort discrete was a signal from the abort button in the cockpit that the astronaut could press to command an immediate abort and return to orbit if something went wrong during the descent. Actually there were two buttons, guarded by a small door so they could not be pushed accidentally. The button labeled Abort started the return to orbit in program P70, using the descent engine. The Abort Stage button dumped the descent stage, selected P71, and continued to orbit using the ascent engine. In this case the spurious signal came from the Abort button. The abort discretes were monitored by the routine I had nicknamed ROSENCRANTZ, officially R11.

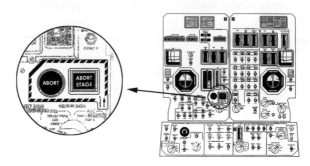

The abort and abort-stage buttons in the LM cockpit. On Apollo 14 the abort button, because of internal contamination, sent a spurious abort indication to the computer

Bruce came back to my office about 1:30 AM and told me the discrete had come and gone several times. It could be turned off by tapping on the panel. Evidently some sort of metallic contamination was floating around inside the switch. No one could predict where it might drift, or when. Was there a way to bypass the aborts monitor?

Now Bruce had my full attention. It was my code after all, circa 1967. We went around the corner to the large office shared by Dave Moore and Sharon Albert where we found a listing of the Apollo 14 flight rope, LUMINARY 178.

At first glance it seemed simple. There was a *flag* called LETABBIT (let-abort bit), a single bit of a word in erasable memory designated as a *flagword*, which could be used to turn the aborts monitor on and off explicitly. That was how the monitor was prevented from operating in the period leading up to TIG—and that was the catch. The LETABBIT bit would be set at the moment of descent engine ignition to turn the monitor on. That meant that before anything could be done about it the aborts monitor would be off and running, four times every second, ready to command an entirely unnecessary abort and leave the Fra Mauro plain unexplored again.

Ignition was a vulnerable time. There would be vibration. Thrust applied by the engine would create gravity inside the switch. Which way would the solder ball go? Could the LM pilot, punching the DSKY, reset LETABBIT in time—bearing in mind that you did not want astronauts typing hurriedly on the DSKY when they were reaching deep inside the software?

That was the crux of the problem. How could I eliminate the window of vulnerability between ignition and the resetting of LETABBIT? It was almost as bad if the spurious signal occurred just before ignition, perhaps during the ullage burn that began at TIG minus 7.5 seconds. Would the astronauts tap frantically on the panel as ignition approached to make it go away? If it persisted the abort could be prevented, but at the cost of the landing attempt, at least until the next orbit when the same thing might happen again. Something better was needed.

I saw that the only way to prevent the monitor from looking at the abort signals at all was to make it think that the deepest level of abort was already in progress. This could be done by setting a register called MODREG to 71 to indicate P71, the abort-stage mode, instead of 63 to indicate P63. Under cover of the deceptive MODREG, LETABBIT could be reset without hurrying, and then MODREG could be restored to the rightful number.

MODREG was the master indication of which program was in progress. It was displayed in its own space on the DSKY. Setting MODREG to 71 during P63 seemed radical, but perhaps it was not as dangerous as it sounded. It would not actually initiate the abort programs. In the period leading up to ignition, BURNBABY—the master ignition routine Peter Adler and I had written two and a half years before—was calling the shots, and the paths taken by BURNBABY were controlled by a parameter that was independent of MODREG. Mostly.

I wrote out the keystrokes to change MODREG and to reset LETABBIT and with that, Peter Volante, Sam Drake and a few others who had clustered around were off to the hybrid simulator to try it out. It was a key moment. I was looking around before going to the hybrid lab myself when I realized the others were ahead of me. I could stay on the second floor studying the listing, tying up loose ends, and talking by phone to the cockpit upstairs and to Russ Larson in Houston.

Reading the code, I saw that there were indeed two places in BURNBABY where MODREG was checked. That meant two things. The countdown to ignition would not be displayed properly. That could be fixed by waiting until the countdown started before setting MODREG to 71. The other consequence was that the task named ZOOM that was intended to throttle-up the descent engine to maximum, exactly 26 seconds after ignition, would not be scheduled. The engine would have to be throttled up manually—a procedure that had been rehearsed by the astronauts for other contingencies.

At that point I went upstairs to the cockpit to watch a run with what I thought was the finished procedure. The spacecraft held a fixed attitude and crashed into the Moon at 600 feet per second. I had overlooked the fact that the missing ZOOM task had the additional duty of engaging the guidance equation. That was the last wrinkle. I added the keystrokes to turn guidance on. Everything worked. We made a second run with some restarts thrown in.

Meanwhile Jack Garman in Houston raised the idea of putting some new code in erasable memory and setting the indexes that controlled BURNBABY so it would be executed instead of the code that set LETABBIT to turn on the monitor. I had thought of that too, but it would have been trickier to develop and test in the time available.

Russ Larson, in the AGC support room at mission control, started selling our procedure. Unfortunately he was overeager. He had relayed the procedure to the simulator in Houston before the last step was added—so they also had crashed. Now I very carefully described the complete procedure to Houston:

(1) After the display of the countdown toward engine ignition (Noun 62) starts, but before ignition, key in

Verb 21 Noun 1 Enter 1010 Enter 107 Enter

to set the mode register to 71, indicating an abort in progress. Verb 21 Noun 1 means "load full word," the number 1010 is the address of MODREG, 107 is 71 in octal.

(2) Exactly 26 seconds after ignition, manually advance the descent engine throttle to 100%.

(3) Key in

Verb 25 Noun 7 Enter 101 Enter 200 Enter 1 Enter

to enable the landing guidance equations. Verb 25 Noun 7 means "set bit," 101 is the address of FLAGWRD5, 200 specifies bit 8 (ZOOMBIT), and 1 is the new value.

(4) Key in

Verb 25 Noun 7 Enter 105 Enter 400 Enter 0 Enter

to explicitly disable the abort monitor by resetting the flag word bit that controls the monitor. Verb 25 Noun 7 means "set bit," 105 is the address of FLAGWRD9, 400 specifies bit 9 (LETABBIT), and 0 is the new value.

(5) Key in

Verb 21 Noun 1 Enter 1010 Enter 77 Enter

to set the mode register back to its proper value of 63 (77 octal).

(6) Return the manual throttle to its minimum setting.

The throttle stays at 100% because it is now being commanded by the guidance equation. If this step were omitted the throttle would be forced to stay at 100% when the guidance equation later requests partial thrust, with bad results.

It was now about an hour before the landing and the LM was behind the Moon. The procedure needed to be ready when it re-emerged. Up to this point Houston had been planning to have the astronauts start the landing with the autopilot in ATT HOLD so that if the abort occurred the spacecraft would not maneuver. The LM pilot would reset the LETABBIT bit as soon as possible. If no abort occurred in the meantime the landing could continue. Otherwise the engine would be shut down manually as quickly as possible. If the short burn did not change the orbital parameters too much another attempt would be made on the next pass two hours later.

That plan was a crap-shoot. Our procedure eliminated the window of vulnerability completely. When they saw the procedure in Houston, Garman recalled, "everybody went, 'Yep, that's it'."

The LM came around the bend and communication was reestablished. The procedure was read up to the spacecraft. We listened carefully to Capcom's every syllable. It was perfect except for one detail. Larson noted on the loop that the instruction to lower the manual throttle to minimum had not been read. Garman said "Roger," and the instruction was relayed.

I asked, because I had misunderstood, to make sure the throttle control switch was not going to be switched to manual, which was unnecessary. Garman asked if the ATT HOLD mode should be used at all. I replied, "AUTO all the way." Garman asked if some of the keystrokes could be put in between ignition and throttle-up. I replied that they could be, but recommended against it because the most important thing was to throttle up on time and the other things could wait. Running without guidance for half a minute longer was fine because the LM hardly maneuvered at all during this period even with guidance engaged.

There was an exhilaration—like an orchestra, playing in perfect synchronization, lengthening its stride as it approaches the finale. Then I remembered Allan asleep in the women's room and sent Dave Moore to wake him. They set about to run an all-digital test of the procedure using the environmental simulation.

Onboard, Shepherd and Mitchell "had a great deal of confidence that what [we] were passing up was going to work." They had practiced for so many bizarre contingencies that it almost seemed routine. LM Pilot Edgar Mitchell operated the DSKY, punching in 61 keystrokes that had to be perfect, but did not have to be rushed. When the guidance bit was set the LM maneuvered a little and to Shepard "it was apparent that guidance had initiated and PGNCS was happy with itself." At the very moment the engine was throttled-up Dave Moore rushed into the SCAMA room with the results of a successful digital test.

There was one more scare. The landing radar failed to lock onto the surface when expected. It would have been impossible to land safely without it. Shepard later hinted he might have tried but he was just teasing. It would have meant outright defiance of Houston and put at risk both the future of the space program and his own golden reputation as an aviator, not to speak of his own golden tuchas.

The LM was down to about 18,000 feet when Flight Controller Dick Thorson suggested cycling the landing radar circuit breaker — turning the radar off and back on — and it worked. And thus Alan Shepard and Edgar Mitchell, in the LM Antares, touched down in the Fra Mauro Highlands, south of the great crater Copernicus.

MY FIFTEEN MINUTES

Coming after the drama of Apollo 13, Apollo 14 got extra attention. Some people thought another failure might have ended the Apollo program after only two landings. The story of a young engineer who quickly devised a workaround for a problem in flight got more attention than anticipated — at least by me.

During the next day I spoke to all the Boston newspapers and television stations, UPI, AP, and CBS news. Someone called my mother in Atlanta to say, "Don's famous." The *Memphis Commercial Appeal* had a local angle and ran with it; they gave more space to the Isetta I had interred in the Mississippi River in 1961 that to the spaceflight.

The lead paragraph of the front-page story in the *New York Times* contained a misapprehension that has persisted:

> It took some ingenious rewriting of a computer program and about 60 rapid-fire punches on a cockpit keyboard to clear the way for the Apollo lunar landing yesterday.

No program was rewritten — that would have been the hard way — the program was deceived. I entered the story in the 21st of its 26 paragraphs:

> [The answer] was finally produced at the M.I.T. in a three-story brick building that had been a warehouse for women's underwear and hosiery. The man who produced it was an engineer named Donald E. Eyles.

> Feverishly juggling alternatives, Mr. Eyles came up with a program that could be inserted in the computer before the descent began — before a spurious signal could start an abort.

As a resident of Boston who had done something illustrious I was invited by Gabriel Piemonte, the President of the Boston City Council, to address that body. I gave a short speech, in my Brooks Brothers suit but without a haircut, thanking the Council for the resolution they passed in my honor, taking care to spread the credit.

For NASA's film about the mission we staged a reenactment. Sam Drake and I are in the LM cockpit on the third floor. I appear to be reading the procedure from a piece of paper. That is accurate enough, except that in the reenactment I am dressed in a button-down shirt and tie and good trousers instead of a ribbed sweater and corduroy bell-bottoms. However, a photograph of me thus attired had also been taken and sent out on the wires. Someone sent me the clipping from a French-language newspaper in which the caption called me "Le Sauveur," and truly, with long hair and a moustache, I did resemble the Son of God.

Then I heard from representatives of David Frost, who invited me to come to New York to appear on his television show along with the Apollo 14 astronauts and the geologist Dr. Paul Gast. I came on last and answered a few unchallenging questions about the event.

Frost but not Nixon. I will explain this cautiously, with a combination of my own and Ralph Ragan's recollections. Ragan was our Deputy Director for NASA Projects, a top guy, tall and angular, friendly but also a little forbidding, corner office on the first floor. He called me in to ask how I would feel about going to the White House. It was not an invitation, he emphasized, just a sounding out.

It was a serious question for me. I had to weigh my loyalty to the Instrumentation Laboratory against my disdain for Richard Nixon. Added to that I had, had always had, a bad attitude towards authority. The higher the authority the stronger my impulse to tweak it. I would have been one synaptic event away from making front-page news, as Eartha Kitt had done two years before when she said to Lady Bird Johnson, "You send the best of this country off to be shot and maimed." Could I be trusted, could I trust myself, to avoid an expression of opinion that would embarrass and damage the Laboratory and make me a liability to the space program?

I promised Ragan an answer the next day. I needed to bounce it around with someone. My question was, if I met Nixon, did I have a positive obligation to speak up? I cannot say that anyone I spoke to had a strong opinion either way. I did go so far as to experiment with writing a speech:

> Mr. President, thank you for this honor. The most serious objection to the space program is that it is merely another plaything of our bloated defense industry. I believe it is more than that, I believe that curiosity and love of adventure are a truer part of human nature than paranoia. I look forward to the day when the effort we are now devoting to killing has been used to heal the earth — I pray it arrives soon — and I expect that on that day space exploration will be more important than ever. In fact, if I am proud to receive this recognition, it is because it comes near the start of an enterprise that will outlive repression, pollution, stupid expenditures on ABM and SST, sneaky, bloody wars in Asia, and even nations themselves — assuming only that humanity survives.

But in the morning I called Ragan and said no. Now, almost fifty years later, would I rather be dining out on my story of visiting Nixon's White House and meeting Pat and Tricia and Julie and the great crook himself — or confiding to these pages the actual ambiguous story and my past and present ambivalence about my decision? Hard to say.

With Dave Hoag and without ambivalence I traveled to Houston for an awards ceremony at which, with Alan Shepard and his crew on the stage, George Low presented me with the NASA Public Service Award. The citation reads:

> He was first to conceive the work-around for the Lunar Module abort switch failure, thus permitting the lunar landing to proceed. He and his Massachusetts Institute of Technology colleagues developed, simulated and refined the procedure in the very short span of time that was available before powered descent to the lunar surface.

The "first to conceive" wording came from a text I had provided when asked. I was trying to be modest and I could not say with certainty that no one else had been thinking along the same lines. So far as I know the "conception" was mine alone. If you consider the development, simulation, and refinement together, not forgetting the salesmanship of Russ Larson in Houston, it was very much a team effort and a smooth one at that.

Our next stop was Bethpage where Hoag and I were treated to lunch with the top executives of Grumman and given the VIP tour. Donning white coats and caps to contain our hair we entered the clean room in Plant 5 where LM-11, destined for Apollo 16, was nearing completion. Grumman was flying high after their spacecraft saved the lives of the Apollo 13 crew. They must have loved me for preventing their contaminated switch from ruining the next mission.

After Apollo 13, Grumman had submitted a mock bill to North American Rockwell (the maker of the Command Module) in which the main item was $400,004 in towing charges based on mileage. Now MIT submitted a bill to Grumman for "switch repair." Three hours of my time came to $37.08, with the notation, "Fortunately able to solve with less expensive engineer rather than replacement part by technician," and at the bottom the handwritten note, "Please use OEM parts in the future."

Maybe it was the Jesus picture that made Jann Wenner send Tim Crouse to write me up for *Rolling Stone*. We hung out for a couple of days in Cambridge bars, and the story appeared in mid-March in the issue with a sepia-toned Muhammad Ali, grimacing in a boxing helmet, on the outside cover. Crouse led off by quoting the following doggerel, which he had seen posted at the Laboratory:

> *Things on board went haywire*
> *Lights flashed red and green*
> *The Rube Goldbergs down in Cambridge*
> *Descended on the scene.*

> *"We are lost" the captain shouted*
> *Alan Shepard was his name*
> *But the boys at Draper shouted*
> *"Ain't the way we play the game."*

Crouse's story began on page one with the headline, "Extra! Weird-Looking Freak Saves Apollo 14!" placed under a large photograph of the musician Shawn Phillips in a checked suit and hair to his elbows. My own face, and hair not quite to my shoulders, popped up on page six.

I was still under the influence of *The Greening of America*. With Charles Reich, I hoped and almost believed that our society really had turned a corner.

> Eyles is one of a growing breed of Consciousness III scientists and tech-nicians—lab workers who allow their imaginations to run free and who can appreciate the cosmic implications of ecology and space exploration.

I had been annoyed after Apollo 8 when NASA Administrator Thomas Paine characterized the mission as a "the triumph of the squares, the guys with computers and slide-rulers who read the Bible on Christmas Eve." Paine probably thought that sounded nice, but the Administrator should have known better than to disparage the independent thinkers who were the essence of the space program. If you were not a square it was not your triumph? I took that personally. I was at pains to claim Apollo 14, at least, as a triumph of the heads.

In fact, I viewed Apollo as a triumph *against* the squares, *in spite of* the squares, in the spirit of William Bainbridge, writing five years later, who portrayed spaceflight as a movement dedicated to explora-tion, which advances when it can exploit a patron looking for a way to leap ahead of an opponent. Just so, Sputnik shock and Kennedy vigah had launched a daring voyage of exploration with no military utility whatsoever.

I was still waiting for a reporter to ask me the question I was asked at parties—until Crouse went there. Why were we spending all that money going to the Moon when so much needs to be done on Earth? Why, I said, do all those things, but take the funds from warmaking, not from spaceflight, because exploration represents one of human-ity's nobler qualities, its desire to know more—and if our civilization survives its knowledge, our destiny.

As my quarter hour wound down I became philosophical about the experience of fame. The lens of journalism is cloudy, of necessity, even when the journalists are as honest and responsible as I experienced them. It was AM radio, with static, not FM. My clear voice never car-ried through. The journalist is never as committed to your story as you are. You will quickly begin to see yourself as a commodity. It is a loss of innocence.

But it was more interesting than that. It was as though a fuzzy parallel figure had come into existence who was based on me, that might sporadically reconnect with me, but who inhabited another, separate dimension where he was not under my control. And he endures, to my amusement, and sometimes embarrassment, as when I open a book about Apollo and see my name in the index, but not Doc Draper's or Dick Battin's or Hal Laning's. All you can do is laugh.

Surely the least trustworthy form of history of all is the astronaut memoir "written with" a professional writer. Careful research to cross-check interview material is probably not part of the writer's contract; conversely, astronauts, being generalists, may not retain the important details, and, being pilots, may have a tendency to embellish. In one such book the myth was created (and in others repeated) that

> A telephone call roused Donald Eyles, MIT's computer whiz, out of a sound sleep in Massachusetts. He threw a coat over his pajamas. By the time he reached the front door, an Air Force car was pulling into his driveway. Moments later he was on his way to his office at Draper Labs.

Driveway? On Beacon Hill? I had gone to sleep with a lunar landing in the offing? Pajamas?

In 1997, when Tom Hanks's company put together a twelve-part miniseries about Apollo for Home Box Office, the writer Erik Bork did contact me, and I helped him get the technical points right in the Apollo 14 episode. When the show was broadcast I was at least in the building, not at home, but I was *again* asleep (accompanied by an uncredited yellow Lab who thought it was her scene) and I was a twitchy guy with a white Afro who walked in and demanded coffee—nothing like the cool Coke-drinking original.

I provided the archetype, it would appear, for the young computer engineer, probably "alternative" in some way involving scruffiness, skin color or apparent lifestyle, who pops up out of nowhere with an idea that saves a space mission—as most recently seen in the character Rich Purnell in the film, *The Martian*.

———

During all the commotion something had been nagging at me. Why had the landing radar failed to lock on when it should have? Was there something about my procedure, something I had overlooked, that had affected the radar? Shepard and Mitchell were only a minute from a mandatory abort when Houston's suggestion to cycle the circuit breaker brought the radar back to life. Had the idea for which I was being lionized almost ruined the landing I had set out to save?

Ten days later our radar expert, Walter Tanner, had it figured out. It had nothing to do with the procedure. Because of an unexpectedly strong radar return from the surface that had occurred even before the landing began, the radar had switched to a low-range mode that prevented acquisition at the normal altitude. Turning the radar off and on had reset the mode. The effect would be avoided on later missions by not energizing the radar so early in the sequence.

PART THREE ⚓ EXPLORING

MISSIONS OF EXPLORATION

APOLLO 15
July-August, 1971
Dave Scott CDR, Jim Irwin LMP, Al Worden CMP
LM-10 — LUMINARY 210
Hadley Rille (26.132°N, 3.634°E)

APOLLO 16
April, 1972
John Young CDR, Charlie Duke LMP, Ken Mattingly CMP
LM-11 — LUMINARY 210
Descartes Highands (8.973°S, 15.498°E)

APOLLO 17
December, 1972
Gene Cernan CDR, Jack Schmitt LMP, Ron Evans CMP
LM-12 — LUMINARY 210
Taurus-Littrow Valley (20.191°N, 30.772°E)

APOLLO 15

Revision 99 of LUMINARY flew on Apollo 11, revision 116 on Apollo 12, and revision 131 on Apollo 13. In the nearly 10 months that went by before Alan Shepard's mission, as we dealt with issues like TLOSS and the throttle instability, and added new capabilities such as the terrain model and the new landing analog displays, LUMINARY had reached revision 178. Now we were moving toward the last LUMINARY, revision 210, which would fly on Apollo 15, Apollo 16, and Apollo 17 without modification.

Apollo 15 would be the first of a new type of mission that was less about getting to the Moon and more about exploring it after arriving. The LM would stay for nearly three days and Dave Scott and Jim Irwin would venture outside the spacecraft three times. Best of all there was a car, a sort of electric buckboard called the Lunar Rover, folded Houdini-style into the side of the descent stage, that would give the explorers a range limited only by the distance they could walk back if the jalopy broke down.

The new mission had little impact on the landing guidance. The LM would come in steeper because of the irregular terrain it had to fly over, but that was accomplished just by changing the guidance targets. The LM was heavier, which cost fuel, but more fuel was available because the tanks had been enlarged, and for good measure the orbit-lowering DOI burn that came before the powered descent was to be performed, before the LM separated, using the engine in the Service Module, which had fuel to spare. After the burn and separation the CSM would hustle back to the higher orbit to wait for the LM to return.

We made some changes to simplify the crew procedures, such as adding DELTAH (the number used in evaluating landing radar data) to the standard P63 display in place of forward velocity, which had never proved useful. And finally we learned our lesson about *discretes,* as we called those on-off signals like the spurious abort indication on Apollo 14. We installed a comprehensive system of overrides. Craig Schulenberg and Peter Weissman worked out the procedures for selecting an abort using the DSKY if the abort button had to be locked out. Larry Berman did an analysis of how an abort trajectory might be affected if guidance activation was delayed by the DSKY work.

And Col. Scott had his way with the windmill. All the instruments in the cockpit were now fly-to and consistent with the AGS, although in the case of the cross-pointers a hardware change had been necessary.

In the Spring I finished my paper for the conference in Dubrovnik, ponderously titled, "Apollo LM Guidance and Pilot-Assistance during the Final Stage of Lunar Descent — Software Considerations." I described the final state of the P66 LPD capability, as it was running in ZERLINA 56, software that still represents the state of the art for a piloted landing on an airless body with inadequately surveyed terrain — the sort of landing we may not do again until we go to play bowls with the moons of Jupiter and Saturn.

In early May I traveled back to Cape Canaveral for the Apollo 15 crew training, held again in the Flight Crew Support Building. It was a three day meeting with more than twenty presenters and a more serious tone than when we met with the Apollo 12 and Apollo 14 crews in the same room. Allan Klumpp and I played a small part on the second day. Scott, having been Pete Conrad's backup on Apollo 12, was already very well prepared.

As the launch approached, the main thing between me and sloth was something called erasable memory programs, EMPs for short. The AGC could execute code in erasable memory just as easily as it executed the permanent code in fixed memory. This opened up the possibility of loading small programs into unused areas of erasable to deal with miscellaneous problems that might come up. The memory areas that we used were located in the Executive's queues. We were confident now that jobs would not stack up, as they had on Apollo 11, and that some memory would remain unused.

NASA's interest in EMPs may have been piqued by the abort-switch workaround on Apollo 14, which was widely but inaccurately described as "a program that could be inserted in the computer," but in fact the technique was already in use. The burn that sent the LM back to the Moon—reduced when its job was done to a lifeless mass hitting at a known spot to help the seismologists calibrate their instruments—was conducted by an erasable memory program fittingly called P99. Dave Moore wrote P99, and three days after Apollo 14 splashed down, amid the hoopla I was experiencing, he was at pains to make it known that the LM's successful deorbit on Apollo 14 was performed by his EMP.

EMPs could be used to work around various hardware malfunctions—glitches in the electronics, bum transistors, renegade bits, meter crap-outs, broken DSKY keys, loose balls of solder. We saw the prospect of a whole library of these little programs, ready to be inserted and activated if they were needed. Eventually there would be about a dozen EMPs for the LM, more still for the Command Module. If we had learned anything at all it was that what would bite us next would never be anything we anticipated, and not every problem had an EMP solution, but by trying to think ahead we were really training ourselves to deal, again, with whatever surprise did occur.

Working with Allan Klumpp and Craig Schulenberg, I developed an elaborate erasable memory program, EMP 103, that would allow a landing to proceed despite the failure of one or more of the interface units, called CDUs, that told the computer the three gimbal angles from the IMU that defined the LM's attitude. Qualifying EMP 103 for flight was the tricky part because both the MIT system and TRW's abort system were employed simultaneously. AGS would provide flight control and PGNCS would navigate and guide, while the astronaut controlled attitude and throttle manually in response to cues provided by our system.

Our hybrid simulator in Cambridge did not have an AGS. The LM simulator at the Cape did, of course, but the intense training by the prime crew left little time for software development. In the last few weeks before launch I could barely enter the building, much less the LM cockpit, because of the quarantine procedures that were set up after the measles incident before Apollo 13.

The beauty of it was, when the crew launched, simulator time became plentiful.

—

I flew to the Cape the day before the Apollo 15 liftoff, early enough to spend a few hours on the beach. The Islander Motel was booked solid but Doug Melvin offered me a comfortable sofa in the family quarters until the next day when the press corps cleared out.

It was still dark when I arrived at the press village near the VAB — a small grandstand surrounded by trailers and temporary buildings containing TV studios. Further back were smaller trailers where technicians from Nikon, Canon or Olympus would give your camera a tune up.

Three miles east the rocket was sublime in its peacock tail of spotlights against a sky tinted by a faint hint of dawn. The air freshened as dawn approached and there were streaks of gold and pink in the sky as Walter Cronkite made his entrance, seemingly already in make-up, leading an entourage of men in suits followed by a woman carrying a portable typewriter. In the grandstand Doc Draper, in a tropical suit and bow tie, worked the house, paying special attention to Mary Bubb, then a statuesque fifty, a reporter who had for many years covered spaceflight for Fairchild Publications. As she did for every launch, Bubb wore a hat that translated the mission patch into three dimensions — in this case chevrons of red, white and blue elevated on dowels above a gray lunar dome. (The patch was an evolved version of a design by Emilio Pucci.)

At liftoff I was at the edge of the turning basin, surrounded by press photographers. As smoke burst from the flame trenches the buzz of shutters and motor drives rose in a reedy crescendo — overcome a quarter minute later by the great bourdon note with its embellishing pops and cracks as the great rocket took to the Air with Fire, shaking the Earth and the Water.

Launch day at the simulator proved to be for entertaining VIPs, not serious work. Moon-walking hot-rodder Pete Conrad came through with two race car drivers that someone identified as Dan Gurney and Roger Penske.

A simple fixed-base simulation of the lunar rover had been improvised since my last visit. You sat in the thing facing a television monitor that showed a view of the lunar surface that was responsive to the vehicle's control stick. The rover looked semi-authentic from the driver and passenger's position. Outside someone had added cardboard fenders to make the thing look like a comic-strip jalopy.

The image in the monitor came from the same terrain model that filled the LM's windows, except in this case the camera in the L&A just skimmed the terrain. There was a photocell sensor that prevented the camera from physically penetrating the surface. While I was there the photocell failed, which caused the brakes to be set. Therefore the terrain could not be lowered to replace the photocell. I remembered the day in a fancy meeting room in Houston when the electricity went out during a thunderstorm and we could not let in daylight because the drapes were electrically operated. This time a technician "went in without a print" (but with a flourish) and managed to release the brakes. When the fun died down I went off to visit the VAB. With John Young's mission still nine months away I found all four bays empty, but several second and third stages were on hand.

I spent the next two days in the LM cockpit, proving that EMP 103 worked as intended, then flew back to my usual post in Cambridge to monitor a landing that was, for the first time—as I hardly dare to breathe even forty-five years later—routine.

Gene Cernan, the Apollo 17 commander, said to Dave Scott after his own mission, "You guys had the best site." Scott's landing site in the Sea of Rains gave access to a formation called the high Apennine Escarpment, and to Hadley Rille, a meandering gorge over 1000 feet deep. In preparation for the mission—and largely on their own initiative—Scott and LM Pilot Irwin had trained with field geologists in desert terrain thought to resemble the Moon.

The LM stayed on the Moon 67 hours. Scott and Jim Irwin performed three surface EVAs. The lunar rover gave them a radius of seven kilometers. As he collected a suite of rock samples meant to characterize the geology of the site, Scott became so absorbed in what he was doing that he lost awareness that he was a quarter of a million miles from home, wearing a bulky spacesuit in one-sixth gravity.

The training and the concentration paid off when Scott and Irwin spotted what has become known as the Genesis Rock — and they knew it immediately:

Scott: Aaah.

Irwin: Almost see twinning in there.

Scott: Guess what we just found. [laughing] Guess what we just found! I think we found what we came for.

Irwin: [laughing] Crystalline rock, huh?

Scott: Yes, sir. You better believe it.

A moment later amid more jubilation they correctly identified the sample as anorthosite, and indeed it proved to be a piece of ancient crust dating back more than four billion years, almost to the formation of the Solar System, an object of incredible antiquity that had somehow survived the pulverizing bombardment the Moon has endured.

Doc Draper had a wide circle of friends. We heard afterward that when the astronauts were having trouble with the drill used to extract core samples, Doc, sitting in the VIP viewing room behind mission control, received a call from Howard Hughes, who knew a lot about drilling equipment, offering help.

BLOCK ISLAND, DUBROVNIK

Many hours of surface activity were broadcast live on commercial television. The video from a camera mounted on the rover was of high quality. At a site with mountains and canyons, seen from changing perspectives as Scott and Irwin roamed, the Moon became three-dimensional as never before. I watched almost every minute on a small black-and-white TV in the dingy apartment Amy was sharing with two girlfriends for the summer. She had graduated and at the end of the summer would move to New York and take a good job at Time Inc.

Lenny Kaye was often in Boston to work with a band called The Sidewinders, fronted by Andy Paley. Some nights in my apartment on Lime Street, with Tim on harmonica, Lenny on acoustic guitar, and me banging on something or other, we played the blues. On one of those evenings a 40-inch water main ruptured at the corner of Charles and Beacon Streets and several blocks were flooded to ankle depth. Someone put loudspeakers in their window and a crowd danced sloppily in the street. After a while Mayor Kevin White, who lived a few blocks away, waded in with his trousers rolled up and very reasonably asked everybody to go home now so the neighbors could go to sleep. White had a gift for this sort of interaction. Someone shouted, "Take off his pants," but White's gambit worked. The next day the front page of the tabloid *Boston Record-American* had a large picture in which Lenny could be seen standing near the Mayor.

The weekend after Apollo 15 landed, the crew on their way home, Jimmy the Flea played its only gig. The venue was the Block Island Inn, on that craggy, Brontëan island off the Rhode Island coast.

It was a Lenny Kaye caper. The band was named, he said, after "the justly famous Jimmy the Flea of Pawnee-on-the-Shawnee, Pennsylvania." Two of its members already had entomological backgrounds; guitarist Ed Finney from Memphis, and Bob Palmer (who later wrote about rock-and-roll for the *New York Times*), on clarinet and Sock-Em hammer, were from a band called The Insect Trust. Steve Krevsky on drums, Patrick O'Connor, bass, Tim White, harp, Lenny on guitars, and yours truly on conga drum, rounded out the septet.

I bought the drum for the occasion. My skills were minimal but I could beat the thing in time and I suppose I added something to the texture. Somebody mentioned Santana. I was tolerated by the real musicians. Here is Friday night's playlist:

Who Do You Love
Me and You and a Dog Named Blue
Come on Everybody
Lucille
Sittin' on the Dock of the Bay
Route 66

Around and Around
Letters from Atlanta
Street Fighting Man
Good Morning Little Schoolgirl
Kootchie Kootchie Man
Brown Eyed Handsome Man
Tough Mean Claudine

And so I turned 28, marveling at the melting away of years.

Then it was off to Dubrovnik, Yugoslavia (now Croatia) for a Symposium on Automatic Control in Space organized by the International Federation of Automatic Control. I came by way of Rome and Venice. Peter Adler travelled via Munich and arrived on a new BMW motorcycle. Allan Klumpp and a few others flew in to Belgrade.

My paper described both the final landing software, as it flew, and its final evolution, including my implementation of John Young's P66 LPD concept. There were interesting papers from both sides of the Iron Curtain, some of them about the rovers that were likely to precede human explorers to Mars. With a variety of accents, a bad sound system, and a general lack of "Powerpoint skills" all around, the *presentations* were not necessarily interesting — my own not excepted.

Dubrovnik, however, was fascinating. Peter and I shared a room in the Hotel Excelsior, located on the water a short walk from the old city. There was a wide stone quay for sunning and swimming, and through an arched door a small discothèque that throbbed late into the night. Dubrovnik, it seemed, was where young Yugoslavians came to party. One night a gale blew sheets of saltwater off the Adriatic, which only made the disco more cozy as we burned the candle at both ends.

The conference was held in the old Dominican monastery, a building that like the entire old city was constructed from a single material. Every building, the pavement under our feet, the walls and towers that had defended the city for centuries from Saracen and Venetian, were all built of the same butter-colored limestone. The fortifications were largely intact. You could circumnavigate the city on the battlements. (Since that time Dubrovnik has suffered under bombardment by modern weapons.)

We had little contact with the Russians. In a sense we were there to gloat, so it would have been natural for them to feign indifference. We were oblivious to the tensions among the nationalities encompassed by "Yugoslavia." When at dinner with one of the senior organizers I expressed admiration for "your country" — referring to its resistance against the Nazis and Tito's assertion of independence from the USSR — the remark received an icy reception to the effect of, "What do you know about it?" We *ate* very well. The cheap caviar and the asparagus soup stick in my mind, and the strong beer.

With the conference over, Peter Adler and I set out on the BMW, me in back, driving south along the Adriatic Coast. We took the land route around the amazing terrain near Kotor; in Budva gazed out at the unattainable island resort of Sveti Stefan; and drove on to Bar in Montenegro, about 20 miles from the Albanian border.

But a day later, already weary of the motorcycle, we made a new plan: Venice by sea. Back in Dubrovnik we booked passage on the motor ship *Jugoslavija*, one of the small liners that plied the Dalmatian coast. The motorcycle was swung aboard in a cargo net. We cruised north through the night, not sleeping, calling at Korcula, Hvar, Split, Zadar, Rab, and Pula, sometimes creeping through narrow channels between ghostly ruins, then tying up at a wharf where merriment spilled out of quayside bars. As night gave way to gray day, the towers of La Serenissima began to spike the horizon. We slipped through another medieval passage into the Lagoon, cruised smartly between the Piazza San Marco to starboard and San Giorgio Maggiore to port, continued along the Canale della Giudecca, and approached a long wharf, where, with the captain and the pilot on the bridge and a powerful tugboat standing by, there appeared to be some confusion between ship and shore. "Dove il imbarcadero?" shouted the Venice pilot in operatic baritone. The ship drifted obliquely toward the wharf. A mooring line was thrown but not picked up. The ship, slow but unchecked, rammed a dockside crane, which teetered, and teetered, and crashed onto the forecastle.

HAYSTACK

With Apollo 15 successfully flown, that incredible hunk of lunar anorthosite safe in the Lunar Receiving Laboratory in Houston, and LUMINARY frozen at 210, there was a sense of decline. The Russian director Andrei Tarkovskiy in his film *Solaris* captures this sense of a project winding down, although happily our apparitions never became corporeal. My job, I suspected, might soon become less exciting. I might even face a choice between a change of career and working on a weapons project I found repugnant.

Allan Klumpp was already looking beyond the Moon, producing a critique of the Viking spacecraft that would land on the Red Planet in 1975, and a twenty page memo on the guidance and navigation requirements for a Mars spacecraft powered by a nuclear engine.

It was hard winter when I heard from Tim Ferris. I was still working on erasable memory programs, those semi-clever little applets we called EMPs. At the Orpheum Theatre Sarah Caldwell had just given us, in its first staged performance in America, Hector Berlioz's epic portrayal of the fall of Troy, *Les Troyens*, making the most of its sublime melodies and its huge potential for spectacle.

Ferris was a reporter for *Rolling Stone* who must already have been thinking about the book that became *Coming of Age in the Milky Way*. I did not have much to show him but I remembered an article in the MIT newspaper, *The Tech*, about the new Wallace Observatory, situated on a hilltop in Westford, Massachusetts. Its 24 inch and 16 inch telescopes were integrated with computers to an extent that was unusual in 1972. We decided to go have a look and I made a call to prepare the way.

We found the place down a half-mile gravel driveway in scrub land somewhere between Lowell and Fitchburg—two white domes connected to a little house where we found Grant Snellen, an electrical engineer and computer expert as well as an astronomer. He had previously worked at Mount Palomar, and early in our rambling conversation he told us about the time the astronomer Allan Sandage, his former colleague, dropped a peanut butter sandwich on the 200-inch mirror. That made Ferris hungry so Snellen made him a peanut butter sandwich — or maybe it was the sandwich that prompted the anecdote. We all had hot tea in mugs that we cupped our hands around.

The facility had a comfortable common room with kitchenette, a dormitory where students working late were encouraged to sleep over, a room for the computer and telescope control console, and the two domes with their handsome instruments. The site often had "good seeing" in winter but that was not the case tonight; Ferris and I were the bozos who visited an astronomical observatory on a cloudy night.

Snellen was working on the equipment and happy for company. He showed us how the telescopes could be controlled from the computer console — providing capabilities to find and track objects that are available today to every backyard astronomer. Stan Zisk arrived from the nearby Haystack Observatory, where he had been doing radar topography of the lunar surface using Haystack's big instrument, an enclosed 120-foot radio telescope that could also emit pulses and receive the signals that bounced back. Tonight the dish was pointed at a secret satellite in geosynchronous orbit. From its radar reflection Zisk said he thought it was a knobby thing. Somehow that led us to the subject of Space War.

For someone familiar with computer games, circa 2017, Space War would be sensory deprivation, but at the time we were going to the Moon it was the cool computer game that people at MIT liked to talk about. Rival ships were in orbit around a star. The ships and the torpedoes they fired at each other followed the sometimes counterintuitive rules of orbital mechanics — all reduced to the two dimensions of the CRT screen. (I had never played, having better toys.)

The real result of this conversation was that, having come this far, it would be crazy for us not to visit Haystack. Zisk got on the phone to find someone to show us around.

It was only a few miles to the other observatory but much of that was on an unpaved road through the frozen taiga, until giant shapes began to materialize in the gloom: a sixty-foot dome, an open dish of about fifty feet, a large fixed antenna made of wire mesh, and finally the looming white dome that housed the 120 foot instrument.

Radio-astronomer Hooker Danforth, spruce in tie and tweed jacket and maybe slightly annoyed in the middle of the night, gave us the tour. Like the optical instruments at Wallace the antenna was controlled by a Univac computer. There were plans to tie the two observatories together so the optical instruments could provide a finder-scope for the narrow beam of the big dish. The dome was essentially a sphere. Like a concert hall it looked bigger from the inside than the outside. The struts that made up the dome seemed at first to form a regular pattern à la Buckminster Fuller, but if you looked carefully the pattern evaporated—an arrangement designed to avoid resonances. There were interchangeable room-sized modules that could be placed at the focus point of the dish to make it easier to switch experiments.

At that moment the telescope was observing what they now said was a Comsat. Every few seconds a large "high voltage" sign blinked on and a buzzer sounded, as a highly directional radar pulse was transmitted. On a CRT we saw a plot of the amplitude versus the wavelength of the echo, to the uneducated eye simply a sharp spike. The group clustered around the monitor was interested in a small bump, just barely above the noise, next to the main spike—as though there were a second unknown object in close vicinity.

So it was back through the sci-fi domescape to the paved road and back to Boston, with a stop at a deserted restaurant where we got to talking and I described a little hypothesis I had cooked up about quasars.

Quasars are "quasi-stellar objects." They resemble stars, but their spectra exhibit a red-shift—a Doppler shift caused by their movement away from us—that seems to place them at the far edges of the expanding universe, at such distances that exotic theories are required to explain how they can be so luminous. Quasars might be relatively local phenomena (within our own galaxy) except that we do not see the corresponding blue-shifted objects we would expect to see if there were rogue stars whizzing around willy-nilly.

Back at the Wallace Observatory Snellen had wrinkled his nose when the name Carl Sagan came up, but I was still thinking about the book, *Intelligent Life in the Universe*, that Sagan had co-annotated with the Russian astrophysicist, I.S. Shklovskii.

In the book Sagan described a scale proposed by Shklovskii's colleague N.S. Kardashev, which ranks civilizations according to whether they have harnessed the resources of a planet, a star system, or a galaxy. Humanity is at best a Type I civilization, squandering the common wealth of our only planet. A Type III civilization that possesses a galaxy is almost beyond imagining. But Type II, a civilization that controls a star, invites speculation. The usual example is a civilization that is driven by Malthusian pressures to construct a Dyson Sphere, a structure suggested by Freeman J. Dyson in 1960 that completely surrounds the star so that all its energy can be captured.

But if a Dyson sphere is feasible, then a combustion chamber built around a star is no great leap. Much the same engineering problems would have to be solved — except that now my own disciplines of guidance, navigation and control would also come into play. Such a system could propel itself with steady acceleration for the life of the star.

What would it look like? Usually it would be invisible. It would only be visible to us if it happened to be flying directly away from Earth so that we could look into the combustion chamber. In that case it would resemble a star, but since we would only see it if it happened to be accelerating away from us, its spectrum would tend to show an unusual red-shift. It might look, in other words, much like a quasar.

Could quasars, I wondered, be star-powered ships constructed by alien civilizations within our own galaxy? Have whole civilizations set themselves to wander? Or are there beings out there with existences so elongated in time that they might seem a bit slow on the uptake, but for whom a voyage across the galaxy in a star-powered transport is like a hop to Atlanta? Do civilizations eventually face, will *our* civilization someday fiercely debate, the choice between committing ourselves to rove, or living invisibly in a sealed sphere, huddled shoulder-to-shoulder around the hearth of a single sun and perhaps forgetting that there is a whole cosmos outside?

The funny thing was, unlike most hypotheses regarding quasars, this one, if true, could be confirmed — if meaningful radio signals happened to be recognized. The other funny thing was that unusual radio-frequency emissions from a quasar *had* already been noticed.

The same N.S. Kardashev who thought up Type II civilizations identified a quasar-like radio source designated CTA 102 that he thought might be of intelligent origin. But, wrote Sagan, the object was subsequently identified "from its spectrum" as a quasar.

> [T]he argument for the artificial origin of the CTA 102 radio source does seem considerably eroded by its identification as a quasar, despite the fact that we do not fully understand the origin and nature of quasars.

Peculiar radio signals from an object of unknown "origin and nature"? It was something to think about.

Alas for my Nobel Prize aspirations, in the years since my drive back to Boston with Tim Ferris, more and more quasars have been associated with very distant galaxies, seeming to confirm that they are embedded in the expanding fabric of the universe. The mystery that remains is why, if Type II civilizations do exist in our galaxy, we do *not* observe their star-powered ships.

But if our civilization survives its self-destructiveness long enough to at last detect another that has survived its, there will surely be clues that in retrospect will seem to have been staring us in the face.

APOLLO 16

I was Ishmael, drawn along on a mad voyage (and living to tell the tale). I was Candide, living in a perfect world of rockets and personal liberation (while a war raged outside). I was often a clueless Holden Caulfield—but in my romantic imagination I was E.T.A. Hoffmann, bewitched by a succession of extraordinary women—glimpsed now in candlelit scenes reflected in memory's funhouse mirror.

You know by now that this is not one of those stories in which the hero meets and marries his one true love, about whom not much more needs to be said. This is the story of six and a half years in the life of a single man in his twenties, who reached that age at a time of a new sexual freedom, post-pill and pre-AIDS, of which both men and women—but perhaps especially women—were eager to take advantage. Considering the energy I put into finding love during these years, it would be a lie, and an injustice, to exclude from this narrative the women in whose arms I found it. Individually you were fascinating, collectively, life-affirming.

The sense of wonder that I was feeling in the company of women may not easily be believed in these jaded millennial times in which I write. Alongside the promptings of physical desire, it was my hunger for knowledge that I most desired to gratify. Each new relationship was a new continent, with its own geography, its own chemistry, its own surprises, where a new language was spoken. But on the other side of that coin — as perhaps I have been trying to conceal in these pages — was a fear. Fear of intimacy as entanglement. Fear of a future without novelty and adventure. Fear of missing something. Or, to turn over the coin again, had I somehow grown up without a normal fear of chaos and uncertainty, like growing up without a fear of heights?

Love? I had not used the word since high-school puppy-love days, but sometimes I felt a fullness, a contentment, an involvement, when saying it would not have been dishonest — but always underneath was the restlessness, the curiosity about what might come next.

I must have met Carol in the late summer of 1971, and Cathy early the next. In a roseate permutation whose details are not clear to me now, they enriched my life during the last years of Apollo.

Carol was watching from an upstairs window at MIT. I waved, she blew a kiss, I counted floors and windows and found her in the offices of the music department. And so we began with movies, Chinese food, and more and more intimate caresses. Then for a while we stuck to the old sofa in my living room and observed the propriety of a few square inches of cloth between us — until an afternoon on Lime Street when she stood up and made a small sound and pulled her wispy garment down to her knees, and hobbled as I led her into the bedroom before helping her kick them off entirely. She was taller than me and very slim. Sometimes we would undress and stand a bare inch or two apart, breathing each other in, not touching at all yet.

Cathy was shapely and compact, Carol's opposite in that way, but our attraction was equally immediate. We met while bicycling along the Charles River, smoked a joint under a tree near Jamaica Pond, dined at the Paramount Diner on Charles Street, and spent the evening together. The next weekend, with her roommates conveniently absent, we roamed her large apartment naked, and she made love to me generously from that day forward. The enduring tableau is framed by the round mirror propped against the wall in my bedroom: the concentration on her face, the long hair spilling over her shoulders....

They own a piece of my heart still. The same goes for all the women I have named in this book. I remember how we met, where we hung out, enough about how they thrilled me that the thrill echoes still. More elusive is how it ended, how this fit in with that, and in general, *when*. There are no Luminary memos to refer to.

Memory foreshortens. Maybe I have painted the flowers thicker on the ground than they would seem if plotted on a graph. I had many initiatives rebuffed, many bewilderments. I missed many signals, fled from others, spent many a lonely night.

Walking home across the Longfellow Bridge in the pre-dawn, shaking off the trance of working out something intricate, inhaling the cold, clean air off the North Atlantic, Venus burning blue above, I had felt the existential loneliness of a man who located himself among the tangled coordinate systems of the starry universe, and craved a completion he had not yet experienced and could not name.

But in the corporeal intensity of the later loves a question seemed to have been answered. I had learned at last to lose myself in the experience—and in the radiated heat, the textures of skin, the contours we traced with our hands, the tastes and aromas and sounds and glances, and in the ultimate high-bandwidth intimacy itself, I could not doubt the connection to an independent, equally-involved individual. If Descartes proved one's own existence with *cogito ergo sum*, then in lovemaking the existence of the *other* was, in bravura fashion, demonstrated. It refuted the solipsism I had felt on the Longfellow Bridge, exploded the phony duality of thought and flesh, and opened the door to the life-loves that would follow.

John Young took flight on April 16, 1972. Again I attended the spectacle at Cape Canaveral, and again spent a productive day in the LM simulator before flying back to Boston to monitor the landing from the classroom.

The most serious scare was a problem with the SPS, the big engine in the Service Module that would be needed to leave lunar orbit and return to Earth. The problem only affected the backup system but a strict reading of the mission rules said that a landing should not be attempted. The LM might need its fuel to propel the crew back home instead of using it to land on the Moon. After a delay of one revolution, two hours, the rules were bent enough to allow what proved to be a very smooth landing.

The LM touched down in highland terrain in a region called Descartes, where geologists hoped ancient crust material would be found. Young was able to place the LM on one of the few level spots in the vicinity. During three outings on the surface in the lunar rover, Young and Charlie Duke collected over 200 pounds of soil and rock — but nary a pebble of the volcanic material scientists had expected them to find.

While Young and Duke were on the Moon the Space Shuttle program was approved. We understood that the circumstances that had given MIT responsibility for the Apollo guidance system would not come again. The Lab, as a not-for-profit organization, could only work for the government when it was judged to be a "sole source" — the only organization able to do the job. That argument, which had been difficult enough in 1961, was impossible in 1971.

We still had a role. Our hardware experts were thinking about how to achieve "fault-tolerance" by running multiple computers in parallel and watching for divergence. On the software side we were considering how the various phases and functions would be organized, and how these would be represented to the crew on the Shuttle's CRT displays, which would be far more capable than our Apollo DSKY. We evolved a concept we called *mode/spec/disp*. It was really a distillation of the Apollo experience. *Modes* were the mutually-exclusive programs that corresponded to the mission phase the spacecraft was flying at the time. We likened the mode-selector to a rotary switch that could only be in one position at a time. *Specs*, or *specialists* (a term I coined for the purpose), were smaller task-oriented programs that could operate within modes and in parallel with other specs. Specs were like a row of toggle switches that could be on or off independently. *Disps* were simply displays: presentations of information without associated processing.

We claimed that these categories were necessary and sufficient to organize the computer activity on a manned spacecraft. Every display screen on the spacecraft would indicate the same Mode, but on individual screens the mode displays could be overlaid — almost like windows — by the displays associated with specs and disps. Some of this stuck in the Shuttle design although it did not fall to us to implement it except in simulations.

In May 1972 Sarah Caldwell gave us Verdi's *La Traviata* with a scintillating Beverly Sills in the title role. On a hot Tuesday night in July I was in Boston Garden with Emily and Tim for the Rolling Stones. I had failed to snag tickets when the band came in 1969 so I tried something different. Well before tickets went on sale, I sent a check for thirty dollars, payee blank, to the Boston Garden box office, with a stamped, self-addressed envelope and a polite note asking for four tickets, adding, "please keep the excess if I have enclosed too much." It worked! Four six-dollar tickets came back. Pretty good seats. As Ralph Ragan said, procurement was a little different in those days.

We got more than we bargained for and were happy to have equipped ourselves with a couple of joints and a plastic witch-hazel bottle full of Jack Daniel's whisky tucked into Tim's sock.

Stevie Wonder played a long opening set and we got ready for the Stones. But there was a long pause. Then a growing restlessness. And finally it was Boston Mayor Kevin White who came on stage. "The Stones were busted in Rhode Island two hours ago," he declared — Keith had been caught with drugs and Mick busted for sass — 'but," the Mayor continued, his voice rising with each phrase, "I called the governor!... and I got them out!!... and they're on their way here now!!!"

White already had one angry crowd on his hands and did not want another. In the South End, riots that had started two days earlier with an incident in Blackstone Park during a Puerto Rican festival were flaring up again. "Part of my city is in flames," White told us, "I need to remove the police detail from this building." Once more White set an example of reasonableness. By trusting, he was trusted. The Garden stayed cool. Just before one in the morning the Rolling Stones swaggered on stage and tore into "Brown Sugar."

DINNER WITH DOC

Again I traveled to the Cape, again to witness the blast-off of man-bearing Saturn, this time with a new element of spectacle laid on, as if the celestial mechanics that made it necessary intended to honor the final Moon mission. We will launch at night. Bound to be a party.

Once more, as soon as the crew departed I would take over the LM simulator to work on erasable memory programs — those snippets of code that we could load into erasable memory to work around certain malfunctions. Don Millard and Phyllis Rye came down with their own EMPs to work on. (Word had gotten around about the LMS time that was available during the first few days of a mission.) We would all fly home in time to monitor the landing from our usual posts in Cambridge.

Erasable memory programs were not much fun in themselves. In return for insurance against an unlikely eventuality, each EMP had to be described on paper, tested under a spectrum of circumstances, and taught to the flight controllers and crew. The what-ifs could go on and on. Occasionally the question was silly, sometimes easy to answer, but often the response was, "Probably that would work but I'd better make a run to make sure."

EMPs were one thing, but my trip to the Cape had another aspect — stemming from Apollo 14 and the larger perspective about the space program that being interviewed had led me to consider. And had I not been learning — in Le Coq, the Whitehaven High School literary magazine, in a raft of undergraduate papers (some on contract), and lately at MIT, writing with no other purpose than to get a point across — that being able to express an idea with clarity on paper is a good first test of the validity of the idea?

In short, my ambition to write about what we were doing was emerging. Was it not, in fact, my duty? I could write and I was on the spot. Would we not like to have the recollections of a junior officer on the *Santa Maria*—and, thinking big circa 1972, what better venue than *Rolling Stone*?

Jann Wenner took my call. Of course he remembered Timothy Crouse's "Weird Looking Freak" story for *Rolling Stone* the previous year.

Would he consider a story from me of perhaps 2500 words on the subject of Cape Canaveral and Apollo 17, I asked. He would be "interested" to see what I "would write." If my piece turned out "interesting" he would "certainly consider" running it. "What people want to read about is people and what they are doing that excites them," he added. I sensed a polite skepticism, California style, for which I could hardly blame him.

But I may have sparked a train of thought. The day before I left for the Cape, Wenner called me—catching me in front of a fire trying to roll a joint with chapped fingers. He had commissioned Tom Wolfe to write a series of stories about Apollo. Would I meet with Wolfe and Annie Leibovitz at the Cape? "Maybe you will become a character in Wolfe's masterpiece." Again a sense of disconnection, but of course I would be happy to meet with Wolfe and Leibovitz.

I grabbed a copy of *The Electric Kool-Aid Acid Test* to read on the airplane that took me in a few hours from slushy Boston to Daytona Beach, where the temperature was 80 degrees. Avis was down to a purple Dodge Dart that looked a little the worse for wear. I took I-95 to 520 and 520 to A1A, the seaward version of US 1, drove south past Carl McIntyre's Freedom Center, the Hilton, the topless shoe shine parlor, the rental offices for the new condo buildings, and on to Cocoa Beach and a downstairs room at the Islander.

Phyllis Rye called from the Motel 6 to say that we were invited to dine with Doc Draper that evening. I went to the Dairy Queen out on the highway for a milkshake—caught myself striding along like an alien—took a deep breath. Back at the Islander I borrowed a pair of scissors and converted a pair of corduroys into swimming trunks. The beach was deeply scalloped in its winter mode, the water, chilly and unpopulated, but I was keyed up enough from fast travel and the events in store that it could have been New Year's Day at the L Street Bathhouse in South Boston. I advanced as far as I dared into the thumping surf. The waves broke just before they reached me and every eight seconds my head was submerged in foam.

It was getting darker and there were lights out at sea, tracking ships in my imagining. Miles to the north, Canaveral, the Cape of Currents, curved out into the Atlantic. Several gantries were gaily lit while others sported only a blinking red light at the top. Canaveral Light winked white three times in a pattern that repeated every minute. The Saturn complex itself, 15 miles away, was invisible behind the bright lights of Port Canaveral.

We dined at a restaurant called the River's Edge (now Jack Baker's Lobster Shanty) located several miles south of Cocoa Beach on the sluggish waterway called the Banana River that runs between the beach and the mainland. Doc presided in grand style, ordering us all second and third pre-dinner drinks as soon as our glasses were half empty—followed by oysters, steak and wine, and more wine. He was accompanied by two handsome Frenchwomen who were officials at the Paris-based International Academy of Astronautics of which he was then President. Doc prodded the conversation but mostly listened.

Peter Weissman, an autopilot guy, ended up sitting next to Doc and relished it. Joe Mori, who ran our mainframes, was there on a junket he richly deserved. Rye and Millard were here to work on erasable memory programs. Ken Kito was a sharp hardware guy stationed at the Cape, Malcolm Johnston our cool pipeline to the hot pilots and fast thinkers in Houston.

Phil Felleman, next to me, promised me the abort switch from the hybrid simulator when it was dismantled (forgotten) and that brought the discussion around to Apollo 14 and its commander, Alan Shepard. Since our merry crew-training meeting with Shepard and his crew a book had come out, titled *The Making of an Ex-Astronaut*, in which Brian O'Leary portrayed Shepard as a sadistic martinet. Malcolm did not disagree, "You'd think the guy would at least nod to me when we pass in the hallway," he said. Happily I had only seen Shepard happy. "You made him happy," someone said, "He really, really wanted to go to the Moon." In fact, Shepard seemed well-liked by everybody at the Cape. It was easier for astronauts to relax here.

It came up that only two days ago Shepard's capable LM pilot, Edgar Mitchell, had been quoted in the *New York Times Magazine* saying that he had observed a gold ring bent by the use of psychokinesis. He had told Malcolm that he knew a man who could dispel a cloud by pointing at it. Is Mitchell kidding himself, kidding us, or could it happen? None of those alternatives seemed plausible.

Conversations about astronauts always came around to Pete. Conrad was an Ivy Leaguer — Princeton on a Navy scholarship — but he liked to hide it. Malcolm recalled taking Conrad to a party in Cambridge. When a Harvard type (as Malcolm related it) asked Conrad what he did for a living he answered, "I sell toilet seats." Harvard walked away without a word, ducking the provocation and missing a conversation he would still remember.

For Malcolm (who was handsomer) Pete was someone who had spent his life compensating for being a little guy with a big nose and a gap between his teeth, who never got the girl. I did not completely buy that. I thought of him as someone born quick but easily bored, who was bound to move from one startling episode to another. My Conrad was motivated by fun. True, you cannot be having fun if you are screwing up, but in Conrad it was not just about cool competence. That coexisted with another impulse that so relished what he was doing that his delight bubbled forth irrepressibly and infectiously — as when he laughed his way to orbit after being struck by lightning on Apollo 12.

At the head of the table, Doc Draper had the blues. I guess we all did. Over coffee he came out with it, "What can we do to follow going to the Moon?" He meant it two ways. What should the nation do? And what role could his Laboratory play? I suppose for him they were the same thing.

Weissman mentioned problems that needed to be dealt with on Earth: poverty, inequality, the environment. Doc did not respond. Malcolm cleared his throat and mentioned the Space Shuttle. Doc just grunted.

"The Space Shuttle is technically interesting isn't it?"

"Sure," said Doc, "but no one thinks it can't be done."

Doc recalled a meeting in Russia at which five hundred Russian experts gave him five hundred reasons a Moon mission could not be done the way he outlined. When he met the same group after Apollo 11 they cheerfully acknowledged their mistake. That was what Doc really wanted. Always the showman. He wanted a problem that seemed impossible, at least to other people. It was the same stunt he pulled in the B-29 in 1953, and the same bravado he showed in Jim Webb's parlor in 1961. Being told he cannot do something stirred him up. But what? Do what? "I've searched my mind," Doc said.

"He was born before Kitty Hawk," Weissman was thinking, "Isn't the Moon enough for him?" But for us?

No terms, it appeared, were too grandiose to have been applied to what we had accomplished. It was the best thing humans had ever done. We had reached the Emerald City of Oz, but when the curtain was drawn back it revealed, what? A truck. A fine truck, called the Space Shuttle, able to haul twenty-five tons to low Earth orbit. A truck that would be our maintenance dose, our methadone, we for whom the Moon came at the start of our careers and turned us into junkies for a certain very expensive high, now facing cold turkey.

For a moment we were in our own minds. The odd thing was, no one mentioned Mars. We all wanted to go on to Mars with all our heart, and we all knew it was politically impossible. Saying it would only twist the knife in Doc's side.

Yet, at that moment, sailing on to Mars seemed almost easy — a problem much like the one we had just solved except for the amount of fuel required. In Saturn we had the quintessential big booster to move the components of a Mars mission to Earth orbit. We could have learned then the on-orbit assembly skills that building the International Space Station later taught us. We had mature guidance concepts, ever more capable computers — and everyone was at the top of their game. Space medicine would have had to keep up, so we needed a space station in Earth orbit to learn about long stays in zero-G, but were we not doing that already, with Skylab scarcely six months from launch?

I went further still. I wanted permanent colonies on the Red Planet. I wanted to double or triple NASA's budget and assign it bolder and bolder missions — but always at the expense of warmaking, especially the creation of those sinister strategic weapons that were dangerous in themselves and misused so much of our creativity. I thought space exploration had the potential to transform human society. I wanted to rechannel aggression into exploration. It would only make America stronger. Had we not seen how Apollo boosted our moral strength in the world, and how Vietnam bled it away?

Ken Kito drove up to the space center to monitor the guidance system during its last night on Earth. Most of the others went back to their rooms at the Motel 6. Doc and the two Frenchwomen? Who knows?

Back in Cocoa Beach I found my way to the party that Time-Life was hosting in a big tent on the beach a short walk from the Islander—not that I was formally invited, but my sense of entitlement and familiarity with the terrain got me in.

The first person I recognized was Deke Slayton, standing alone, who scowled at me. Then I spied a tall girl in an orange jumpsuit, carrying a big camera, who could only be Annie Leibovitz. It took her a moment to realize who I was but then she seized me by the shoulders and led me over to Tom Wolfe (dressed to perfection) whose first words were "Do you know how many messages I've left at your motel?" (Messages, not the Islander's forte.) We chatted about why I was at the Cape, and I invited him to stop by the simulator the morning after the launch. Annie snapped us as we talked. A person pushed in and began to quiz Wolfe about the subject of his story, his "angle," his attitude toward the space program. The steel band started playing. I slipped away.

The launch was planned for about 10:00 PM the next day. The simulator still belonged to the prime crew. With the weather holding warm that spelled beach day and my skin was buzzing with a sunburn by the time I met Phyllis Rye, and new arrivals Margaret Hamilton and Dan Lickly. We drove north in the purple Dart, taking the historical route past the old launch pads for Margaret's sake.

This was my fourth launch and I had always watched from the press site on the right, or south, side of the Vertical Assembly Building. Tonight, because someone had made new rules and we did not all have the right passes, we were bused in to the VIP viewing area on the other side of the VAB, consisting of a bank of bleacher seats in a scraggly field that stank of whatever they sprayed for the insects.

I stayed with the MIT group for a while but they were content to sit in one place so I went exploring on my own. The area we were in was defined by a loop of the crushed stone track along which the crawler—a motorized platform the size of a supermarket—carried the rocket to the pad. Across the crawler track I found a grove of yellow toadstools, actually supports for idle launch platforms, pylons about fifteen feet tall with ladders leading up to grillwork platforms. I climbed one of the pylons and smoked half a joint, feeling like the caterpillar with his hookah in John Tenniel's illustration for *Alice in Wonderland*. Several other people climbed up and one of them passed around a pipe.

While we loitered the sequencer that controlled the busy prelude to a Saturn launch was clicking and clacking away, opening and closing valves, energizing circuits, testing pressures and voltages, doing all the little chores that were part of getting the big bird off the pad.

Time passed. Too much time passed. A loudspeaker buzzed but it was too far away to understand. A photographer on another pylon shouted, "Holding." I descended from my perch and crossed back to the grandstand. There had been a snag in the launch sequence.

There would have been more excitement over at the press site, more suspense, more sense of the beast tensing at the leash, and simply better information. We would have known that less than three minutes before liftoff the terminal control sequencer had failed to issue a command to pressurize the liquid oxygen tanks in the S-IVB, the Saturn rocket's third stage. We would have been poring over handouts that described the sequencing leading up to launch, and savvy reporters would have been bouncing it around. We would have known that we would still probably have a launch in a couple of hours.

Instead I was stuck in a humid limbo with bored people who did not care much about the details. The night was beginning to feel surreal. Three miles away the slender wand of Saturn stood steaming in a fan of spotlights. Over us loomed the Vertical Assembly Building — so geometric, so lacking in human scale, that it seemed insubstantial in the night — Atlantis risen from Floridian salt marsh.

Behind the bleachers I saw Alabama Governor George Wallace whisked away in a limousine. There were families with tow-headed boys in blue jeans, and budding daughters with piled-up hair walking like tomboys under their taffeta, wide eyes darting right and left. A heavily-decorated general from an African country stood alone, looking so forlorn I wanted to hug him. A Navy four-striper shook out a white handkerchief and spread it daintily on a seat-plank before sitting down. Annie Leibovitz came up from behind in her uniform, orange jumpsuit, and snapped a photo or two.

We found Tom Wolfe standing in crab grass, looking like he did not realize he was in an outer borough, offering around a bag of salted peanuts that there was absolutely nothing to wash down. Wolfe was talking to several exceptionally handsome women whose names I did not catch (or I would be bragging about it now) and a man whose name I had heard from Lenny Kaye: the great record man Ahmet Ertegun. Ertegun was wearing toy dark glasses and a toy NASA hard hat from the gift shop. He asked me to describe the sound of the Saturn V. I urged him, with his expertise, to record it with the highest fidelity. The launch of Skylab, four months away, would be the last chance and it would serve history to capture the vibrations, even if the loudspeakers that could reproduce it did not exist — but perhaps recording it was not technically possible. No, no, said Ertegun, we could record it. (So far as I know he did not.) A kid came around selling cans of warm Pepsi at the opportunistic price of fifty-five cents. Wolfe and I agreed to meet the next day for a real conversation.

And it is almost as though we have forgotten why we are here, at 12:33 AM, when it begins.

Flame and smoke erupt left and right from the flame trenches. By day these symmetrical outbursts resemble smoke. Now we can see that they are laced with bolts of fire. The lateral flames paint the rocket's white shaft a lurid orange.

There is complete silence. Conversation has stopped, but the rocket's vibrations have not yet traveled the three miles from the launch pad. Some people notice animal sounds during this interval.

Every second each of the five F-1 engines on the first stage accelerates 4700 pounds of burning kerosene and oxygen to a velocity of 8300 feet per second and expels it through the engine bell. That is enough to lift 7,500,000 pounds—but the bird is still clamped down. If an engine fails or an important parameter is out of limits the launch can still be scrubbed.

Then we see motion. Majestically the rocket rises. It throws a wiggle like a balanced broomstick to move away from the launch tower. As the tailfins of the rocket pass the top of the structure the sound hits us, that huge, now-familiar percussion that I feel through my feet and sunburned chest.

And as the rising rocket draws its fiery tail free of the Earth the atmosphere catches fire. No color exists anywhere but a ruddy orange. For a moment I turn away, as one turns to look back at the audience during a standing ovation. The thick haze of the windless night is bright in all directions. The VAB is ablaze. The whole Earth is a pagan bonfire. Was this the sky the night the Greeks burned Troy and loosed the ember that became an unimagined empire? Our planet seems to incinerate itself in its instinct to thrust Earth-life outward into the cosmos.

The shaft disappears into darkness leaving the disembodied flame. As Saturn turns to the east the flame becomes less a bolt than a glob and finally a tiny asterisk. The sound goes from roar to crackle to rumble. At about 150 seconds, as staging occurs, we see the flame plume for a moment, disappear, and return as a dancing pinpoint like a twinkling red star as it disappears into the sea mist, leaving a murmur that seems to come from every direction.

DINNER WITH TOM AND ANNIE

The next morning, after a few hours of sleep and a wake-up dip in the ocean I was flogging the purple Dart across the deserted causeway as fast as it would roll. I parked in one of the spots that were "Reserved for Apollo 17 Astronauts."

As usual, EMP 103 was my main concern. It was the granddaddy of all the erasable memory programs with a history going back to before the Apollo 15 mission. EMP 103 tried to cope with failures in the electronics, called the CDUs, that provided the computer with the three gimbal angles from the IMU that defined the spacecraft's attitude.

If the problem affected CDUX, which during the landing corresponded to the LM's yaw angle (its rotation about its vertical axis), the best we could do was prevent the autopilot from reacting to the incorrect information. If the pitch or roll indication failed but the computer was still receiving valid data from the accelerometers, then, from the measured acceleration we could compute and display the approximate CDUY or CDUZ value.

We thought that by now the EMP had reached maturity and that we understood its limitations. The documentation was complete. The crew had practiced with it. Then, just a week before, one of their simulated landings at the Cape had appeared to show that the EMP was causing the computer to compute an inaccurate rate of descent — obviously a number of vital interest during the landing.

Phyllis Rye and Don Millard were deep in conversation with Bob Pearson and I was drinking a Coke with my Adidas up on the console when someone I did not know stopped to scold me. He was concerned with how it looked to the visitors in the gallery over our heads. It was true we tended to forget the visitors were there, but there was extra tension in the air because this building was going to be closed shortly after Apollo 17 returned to Earth. Bob Pearson would have a new job planning where to store equipment and supplies on the Skylab space station. The scolder, perhaps not.

While Rye and Millard made some runs, not landings, related to their EMPs, I had time to wander around the high-bay area for what I knew was the last time. I visited one of the Command Module simulators, climbing the stairway in my socks and crawling in to lie on the center couch. I stared at the dozens of switches and indicators on the wide panel, which felt uncomfortably close to my face. Many of the controls were unfamiliar and there was no window to speak of. I never flew the Command Module or especially wanted to.

I walked to the end of the high bay where the full size mock-up of the LM loomed up. Clustered around its landing gear were dummy versions of the experiments the crew would install on the Moon. There was a lunar rover, a large sandbox filled with simulated lunar soil, and two rolling cranes designed to support five sixths of an astronaut's weight when he practiced in a lunar surface suit. The LM mock-up was for rehearsing the exit from the cockpit and the climb down the ladder to the surface.

I climbed up the back stairway to the cockpit. The hatch was square and in the position of the cabinet doors under your sink if you are looking out the kitchen window. I went down on hands and knees with my posterior toward the open hatch. Grasping handholds in the floor I edged backwards onto the small platform called the front porch, which was corrugated so my toes could find purchase. This would have been even more of a belly crawl if I had been wearing a surface suit with a bulky backpack containing my life support system. Edging further out I felt around for the top rung of the narrow ladder that ran down the front landing gear. The lunar surface was about twelve feet down. My foot found the next rung and then the next as I held on to the porch rails, and then the top rung, and so on. I reached the last step, which was still almost three feet above the floor, and awkwardly jumped backward.

Rye and Millard had managed to make a few runs but today celebrities were being escorted through. A science advisor from the Nixon White House flew lunar landings for an hour, shepherded along by Pearson. I would get my chance tomorrow. I lingered a while because John Wayne was expected — but never showed.

—

It would have been fun to fly a lunar landing with Tom Wolfe, and possibly useful to him, but he did not show up at the LMS. He and Annie Leibovitz picked me up at the Islander that evening and, with Annie in the back seat, Wolfe and I found our common ground as Southerners who had come north to be part of a larger world.

We crossed the first segment of the causeway leading from Cocoa Beach to the mainland and dined at Captain Ed's Tiki Bar (still there). Then it was on to drinks at Ramon's, that temple of astronaut worship (sadly defunct) with its huge sign honoring "Our All American Space Team....The Seven Astronauts" — meaning the original seven Mercury astronauts — and its comfortable booths that reminded me of 1950s hangouts like Chenault's in Memphis.

I could have used this conversation to learn writerly things that would be useful to me at this moment, but ostensibly it was I who was helping Wolfe. And so they bought me gin-and-tonics, or was it rum-and-cokes, and I gushed. Astronaut stories of course. Pete Conrad in the flying bedstead at Ellington. Landing the LMS with Conrad, Dave Scott, John Young. How Wally Schirra got the visitors gallery shut down, when astronauts were present, after he emerged from the simulator one day in droopy briefs and saw a busload of bug-eyed tourists staring at him.

And I tried to give Wolfe a feel for the work I was doing. Programming the guidance computer gave us a wide perspective because the computer had so many roles to play and tentacles reaching out to so many systems on the ground and onboard. We were concerned with everything from an individual transistor deep in a black box to crew training and operational planning. Nothing we did had ever been done before. Computer software was a very responsive medium; once the framework was established you could go from a new guidance idea to seeing it operate in a high-fidelity simulation literally overnight. What we did was technical but it was also literary. We were wielding a language. A piece of code like a poem had to express an idea economically but it also had to scan, had to fall trippingly off the tongue of the central processor. Memory and time were our two constraints and we played them, one against the other, in counterpoint.

Our programs originated far back in time and gradually evolved. There were 111 revisions between the LM program that flew Apollo 11 and the one that was loaded into the computer for Apollo 15, 16, and now 17. The computer was a machine and the behavior of LUMINARY was deterministic, but the human contribution, the uncertain terrain, the accuracy of navigation, the unknown amount of execution time consumed by counting pulses, were hard to predict. We tested the program like behavioral scientists performing an experiment on a living creature and then like unscrupulous surgeons we made changes aimed at perfecting the organism. We watched to see if the behavior was improved or damaged, with the option to undo it, erase the scar, and try something else.

And of course I revealed my aspirations for the space program and my eagerness to fly manned missions to Mars and beyond, exploiting tools like the extraordinary Saturn V and the magnificent launch facilities here at the Cape that we had developed at great cost, but used so far only to launch a handful of Moon missions.

In Wolfe and Leibovitz I had an intelligent and engaged audience — luxury casting in the roles of listener. Wolfe wrote four articles, which appeared in *Rolling Stone* in January, February and March of the new year. The nearest Wolfe came to us at MIT was in part three of the series, where he wrote, in astronaut voice:

> The space program, you have to understand, was the greatest triumph of engineering in the history of engineering. Engineers — not your pure scientists — were the geniuses in the space program, and we mean just what we say by "genius," too. They did things with computers, particularly in the guidance systems, that were so complex, so sophisticated, so far out, things that were gyrating so diceyly out on the tippy Western edge of the equation, that it was just goddamned close to being pure science. Not only that, a few months down the line they had to prove it out with somebody's hide (ours) as the colorful part of the test.

Three weeks later, in an elegantly calligraphic letter, Wolfe thanked me for providing just that insight and disclosed that he was "revving the series up a bit to turn it into a book." As a matter of fact almost nothing from the *Rolling Stone* articles, least of all the quoted line of thought, made it into *The Right Stuff*—unless you count the tension between the engineer's abstraction and the astronaut's posterior that is practically what the book is about.

LAST LANDINGS AT THE LMS

The next morning I began by flying a normal automatic landing from the beginning. I selected the landing program and the familiar sequence began. The activity light burned for a few seconds as the ignition algorithm converged on a time and attitude for ignition. I authorized the maneuver to the burn attitude. Coasting nav brought the state vector forward. The countdown started. At TIG minus 35 seconds the DSKY went blank and at TIG minus 30 returned, indicating that powered flight nav had begun. The tape meters sprang to life and began indicating altitude and rate of descent. At TIG minus 7.5 the ullage burn started with an audible pssssssssss. At TIG minus 5 the display flashed and I approved the burn. At TIG we lit the engine and at TIG plus 26 throttled it up to max—at each stage hearing a throatier sound from under the floor. The landing radar locked on. Throttle down was on time.

At 15,000 feet there was a flash like lightning in the windows. That was an electronic artifact of the surface display being switched on. Now if I stood on my toes and leaned in I could glimpse the lunar horizon at the bottom of the window. Less than a minute later, at 8000 feet, came High Gate, P64 and pitchover—the simulated firings of the maneuvering jets sounding like jazz cymbals—and now the whole area of the Taurus-Littrow landing site was spread out in front of me. "Read me some look angles please, Don." I was alone in the cockpit but the console had a duplicate of the DSKY so Don Millard would play the role of LM pilot from there.

I put in two clicks short and the LM responded by pitching back a few degrees, the note of the engine surging briefly. One click left and the horizon tilted as the LM put on a few degrees of roll.

At 400 feet I took over in P66. "300 feet, down at 10, looking good," said Don Millard, getting into the spirit of it. I put in five up-clicks on the ROD switch. "240 feet, down at 5." I picked out a spot near Camelot crater and slid the LM in that direction. I had plenty of gas so I slowed the descent rate and reduced my horizontal speed until I was practically in a dead hover. I yawed around a bit to look around. (A full 360 was not possible because the simulator would not allow you to look back at the high-intensity lamps that simulated the Sun.) After that there was nothing left but to bring her on down.

That was a normal landing, but my main concern today was the descent-rate error caused by EMP 103. The first thing I wanted to find out was whether the error persisted to low altitude. An error that was inconsequential at 10,000 feet might be disastrous at 500. We thought the altitude-rate discrepancy might be caused by an error in the pitch angle that was computed by the EMP, which in turn compromised the accuracy of the landing radar data.

We made several runs to try out solutions. We found we could reduce the error considerably, and totally eliminate it before we reached 1000 feet, simply by changing the weighting factor used by navigation when it incorporated landing radar data. If EMP 103 was called on we would recommend this adjustment. The odd thing was that both decreasing and increasing the boldness with which radar data was incorporated improved the result. In one case the error did not build up as high. In the other it was corrected faster when the LM slowed down.

For a finale I tried a far-out case. Could I land successfully with an outrageous pitch error of 4 degrees? The error led to an altitude-rate error of over 100 feet per second in the downward direction. I pretended not to notice until High Gate when the surface became visible out the window. Overriding the automatic throttle manually I avoided crashing but I did not ease up soon enough and found myself at 2000 feet with fuel down to 3 percent. I nursed the LM down to about 1200 before the engine went silent and I crashed, thankfully without sound effects. In all I flew about twenty landings, most of them full-length. It was a good days work, if you can call it work to play with such a toy.

That was not quite all. Phyllis Rye had plenty of hours in our plywood LM in Cambridge but she had never flown a lunar landing in the LMS. Now she wanted the VIP treatment. I moved over to the LM pilot's position and we started at 15,000 feet to avoid the tedium of the braking phase—so jaded had we become—and she brought the LM down handily.

The next day I checked out of the Islander and drove back to Daytona for my flight to Boston, taking the shortcut through the space center. I stopped at the Flight Crew Support Building to have a last look around and found Bob Pearson at the LMS console, listening to the conversation between Houston and Apollo 17 on a squawk box.

Purely for fun, I flew two landings. In the first run I chose to yaw around to the right near the end to look at Camelot crater, and that gave me trouble nulling out my horizontal velocity, which in turn made me neglect my altitude-rate. I touched down at about 7 feet per second—within the capacity of the landing gear but not pretty. In the second run, my last landing and perhaps one of the very last ever flown on this simulator, I set her down gently on the shelf between the craters called Camelot and Horatio.

Pearson showed me the last page of the crew-training log, which recorded three landings flown by Gene Cernan and Jack Schmitt the day before they launched. At the end Pearson had written, "End of another era."

THE ARTIFACT

While I was rattling up the interstate toward Daytona in the purple Dart—which had not fallen apart despite my best efforts—Apollo 17 burned the CSM's main engine to slow the two spacecraft and bring them into a 60-mile orbit around the Moon. The next morning I was in the SCAMA room at MIT to listen to LM activation, separation, descent orbit insertion, and the powered lunar descent.

Cernan:	Stand by for pitchover, Jack.
Schmitt:	8000
Cernan:	I'll need the PRO [to enable redesignation].

Schmitt: I'll give it to you.

Cernan: Pitchover.

Schmitt: There it is. PROCEEDed.

Cernan: And there it is, Houston. There's Camelot!

Schmitt: Wow!.

Cernan: Wow! Right on target.

Schmitt: I see it.

Cernan: We got them all.

Schmitt: [reading LPD angles] 42 degrees, 37 degrees through 5500. 38 degrees...

Houston: Challenger, you're GO for landing.

Schmitt: ...5000 feet; 42 degrees through 4000; 47 now; 47 degrees through 3500; 49 degrees. 3000 feet. 53 degrees....

Cernan: Okay, I've got Bargea; I've got Poppie; I've got the Triangle.

Schmitt: At 2500 feet, 52 degrees. H-dot [descent rate] is good. At 2000, H-dot is good. Fuel is good. 1500 feet, 54 degrees, Gene. Approaching a thousand. Approaching a thousand feet; 57 degrees. Okay, you're through a thousand, and I'm taking...Radar altitude and PGNS altitudes agree. You're through 800 feet. H-dot's a little high.

Cernan: Okay, I don't need the [LPD] numbers any more.

Schmitt: Okay. You're 31 feet per second, going down through 500. 25 feet per second through 400. That's a little high, Geno.

Cernan: Okay.

Schmitt: 300 feet, 15 feet per second. A little high. H-dot's a little high.

Cernan: Okay, I've got P66.

> Schmitt: Okay; 9 feet per second down at 200. Going down at 5.
> Going down at 5. Going down at 10 (fps); cut the H-dot.
> The fuel's good. 110 feet. Stand by for some dust. Little
> forward, Gene. Moving forward a little. 90 feet. Little
> forward velocity. 80 feet; going down at 3. Getting a little
> dust. We're at 60 feet; going down about 2. Very little
> dust. Very little dust, 40 feet, going down at 3.

> Cernan: Stand by for touchdown.

And so we landed, for the sixth time, smooth as silk with no exclamation points except the ones that were de rigueur when the landing site was recognized at pitchover.

There were perhaps three score people in the room. A few I knew very well, especially my mentor and friend Allan Klumpp. After touchdown we shook hands and indulged in a moment of mutual congratulation—and relief.

We had not killed anyone. Each of us, at one time or another, had visions of being called to account for some fatal blunder that we had committed and failed to detect. The pain of that was hard to imagine, but if the fear was too much you could switch to nuclear missiles where if you screwed up it would hardly be noticed.

Were we lucky or were we good? Both I think. To a point we made our own luck. The main ingredient in that was honesty, with ourselves above all.

Cernan and Schmitt performed three surface EVAs with a total time of over twenty-one hours and ventured in the lunar rover over four miles from, and out of sight of, the craft that was their only way home—surely as far out on a limb as humans have ever gone.

I watched the television coverage of the surface activity at home. Late in the third EVA there was a moment, at about 7 days and 46 minutes mission elapsed time, that produced something new, a frisson, a horripilation, that was different from all the previous thrills.

While Cernan and Schmitt gathered some final samples, the TV camera on the lunar rover, controlled by the ground, scanned the landscape. The focus settled on an object that appeared to rest on a hillside perhaps half a mile away—although distances on the Moon were hard to judge.

To the left and uphill was a lumpy part, possibly a sphere or dodecahedron. Extending downhill from it was a shaft in the general shape of a fuselage, but with a slight curve as though it had bent on impact to conform to the shape of the hill. The camera moved away from the object and then returned.

A long half-minute went by while I stared. Could this be contact, almost as Arthur C. Clarke had imagined it, in an alien object discovered on the Moon? Houston finally spoke up, sounding slightly tense:

Houston:	Okay, 17. What's out there in the distance on a hillside in the field-of-view of the camera? The camera is pointing at it. Oh I'll bet...
Cernan:	We've got to get a distance. Which hill? Let me see where you're...
Houston:	...that's the flag, I bet, on the charge.
Cernan:	Yeah, you're looking right at it, but it's only 10 meters away.
Houston:	Okay. It's hanging in front of the hills. That's the problem.
Cernan:	You're looking right at the flag.
Houston:	Okay. It's hanging in front of the hills. We thought we had an artifact or something like that. Okay. Press on.

The astronauts had just placed one of eight explosive charges that would be detonated after they left the Moon in an experiment designed to illuminate the structure of the upper lunar crust. Each charge had a slim antenna, and attached to the top was a gewgaw intended to prevent the astronauts from stumbling over the device. The antenna was so thin that it was invisible, at least on my black-and-white television, and that was apparently also the case on the screens at mission control. The angle of the flag lined up perfectly with the slope of the hillside behind it.

For just a moment serious people had entertained the possibility that we had made contact with an alien civilization. Apollo may have been an epochal accomplishment, I thought, but it was only the rehearsal for a great deal more.

EPILOGUE

We were flying ambitious missions with panache. The astronaut was reinvented as a nervy but vulnerable human being. Ziggy Stardust came with a song and a movie and an attitude. A hippie software engineer was written up in *Rolling Stone*. Mailer and Wolfe tried on perspectives while Clarke and Kubrick ushered us from chimpanzees to contact, and beyond, to a simulation of the epiphanies promised by spaceflight's radical potential to shatter paradigms.

Every launch was a glittery party shared with the whole world, and the scene was an almost utopian vision of the scientists and artists of the age, the border between them blurred, marching into the starship that we had launched, that will carry them to who knows what new places and experiences — or so it seemed, until you remembered that the moment had lived only so briefly, like lightning, or a mirage, or the unknown object trailing a blue flame that I saw at Tanglewood.

Some of us were more ambitious than others.

George Cherry moved around restlessly. He led a futile effort to demilitarize the Laboratory, then turned around and worked for the Air Force at Edwards Air Force Base. By 1974 he was in Washington at NASA headquarters, where he saw "more dead wood than you can imagine." Later he wrote computer-language manuals. Finally he retired to coastal Maine and walked his dogs along the shore.

Allan Klumpp returned to the Jet Propulsion Lab where he worked on the guidance system for the Galileo spacecraft that was launched to Jupiter in 1989. In retirement he has applied his restless mind to devising solutions to the environmental and energy crises.

Peter Adler went to law school, specialized in intellectual property, and learned the ropes on the team that represented Polaroid in its successful lawsuit charging Kodak with infringing its instant-photography patents. I attended the trial and enjoyed, far more then he did, a half day of Edwin Land's testimony.

Dana Densmore left MIT in 1977 and worked in industry for a while, later moving to Santa Fe and joining the faculty of St. John's College, where she taught the history of ancient and medieval mathematics and physics. In 1995 she published, *Newton's Principia: The Central Argument.* With William Donahue she founded and operates Green Lion Press.

I was less ambitious. I stayed at the Laboratory. Or was I the most ambitious of all. I wanted to be there when Brigadoon next rose from the Florida mists and manned spaceflight entered its next golden age, something I tended to think was right around the corner. Perhaps for me, as for F. Scott Fitzgerald, "the compensation of a very early success was a conviction that life was a romantic matter." Like him I continued to seek "the eternal Canaveral by the Sea*."

I managed to stay involved in manned spaceflight, at one remove, helping to build several simulations of the Space Shuttle guidance system. I led the development of a Space Station simulation that explored ways to use computer graphics in space.

During the main years of this memoir I was never quite one of the grown-ups, but as our ages equalized I joined a weekly tennis group with Norm Sears, Hal Laning and Dick Battin, getting to know these giants better than I had ever imagined. I especially enjoyed partnering Hal, who at 80 played one quarter of the court with guile and precision, while I ran around flailing at everything else. When Dick missed a shot Norm liked to taunt him with the fly Dick had bisected in the air with a pair of scissors. "Show me the fly," Dick would respond.

For one of our Shuttle simulations I designed a system called Timeliner that made it possible to write scripts to sequence the simulation, using

---

* With apologies, I have adapted Fitzgerald's wording "eternal Carnival by the Sea."

a simple language based on temporal constructs such as *when* and *whenever*. A US patent was granted in 1998.

Timeliner started as a simulation tool but I thought it would also be useful onboard a spacecraft. Flight software takes two forms: specialized systems that do things like guidance, navigation and control and function iteratively; and other programs that run through just once to kick off the steps that must occur in sequence to accomplish a task or a phase of the mission. Timeliner scripts provide the second type of software, with the advantage that new scripts can be created by the operational experts, and uploaded to the spacecraft, to use the onboard systems in new ways, as necessity and imagination inspire. If the specialized systems are the kitchen appliances, Timeliner scripts are the recipes.

When the Laboratory started building yet another Space Station simulation, I was in a position to propose Timeliner for use as the *user interface language* aboard the International Space Station, where it would provide just the capability I had imagined. Once more, as he had during Apollo 14, Russ Larson worked to sell my concept to NASA, only this time it took two years instead of two hours. We were in competition with a proposal from the Federal Systems Division of IBM that was less capable and more expensive; yet, so arrogant were the corporations who had carved up the Space Station pie, that we were perceived as the party-crashers. The showdown came at a meeting of the Software Control Board chaired by Dick Thorson — the man who had manned the LM console in mission control during the abort-switch incident on Apollo 14. The room was packed with the young flight controllers and payload operations experts that Larson and I had cultivated for two years, and sitting in a chair directly behind Thorson, with a metal fork from the cafeteria in his shirt pocket, pointing up, was Gene Kranz. For a moment the old spirit of Apollo was in the room, and when the decision went in our favor it was a poke in the eye to the corporate-political complex that manned spaceflight had become.

And so we adapted our interfaces to connect to the Space Station systems and added displays so astronauts could oversee what Timeliner was doing. As I write this in 2017, three versions of Timeliner are in use aboard the International Space Station. IBM sold off Federal Systems soon after the decision. Probably just a coincidence.

Timeliner was one of the specific technologies cited when in 2010 the Charles Stark Draper Laboratory was awarded the prestigious Collier Trophy, along with other members of the Space Station team. Timeliner has also been licensed for commercial use. Its modular structure makes it easy to adapt to a host system.

Phyllis Rye, a versatile troubleshooter during Apollo, stayed at the Lab and worked closely with me and Larson during the Timeliner campaign. After we got the job she wrote our formal "requirements document" practically overnight, and she coded the module that gave Timeliner the ability to do sines and cosines, square roots, and other mathematical functions. Phyllis, like me but surely few others, wrote flight code for Apollo, and also code that is running, as I write this in 2017, aboard the International Space Station in Earth orbit.

When the space shuttle *Challenger* blew up during boost in January 1986, I was appalled, then incensed. The words with which Lawrence Mulloy, Director of the solid rocket booster program, overruled concerned engineers the day before the launch, "When do you want me to launch, next April?" epitomized for me an arrogantly ignorant management culture that I was sorry to see in such stark display at NASA.

As details emerged about the many signs that the O-rings in the solid fuel boosters did not always seal properly, which had been explained away instead of understood, I saw the root cause of the accident in a failure of intellectual honesty. I put my thoughts into a short essay that I sent to the *New York Times*, and on March 21, 1986 I shared the op-ed page, with James Reston, Russell Baker, and Bruce Babbit.

When the Hubble space telescope was launched a few years later with a flawed main mirror after anomalous test results were misunderstood, and the shuttle *Columbia* disintegrated during entry because of complacency about the shedding of foam insulation by the external tank during boost, those seemed to be further signs of the demise of the culture that had taken us to the Moon and back.

Despite our advances in tiny computers and video games and interconnection, I fear that we no longer have the ability to do what we did in the 1960s. The culture of NASA, dependent for political will on big corporations that are more interested in profit than exploration, and so management heavy that a decision that Allan Klumpp and I could make on our own in an afternoon might require a committee and a month, works against the sort of directness with which we approached our goal.

Politics is another obstacle, when spaceflight serves only as a carcass fought over to bring government spending to the district, or as a stage for trumpeting grandiose, Potemkin goals with barely a pretense of follow-through. Spaceflight represents aspiration, and scientific discovery, and long-range economic growth, and synergies with environmental and energy goals, and a proven avenue for international cooperation, and a substitute for war as a director of our creative energies, and a spirit of generosity and idealism that encompasses all mankind. Why has spaceflight, since JFK and LBJ, never been embraced by the left, but left to the posturings of the political right?

A buckle was closed in 2009 when I picked up the phone and heard the voice of Martin Montague, son of the Magnificent Montague—the legendary disc jockey on radio station KGFJ in Los Angeles. Montague's trademark shout-out was *Burn, Baby! BURN!*—which is also the title of his autobiography. That was all about hot music, not looting and arson, but to Montague's dismay the cry was taken up by rioters in the Watts area of Los Angeles in August, 1965. Montague himself was a voice for calm, while the chief of the Los Angeles police stoked the flames, taunting the rioters as "monkeys."

Martin Montague had been surfing the web and had come across references to the master ignition routine that I wrote with Peter Adler in 1967, which we had naughtily named BURNBABY in allusion to Montague's shout-out, as we had seen it quoted in *Life* Magazine's coverage of the riots.

"So my father is on the Moon?" asked Martin Montague. Yes he is. An Apollo mission drew so many fine filaments with it to the silvery orb.

GLOSSARY
BIBLIOGRAPHY
NOTES
INDEX

GLOSSARY OF ACRONYMS AND CAPITALIZED TERMS

TERM	PRONOUNCED	DESCRIPTION
AGC	A-G-C	Apollo Guidance Computer
AGS	aggs	Abort Guidance System
AMELIA	amelia	Non-flight program for LM created by the author
APS	apps	Ascent Propulsion System, developed by Bell Aerosystems
ATT HOLD	att hold	Autopilot mode in which a deflection of the RHC commands an attitude rate, and returning the stick to detent stops the rate
BSO	B-S-O	Boston Symphony Orchestra
BURNBABY	burn baby	Master ignition routine, controls sequencing leading up to ignition for LM burns (written by the author and Peter Adler)
CDU	C-D-U	Coupling Data Unit, analog-digital converter providing information to the AGC (CDUX, CDUY, CDUZ are gimbal angles from the IMU)
CM	C-M	Command Module, developed by North American Aviation
COLOSSUS	colossus	AGC program for CM, flew on Apollo 8
COMANCHE	comanche	AGC program for CM, flew on Apollo 9-17
CSM	C-S-M	Command and Service Module (when they are joined)
DAP	dap	Digital Autopilot
DELTAH	delta-H	LGC variable, difference between altitude measured by the landing radar and altitude derived from inertial navigation, used during powered descent to evaluate radar data before incorporating it
DIANA	diana	Non-flight program for LM created by the author and Peter Adler
DOI	D-O-I	Descent Orbit Insertion, transfer to orbit from which the powered descent will begin
DPS	dips	Descent Propulsion System, developed by TRW
EMP	E-M-P	Erasable Memory Program
EVA	E-V-A	Extra-Vehiclular Activity, astronaut activity outside the spacecraft. Leaving the LM to explore the lunar surface was termed a "surface EVA."

TERM	PRONOUNCED	DESCRIPTION
FCSB	F-C-S-B	Flight Crew Support Building, building at KSC that housed the LMS
FDAI	F-D-A-I	Flight Director Attitude Indicator, LM cockpit instrument that indicates the LM's orientation, better known as the eight ball
FEBE	phoebe	Prototyte MIT inertial system first flight tested in 1949, named for Greek Sun god Phoebus Apollo
FLAGWRDn	flag word n	LGC words in which individual bits are used as "flags," i.e. boolean (on/off) variables
FMES	fems	Full Mission Engineering Simulator, GAEC's LM simulator in Bethpage, Long Island
FOD	F-O-D	NASA Flight Operations Directorate (the flight controllers), located at MSC
FSRR	fisser	Flight Software Readiness Review
GAEC	G-A-E-C	Grumman Aircraft Engineering Corporation, company based in Bethpage, New York that designed and built the Lunar Module
GSOP	G-sop	Guidance System Operations Plan, requirements document for the PGNCS software
ICD	I-C-D	Interface Control Document
IMU	I-M-U	Inertial Measurement Unit, inertial sensor that provides an attitude reference and measures acceleration
ISP	I-S-P	Specific impulse, expressed in seconds, a measure of the efficiency of a rocket engine
KSC	K-S-C	Kennedy Space Center, located at Cape Canaveral
LCC	L-C-C	Launch Control Center, located near the VAB at KSC
LETABBIT	let-abort-bit	LGC variable, a bit in FLAGWRD9 that when set enables the Aborts Monitor R10 (ROSENCRANTZ)
LGC	L-G-C	LM Guidance Computer, the AGC installed in the Lunar Module
LLTV	L-L-T-V	Lunar Landing Training Vehicle, the "flying bedstead"
LM	lem	Lunar Module, developed by GAEC
LMS	L-M-S	LM Mission Simulator
LOI	L-O-I	Lunar Orbit Insertion
LPD	L-P-D	Landing Point Designator, the system for indicating and changing landing site during P64
LR	L-R	Landing Radar, measures altitude and velocity relative to lunar surface

TERM	PRONOUNCED	DESCRIPTION
LRV	L-R-V	Lunar Roving Vehicle, the car taken to the Moon on Apollo 15, 16, and 17.
L&A	L-n-A	Landing and Ascent, device providing lunar landscape views for the LM windows of the LMS
LUMINARY	luminary	AGC program for LM, flew on Apollo 10-17
MAC	mack	MIT Algebraic Compiler
MET	M-E-T	Mission Elapsed Time
MODREG	mod-reg	LGC variable, indicator of current mission phase
MPAD	M-pad	NASA Mission Planning and Analysis Division, located at MSC
MSC	M-S-C	Manned Spacecraft Center (later Johnson Space Center)
MSFN	miss-fen	Manned Space Flight Network, system of Earth-based antennas for tracking and communications
MSOB	M-S-O-B	Manned Spacecraft Operations Building, at KSC, now the Operations and Checkout (O&C) building
OEM	O-E-M	Original Equipment Manufacturer
P12	P-12	LM mission phase: normal lunar ascent
P40	P-40	LM mission phase: orbital or mid-course maneuver on DPS
P41	P-41	LM mission phase: orbital or mid-course maneuver on RCS
P42	P-42	LM mission phase: orbital or mid-course maneuver on APS
P51	P-51	LM mission phase: IMU alignment
P52	P-52	LM mission phase: IMU alignment
P63	P-63	LM mission phase: lunar landing, braking phase
P64	P-64	LM mission phase: lunar landing, visibility (or approach) phase
P65	P-65	LM mission phase: lunar landing, automatic final landing
P66	P-66	LM mission phase: lunar landing, semi-automatic final landing
P67	P-67	LM mission phase: lunar landing, manual final landing
P70	P-70	LM mission phase: lunar landing abort using DPS
P71	P-71	LM mission phase: lunar landing abort using APS after staging

GLOSSARY

TERM	PRONOUNCED	DESCRIPTION
PCR	P-C-R	Program Change Request
PDI	P-D-I	Powered Descent Initiation, DPS ignition for the powered descent
PGNCS	pings	Primary Guidance, Navigation and Control System, MIT's contractual responsibility
PIPA	pippa	Pulse Integrating Pendulous Accelerometer, mounted on the SM
PIPTIME	pip time	LGC variable, time of the most recent accelerometer reading, i.e. the time corresponding to the most recent navigation update during powered flight
R10	R-10	LM routine: Landing Analog Displays, operates panel instruments
R11	R-11	LM routine: Aborts Monitor, responds to abort and abort-stage buttons during lunar descent
R12	R-12	LM routine: Landing Radar, operates landing radar during lunar descent
R13	R-13	LM routine: Manual Modes Monitor, switches among final landing modes
RCS	R-C-S	Reaction Control System, the maneuvering jets
REFSMMAT	refs-mat	LGC variable, matrix that defines orientation of the SM with respect to the reference coordinate system
RHC	R-H-C	Rotational Hand Controller, used to control attitude maneuvers, also used to signal landing site redesignations during P64
ROD	R-O-D	Rate of descent, pertains to the ROD switch used to increase or decrease descent rate during P66
RR	R-R	Rendezvous Radar
SCAMA	scama	Switched Conference and Monitoring Arrangement, our voice link to mission control.
SCB	S-C-B	Software Control Board
S-IVB	S-4-B	Third stage of the Saturn V rocket
SM	S-M	Service Module, always attached to CM (and collectively called the CSM), except during entry
SM	S-M	Stable Member, inertially stabilized component at core of the IMU upon which are mounted gyroscopes and accelerometers
SOLARIUM	solarium	AGC program for CM, flew on 501 (Apollo 4) and 502 (Apollo 6) missions

TERM	PRONOUNCED	DESCRIPTION
SPS	S-P-S	Service Propulsion System, rocket on the SM, developed by North American Aviation
SUNBURST	sunburst	AGC program for LM, flew on LM-1 Mission (Apollo 6)
SUNDANCE	sundance	AGC program for LM, flew on Apollo 9
SUNDISK	sundisk	AGC program for CM, flew on Apollo 7
SUNSPOT	sunspot	AGC program for CM, would have flown on Apollo 1
SUSANK	susan K *or* sue sank	MAC-language simulation of the lunar landing created by Allan Klumpp, named after his wife
TEI	T-E-I	Trans-Earth Injection, departure from lunar orbit for return to Earth
TIG	tig	Time of Ignition
THC	T-H-C	Translational Hand Controller, also used as manual throttle during lunar descent
TLI	T-L-I	Trans-Lunar Injection, departure from Earth orbit on way to the Moon
TLOSS	T-loss	Time loss, the fraction of processor time taken away by counter activity or other cause, usually expressed as a percentage
TREDES	T-redes	LGC variable, time remaining during which landing site redesignations are possible during P64
TTF	T-T-F	LGC variable, time to fly, the time remaining in P63 or P64, used in denominator of guidance equation
TRW	T-R-W	Thompson Ramo Wooldridge, a California based company that developed the LM's descent engine (DPS) and the abort guidance system (AGS).
UIL	U-I-L	User Interface Language, function provided by the sequencing system Timeliner as installed on the International Space Station
VAB	V-A-B	Vertical (later Vehicle) Assembly Building, structure at KSC where Saturn rockets were prepared for flight
ZERLINA	zerlina	Non-flight program for LM created by the author
ZOOMBIT	zoom-bit	LGC variable, a bit in FLAGWRD5, normally set at DPS throttle-up to enable lunar landing guidance
6L6	6-L-6	Vacuum tube tetrode, typically used in the output stage of audio amplifiers

BIBLIOGRAPHY

As is proper in any memoir, my principal source is my own recollection. I am painfully aware of the tricks memory can play, but it is the role of the memoirist to relate what he believes to be true even when he cannot prove it.

Naturally I have tried to substantiate my recollections as much as possible, drawing on published and online sources of information, and on those work documents I had the foresight to preserve — while regretting that I did not save others that would be useful to me now. Many key documents must exist today, if at all, forgotten in someone's attic or basement. At least, information on paper can survive for centuries. Digital data must be actively maintained at a cost that may become burdensome to future generations having other priorities. Our "paperless" era may prove an even greater mystery for historians.

Sources that have been generally useful or which are cited on multiple occasions are listed below, along with the short name under which they will be referenced in the notes that follow. Many of the listed documents are available online and can be located by searching with the information given here.

Apollo5Report	Apollo 5 Mission Report, NASA MSC-PA-R-68-7.
Apollo7Voice	Apollo 7 Air-to-Ground Voice Transcriptions, NASA, Manned Spaceflight Center.
Apollo9Report	Apollo 9 Mission Report, NASA MSC-PA-R-69-2.
Apollo11Voice	Apollo 11 Technical Air-to-Ground Voice Transcription, NASA, Manned Spaceflight Center, July 1969, with additional reference to JonesTranscripts.
Apollo11Debriefing	Apollo 11 Technical Crew Debriefing, NASA, Manned Spaceflight Center, July 31, 1969.
Apollo11Downlink	Apolllo 11 data downlinked by the LGC during the lunar descent.
Apollo11Report	Apollo 11 Mission Report, NASA MSC-00171, Nov., 1969
Apollo12Voice	Apollo 12 Technical Air-to-Ground Voice Transcription, NASA, Manned Spaceflight Center, Nov. 1969, with additional reference to JonesTranscripts.
Apollo12Debriefing	Apollo 12 Technical Crew Debriefing, NASA, Manned Spaceflight Center, Dec. 1, 1969.
Apollo13Debriefing	Apollo 13 Technical Crew Debriefing, NASA, Manned Spaceflight Center, April 24, 1970.

Apollo14Report   Apollo 14 Mission Report, NASA MSC-04112, May, 1971.

Apollo14Debriefing   Apollo 14 Technical Crew Debriefing, NASA, Manned Spaceflight Center, Feb. 17, 1971.

Apollo15Voice   Apollo 15 Technical Air-to-Ground Voice Transcription, MSC-04558, NASA, Manned Spaceflight Center, July 1971, with additional reference to JonesTranscripts.

Apollo17Voice   Apollo 17 Technical Air-to-Ground Voice Transcription, MSC-07629, NASA, Manned Spaceflight Center, Dec. 1972, with additional reference to JonesTranscripts.

BattinVonKarman   Richard Battin, Von Karman Lecture: "Some Funny Things Happened on the Way to the Moon," *Journal of Guidance, Control, and Dynamics* XV, No. 1, Jan.-Feb. 2002.

BattinBreakwell   Richard Battin, "Second Breakwell Memorial Lecture: 1961 and All That," *Acta Astronautica* XXXIX, No. 6, Sept. 16, 1996.

BattinNarrative   Richard Battin, "Space Guidance Evolution — A Personal Narrative," *Journal of Guidance, Control and Dynamics*, March-April 1982.

BattinTopics   Richard Battin, "On Algebraic Compilers and Planetary Fly-By Orbits," IAA-94-IAA.2.1.618, 1964. (Also: *Acta Astronautica* XXXVIII, No. 12 (p. 895-902).

BlairSmithMemo9   Hugh Blair-Smith, "Block II Instructions," September 30, 1965, revised July 1, 1966.

BlairSmithMemoir   Hugh Blair-Smith, *Left Brains for the Right Stuff*, SDP Publishing, 2015.

CherryExegesis   George Cherry, Memo No. 370-69, "Exegesis of the 1201 and 1202 Alarms Which Occurred During the [Mission G] Lunar Landing," Aug. 4, 1969.

CollinsReflections   "Laboratory aviator extraordinaire: Chip Collins reflects on a 40-year Draper career," D-Notes (internal publication of the Draper Laboratory), May 20, 1988 (p. 3-4).

DensmoreMemos   Memos by Dana Densmore in her role as LUMINARY Assembly Control Supervisor between Nov. 1969 and Feb. 1971 are Luminary Memos Nos. 122, 124, 129, 131, 134, 136, 142, 145, 150, 151, 156, 157, 158, 172, 173, 175, 176, 179, 182, 184, 185, 187, 188, 189, 190, 192, 193, 195, 196, 197, 202, 204, and 205.

DraperRemarks "Remarks by Dr. C. S. Draper," 1969, included in C-5249, *Historical Collection Projects*, edited by J. Scott Ferguson, MIT Historical Collection, Aug. 3, 1979

DuffyMemoir Robert A. Duffy, "Charles Stark Draper, a Biographical Memoir," National Academy of Sciences.

EngineeringApollo Lecture at the indicated date by the indicated person to Professors David Mindell and Larry Young's "Engineering Apollo" course (16.895J) at MIT.

EylesFinalLanding Don Eyles, "Apollo LM Guidance and Pilot-Assistance during the Final Stage of Lunar Descent — Software Considerations," MIT Charles Stark Draper Lab, E-2581, May 1971. Also: Don Eyles, "Apollo LM Guidance Software for the Final Lunar Descent," Automatica, Journal of the International Federation of Automatic Control IX, No. 2, March 1973 (p. 243).

GarmanInterview John R. Garman, interviewed by Kevin M. Rusnak as part of the "NASA Johnson Space Center Oral History Project," Houston, Texas, March 27, 2001.

HallsJourney Eldon C. Hall, *Journey to the Moon, the History of the Apollo Guidance Computer*. American Institute of Aeronautics and Astronautics, 1996.

HansenFirstMan James Hansen, *First Man, The Life of Neil A. Armstrong*. Simon and Schuster, 2005.

HoagsHistory David G. Hoag, "The History of Apollo Onboard Guidance, Navigation and Control," Charles Stark Draper Lab P-357, Sept. 1976. Also: *Journal of Guidance* VI, No. 1, Jan.-Feb. 1983.

InertialGuidance Charles S. Draper, Walter Wrigley, and John Hovorka, *Inertial Guidance*, Pergamon Press, 1960.

JonesTranscripts For the given mission, Eric Jones, "Corrected Transcript and Commentary," Apollo Lunar Surface Journal, available online — especially valuable for its analysis of which astronaut is speaking.

KlumppThrottle Allan Klumpp, "Apollo Vignette – LM Descent Engine Throttle Incident," Dec. 14, 1985.

KlumppP66Auto Allan Klumpp, "Automatic P66", Luminary Memo No. 143, March 24, 1970.

MITApollolOrg   Organization chart of Apollo effort at the MIT Instrumentation Laboratory, dated Feb. 1, 1969, 18 pages, available at www.doneyles.com/LM/ORG.

MITsRoleSoftware   Madeline S. Johnson and Donald R. Giller, "MIT's Role in Project Apollo, Volume V, The Software Effort," Charles Start Draper Laboratory, R-700, March 1971.

MuntzInterpreter   Charles A. Muntz, "User's Guide to the Block II AGC/LGC Interpreter," MIT Instrumentation Laboratory, Report R-489, April 1965.

MuntzMemoir   Unpublished draft memoir written circa 1999 by Charley Muntz, quoted with his permission.

MurrayBlyCox   Charles Murray and Catherine Bly Cox, *Apollo, the Race to the Moon*, Simon and Schuster, 1989.

PreConsiderations   J. H. Laning, J. Frey and M. B. Trageser, "Preliminary considerations on the instrumentation of a photographic reconnaissance of Mars," MIT Instrumentation Laboratory, Report R-174, 1958.

SchulenbergMemos   Memos by Craig Schulenberg in his role as LUMINARY Assembly Control Supervisor between April 1968 and August 1969 are Luminary Memos Nos. 21, 22, 23, 25, 28, 29, 30, 31, 34, 37, 40, 49, 51, 52, 55, 58, 61, 67, 73, 78, 83, 85, 91, 92, 94 (by Bruce McCoy), 103, and 107.

TimesApollo14   *New York Times*, front page story by Richard Witkin, Feb. 6, 1971 (p. 1)

TindallApollo12   Howard W. Tindall Jr., Chief, Apollo Data Priority Coordination, "Apollo 12 Mission Techniques," 69-PA-T-122A, Sept. 24, 1969.

TindallApollo14   Howard W. Tindall Jr., Chairman, Apollo Software Configuration Control Board, "Latest in Luminary for Apollo 14," July 24, 1970.

TindallDeltaGuid   Howard W. Tindall Jr., Chief, Apollo Data Priority Coordination, "Let's Hear it for 'Delta Guidance'!", 69-PA-T-130A, Oct. 21, 1969.

TindallPinpoint   Howard W. Tindall Jr., Chief, Apollo Data Priority Coordination, "How to land next to a Surveyor — a short novel for do it yourselfers," 69-PA-T-114A, Aug. 1, 1969.

NOTES

PROLOGUE

(PAGES 3-5)

LM-1 problem: Conversations and email exchanges with MIT engineer George Silver, who was at Cape Canaveral for the LM-1 launch. Silver related that the problem was understood in the blockhouse at pad 37B, but no telephone link was available to the MIT observers who were at mission control. George Silver drove to the MSOB in thick fog but by the time he arrived and was able to communicate with Houston the decision to turn off the PGNCS had already been made and it was too late to try again. Other information is from Apollo5Report.

Timing of engine-arm command: William R. Hammock, Eldon C. Currie, and Arlie E. Fisher, "Apollo Experience Report — LM Descent Engine," NASA TN D-7143, undated (p. 22).

PART ONE • LEARNING

GROWING UP (PAGES 9-14)

Parents: Don Edgar Eyles (Sr.), 1915-1963, son of Francis L. Eyles and Mary Augustus Brown; and Mary Steed Stipe, 1917-2005, daughter of John Gordon Stipe and Annie Zuleika Dillard.

Moon-lander: *Collier's* Magazine, Oct. 18. 1952.

A play and a musical: These productions were directed by speech teacher Patricia Wheeler with musical direction by Assistant Principal Kenneth Canestrari.

Great books: *Brave New World* and the others mentioned were available in Memphis at an informal bookstore created at Southwestern College (now Rhodes College) by Professor Ray Hill.

Whitehaven: A neighborhood of Memphis founded by Colonel Francis White around 1850 and now best known as the location of Graceland. Whitehaven High School was all-white at the time I attended. At this writing it is all black in consequence of white flight from that area.

Paternalistic pride: Miss McCorkle made the quoted statement in class in 1956-1957. Also: Anna Leigh McCorkle, *Tales of Old Whitehaven*, 1967, Library of Congress Catalog Control No. 67027429.

Ancestors on both sides: Hanson Hard, a doctor in the Union Army, was captured in Paducah, Kentucky by the forces of Nathan Bedford Forrest. He wrote a droll account of being marched south to Mobile, where he was exchanged back to the Union (Library of Congress, Catalog Control No. 79004972). Confederate James Peter Barksdale, after recovering from a Minié ball that passed through both lungs during an action near Pensacola, Florida, was promoted to major and given command of militiamen. On one occasion, with a battalion of 700 young boys and old men armed with obsolete muskets, he defended a supply train against a superior force of General Sheridan's cavalry. He took a position that gave his men good cover and obliged the Yankees to advance on a narrow front limited by the concave bend of a river. The attackers gave up after three assaults and the Union commander is said to have reported that he was opposed by a force of ten thousand Confederates (Captain John A. Barksdale, *Barksdale Family History and Genealogy*, 1940, Library of Congress Control No. 40034264).

Victorian mansion: The Goyer-Lee House, 690 East Adams, abandoned in 1959 by the Memphis Academy of Art and found still empty in 2011.

Guild Art Theatre: Now the Evergreen Theatre. Recollections of Bill Kendall can be found on the Cinema Treasures web site (search for "Evergreen on Poplar"). Under Kendall's auspices in 1969 the theatre hosted a Miss Gay Memphis pageant that was an epochal event for the gay population of the city.

HIRED (PAGES 14-19)

Kennedy speeches: Address to Congress, May 25, 1961, and speech at Rice University in Houston, Sept. 12, 1962. NASA announced the contract award to the MIT Instrumentation Lab on August 9, 1961.

Monkey-malaria infection: Don E. Eyles, G. Robert Coatney and Morton E. Getz, "Vivax-type Malaria Parasite of Macaques Transmissible to Man," Science, July 8, 1960, Vol. 132, No. 3419, (p. 1812-1813).

"Bob, I have monkey malaria.": Robert Coatney et al, *The Primate Malarias*, National Institutes of Health, 1971 (p. 87). The story is retold in Robert S. Desowitz, *The Malaria Capers*, W. W. Norton, New York, 1991. Coatney's book is dedicated to my father and to "the inmates of the United States Penitentiary, Atlanta, Georgia, who volunteered to accept infection with human and simian malarias." My father also worked with prisoners at Joliet Prison in Illinois, where one of the volunteers, who became a skilled technician under my father's tutelage, was the murderer Nathan Leopold.

THE MISSION (PAGES 19-23)

AGC languages: The Basic language is described in <u>BlairSmithMemo9</u>. The language we called Interpretive is described in <u>MuntzInterpreter</u>.

Apollo mission facts: Richard W. Orloff, *Apollo by the Numbers*, NASA, 1996.

THE LUNAR LANDING (PAGES 23-30)

Two papers: George W. Cherry, "E-Guidance — A General Explicit, Optimizing Guidance Law for Rocket-Propelled Spacecraft", MIT Instrumentation Laboratory Report R-456, Aug., 1964; and Allan R. Klumpp, "A Manually Retargeted Automatic Descent and Landing System for LEM," MIT Instrumentation Laboratory Report R-539, March, 1966.

P67 manual mode: In "An Early User's Guide to the Lunar Landing Guidance Programs," written before Apollo 11, George Cherry states that, "Indeed, Neil Armstrong has told me... that simultaneous control of attitude (and horizontal velocity) and throttle (descent rate) is a formidable crew task."

SUSANK (PAGES 30-33)

Whirlwind: Kent C. Redmond and Thomas M. Smith, *Project WHIRLWIND*, Digital Equipment Company, 1980.

MAC language: J. Halcombe Laning Jr. and James S. Miller, "The MAC Algebraic Language System," Charles Stark Draper Laboratory, Nov. 1970.

DOC DRAPER AND INERTIAL NAVIGATION (PAGES 34-42)

General sources: DuffyMemoir, DraperRemarks, and InertialGuidance.

Draper's views on the role of technology: Charles Stark Draper, "Technology, Engineering, Science and Modern Education," *Leonardo* 2:2, 1969 (p. 147–153). In a paper titled "Military Technology and the Future of Mankind" (1970, nothing else known), Draper writes, "The complex of activities directed toward artificially moulding nature into better accord with human desires is called Technology."

"I'm going to develop it": Quoted by Dr. Robert Seamans, interviewed in his office at MIT on Feb. 25, 1987, by Martin Collins and Michael Dennis. Seamans added "I don't think I could quite go that far myself."

Wiesner on Draper: Remarks by Jerome Wiesner at the memorial service for Doc Draper held in Kresge Auditorium, 1987.

"Along in October...": Quoted from Ralph Ragan's account of the meeting with Jim Webb et al in Washington, accessed on the Charles Stark Draper Laboratory web site (but apparently no longer posted there). It's hard to disbelieve Ragan's memory of a fire in the fireplace, which he has reaffirmed to me in conversation, but, oddly, the date of this 1961 meeting is not agreed upon. Donald A. MacKenzie in *Inventing Accuracy* (MIT Press, 1990, p. 190) quotes Ragan as saying it was a "crisp, cold day" in September and that brandy was served. However David Hoag in HoagsHistory (p. 5) states firmly that the meeting was on August 31, a day when Washington, D.C. had a high temperature of 92 degrees (Weather Underground). Draper himself in <u>DraperRemarks</u> (p. 30) places the meeting "immediately after" Kennedy's May 25 speech announcing the Moon challenge, but his letter making his case for flying on the mission is dated November 21, and begins, "Following up on our various conversations of recent days...." I accept the September or October, 1961 date for the occasion described by Ragan, but undoubtedly other meetings took place during this period involving the same individuals. It is even possible that the question-and-response was a ritual catechism that Webb and Draper, who had known each other for twenty years, enjoyed enacting on more than one occasion. The meeting is downplayed by Robert C. Seamans, interviewed by Carol Butler, Cambridge, Massachusetts, June 22, 1999, for the Johnson Space Center Oral History Project (p. 14-13).

"Not really much of a laboratory": Interview with Richard Battin conducted by Professor David Mindell.

"Potentially disastrous consequences": <u>DraperRemarks</u>.

Internal combustion engine: C. S. Draper et al, "Development of a Detonation Detector Suitable for Use in Flight," NACA Technical Note 977, Washington, 144 (reprint of article from 1939). Also, U.S. Patent 2275675, filed May 13, 1938.

Maybe it was 26: According to the *Dictionary of American Naval Fighting Ships* (US Naval History and Heritage Command), the ship initially claimed to have downed 32 enemy aircraft but subsequently reduced the claim to 26. Doc Draper in <u>DraperRemarks</u>, and others, have continued to cite the higher figure.

"When you run a house of ill repute": Quoted by Chip Collins in private conversation.

SPIRE flight: <u>CollinsReflections</u>. The eleven men onboard were Doc Draper, Chip Collins (pilot), Dave Buxton (copilot), Irv Levin and Charles Cameron (flight engineers), Roger Woodbury, John Hursh, Joe Aronson, Don Price (GE resident), and Air Force officers Captain Stevenson and Colonel Robert Jarmon (observers). The date of the flight was Feb. 8, 1953.

From the foot of the stage: As recalled by Bob Duffy, speaking to an audience at the Draper Laboratory.

"There were audible gasps": <u>CollinsReflections</u>.

Gyroscopes: Details about the Apollo gyroscopes were found in Northrop Corporation Electronics Division, PPD-72-E-10350, "Ball Bearing Technology Utilization Document", Oct. 1972.

SUNBURST (PAGES 43-48)

Genealogy of the AGC programs: MITsRoleSoftware. I have, however, simplified the family tree, in that the assemblies being released for manufacture were usually given different names (for Apollo 11 it was LUM99R2 revision 0). Sometimes a program needed to be re-released with minor changes, at a point when new capability was already being added to the main line assembly. That would necessitate creation of an offshoot of the original release with a new name. (For example, the rope for Apollo 13 was released four times, as LUMINARY rev. 130, LUMINARY rev. 131, LUM131 rev. 0, and LM131 rev. 1.) In addition, numerous offline assemblies were created for special purposes, AMELIA and ZERLINA being two examples that figure in this memoir.

FEBE: InertialGuidance (p. 21).

"MIT's weird preoccupation with the Sun": Howard W. Tindall Jr., Chief, Apollo Data Priority Coordination, "Spacecraft computer program names," 67-FM-T-41, May 23, 1967.

Whirlwind instructions: MIT Digital Computer Laboratory, "A Short Guide to Coding Using the Whirlwind I Code of October 1949," included in MIT Instrumentation Lab R-196, June 11, 1951.

SUNBURST description: Drawn from my listing of BURST120 (i.e. SUNBURST rev. 120), the version that flew on LM-1, and does not necessarily apply to SUNBURST as I first encountered it in the late summer[a] of 1966.

COORDINATE SYSTEMS (PAGES 49-53)

Coordinate Systems: Section 5.1.4 of R-567, "Guidance System Operations Plan for LUMINARY," in its various versions.

THE BUILDING (PAGES 53-57)

Uneeda Termite Service: BlairSmithMemoir (p. 106).

CODING AND DEBUGGING (PAGES 57-63)

Interpretive language: MuntzInterpreter.

"Not sufficient thought": Allan Klumpp, handwritten memo, Aug. 14, 1966.

Environmental simulation: F.K. Glick and S.R. Femino, "A Comprehensive Digital Simulation for the Verification of Apollo Flight Software," MIT Instrumentation Laboratory Report E-2475, Jan. 1970

Erasable memory dump: arranged in eight columns of five-digit numbers, each expressing in octal the contents of a 15-bit word, with 32 lines devoted to each of the computer's eight erasable memory banks.

THE GUIDANCE COMPUTER (PAGES 63-72)

"Tell them it's a cubic foot": BattinVonKarman.

Computer hardware: HallsJourney.

Ralph Ragan estimated: Ralph Ragan, interviewed by Ivan Ertel, April 28, 1966, JSC History Office, quoted in HallsJourney (p. 85).

Whirlwind achieved: Bruce S. Old Associates, "Return on Investment in Basic Research – Exploring a Methodology," Report to Office of Naval Research, Nov., 1981.

Two additional bits became available: Hugh Blair-Smith in BlairSmithMemoir (p. 205) attributes this insight to Al Hopkins and wishes he had thought of it himself.

THROTTLE CONTROL (PAGES 72-75)

Basic language: BlairSmithMemo9.

LM Descent Engine: "LEM Descent Engine," MIT Instrumentation Laboratory, Nov. 9, 1965; and in "LEM Propulsion Systems Flight Test Requirements," TRWG #6, Dec. 16, 1965.

FIRE ON HE PAD (PAGES 75-78)

"Never mind, you'll figure it out.": A story told by Norm Sears at his own retirement party.

Organization: According to MITApolloOrg I "reported" through three different chains of command: through Jim Kernan and Dan Lickly to Dick Battin and Norm Sears (who shared a box), through project manager George Cherry to Battin/Sears (and NASA), and through Allan Klumpp and Bill Marscher to Battin/Sears.

Reading: I am able to say what I was reading, here and elsewhere, because I have kept a log of the books I have read, starting in June, 1960.

"What we have here is a Heathkit": Quoted by Malcolm Johnston at EngineeringApollo, April 14, 2011. In Johnston's recollection the conversation was on Thursday night, the eve of the fatal fire. Johnston was at Cape Canaveral working on a technique known as Sim Flight, which allowed the simulation of a maneuver to be run on the spacecraft hardware itself (with engine-on signals interrupted) using the gravity vector as a stand in for rocket thrust. Such a simulation provided an end to end polarity test of the integrated system.

WHAT IF WE LOST POWER? (PAGES 78-83)

Latin American tour: The mixed reception encountered by Neil Armstrong and Dick Gordon is described in <u>HansenFirstMan</u> (p. 296-300).

"One of the senior hardware designers": This and later quotes are from <u>MuntzMemoir</u>. The senior hardware designer was Herb Thaler, who worked for the company (Raytheon) that built the Apollo computer to MIT's design.

WHIMPER TC WHIMPER: Muntz originally wrote this immortal line of code for the Block I program SUNRISE. I have quoted it from a listing of AURORA Revision 12, dated Nov. 1966.

"In a total of over 25 hours of space flight": Edward M. Copps Jr., "Recovery from Transient Failures of the Apollo Guidance Computer," MIT Instrumentation Laboratory Report E-2307, Aug. 1968.

THE HYBRID (PAGES 83-88)

Hybrid simulator: Philip G. Felleman, "Hybrid Simulation of the Apollo Guidance, Navigation and Control System," MIT Instrumentation Lab E-2066, Dec. 1966.

THE RIVALS (PAGES 89-93)

General sources: Conversations with Allan Klumpp and George Cherry occurring during the span of this memoir, and in 2008.

Prominent physician: Dr. Theodore G. Klumpp, drug company executive and head of the drug division of the Food and Drug Administration between 1936 and 1941, died 1997.

Autopilot face off: The competition between the MIT and Bellcomm autopilot concepts is described in Richard J. Gran, "Fly Me to the Moon — Then and Now" (accessed on-line at www.mathworks.com/company/newsletters/articles/fly-me-to-the-moon-then-and-now.html").

AX∗SR∗T, BURNBABY, AND TWIDDLE (PAGES 93-100)

Execution time was cut in half: Don Eyles, AGC Memo No. 25, "New Geometry Routines," May 3, 1967.

"Burn, Baby, Burn": Phrase remembered from the coverage of the Watts riots in Los Angeles in the Aug. 27, 1965 issue of *Life* magazine.

"Much tighter assembly control...": Howard W. Tindall Jr., 67-FM-T-85, "Spacecraft computer program development improvements to be utilized by MIT," Oct. 18, 1967.

Assembly control memos: <u>SchulenbergMemos</u>, <u>DensmoreMemos</u>

When I was sure: Sunlighter No. 57, Aug. 15, 1967.

A very subtle bug: R.A. Sheridan, 23S Memo 72-6, "Impact of 'CCS Q' Simulator Error on Flight Programs," Jan. 25, 1972.

"Not counting your code": Jim Miller in an email message on Feb. 10, 2011.

"Your cute trick": Hugh Blair-Smith in an email message on May 28, 2012.

PUSSYCAT TEAM (PAGES 100-103)

Pussycat Team meeting: The meeting, on November 6, 1967, *may* be documented in Steve Copps, Luminary Memo No. 2, "Tiger Team," November 15, 1967, but I have not yet been able to locate a copy of that document. My accident was also November 6, but I arrived at the Massachusetts General Hospital after midnight and was admitted on November 7.

ROSENCRANTZ AND GUILDENSTERN (PAGES 103-105)

Stainless steel rod: Gerhard Küntscher, *Journal of Bone and Joint Surgery*, American Volume, Jan. 1958 (p. 17-26). In the surgical report dictated for Dr. Boyd by First assistant Dr. James Huddleston the device installed in my femur is erroneously termed a "Kirschner rod."

DANA (PAGES 105-111)

Dana's background: She was born Dana Densmore Allen used her husband's name as Dana DeWolf at the time she enters this story. In 1969 she dropped the "patriarchal" names of her father and husband and became Dana Densmore. Dana's radical roots are described in her sister Martha Allen's memoir of their father Russell Allen, accessed at http://www.wifp.org/russellallen.html but not there when checked later.

Dana's journal: excerpts were generously made available to the author.

Downlink logic: Peter Adler and Dana Densmore, Luminary Memo No. 89, "A Metaphysic of Downrupts," June 23, 1969.

Bob Dylan: The album *John Wesley Harding*, which contained "The Ballad of Frankie Lee and Judas Priest," was released by Columbia Records in December, 1967. The starting point for our interpretation was the resonance between the line "Are you Frankie Lee, whose father is deceased?" and the question "Is God Dead?" as asked on the cover of Time Magazine, April 8, 1966.

"One hang-up to liberation": Dana Densmore, "On Celibacy," No More Fun and Games, A Journal of Female Liberation, Vol. 1, No. 1, Oct. 1968. The drawing referred to was on the cover of the same issue. My interpretation of the drawing is not that intended by the artist or the creators of the journal.

PART TWO • FLYING

AS-502 (PAGES 115-118)

Assignments: George Cherry, Luminary Memo No. 6, "Summary of Information from Level III Testing Status Reports for LUMINARY Development Plan," Jan. 12, 1968. Assignments also described, with variances, in Dan Lickly, Luminary Level 4 Note #24, Oct. 7, 1968.

Birth of LUMINARY: Luminary Memo No. 20, "SUNDANCE Revisions 280, 281, and 282 and LUMINARY Revision 0," Jim Kernan, April 1, 1968.

SOLARIUM: Howard W. Tindall Jr., "Rope Manufacture for AS-502", Jan. 1967.

Saturn anomalies: George C. Marshall Space Flight Center, MPR-SAT-FE-68-3, "Saturn V Launch Vehicle Flight Evaluation Report — AS-502 Apollo 6 Mission," June 25, 1968.

ELIMINATING LINEAR GUIDANCE (PAGES 118-120)

Bureaucratic non sequitur: James J. Fandel, MIT Assistant Director for Personnel Relations, to William B. Alexander, President of the Research, Development and Technical Employees Union, Dec. 2, 1968.

Allan gave me credit: Allan Klumpp, "Status of Lunar Landing Targeting Projected Targeting", Nov. 4, 1968

Memory gain: Don Eyles, Luminary Memo No. 44, "Implementation of 'One-Phase' Guidance in the AGC", Sept. 19, 1968.

THE DOCTORS (PAGES 120-125)

The two men met: BattinNarrative

"Let George do it.": The phrase goes back much further, 1910 according to OEDII, and from at least as long ago as 1931 the name "George" has been used to refer to an automatic system, specifically an aircraft autopilot.

George compiler: Laning, J. H. Jr. and Zierler, N., MIT Instrumentation Laboratory, Engineering Memorandum E-364, "A Program for Translation of Mathematical Equations for Whirlwind I," Jan. 1954.

"Nearly everyone who has had a problem to solve": J. Halcombe Laning, "George User's Manual," quoted in HallsJourney (p. 183).

Backus consulted with Laning: John W. Backus, written communication to Laning dated May 21, 1954, quoted in BattinTopics.

"Dr. Laning was the first person": John W. Backus, written communication to the President's Committee on The National Medal of Science, National

Science Foundation, Aug. 16, 1991, quoted in <u>BattinTopics</u>.

"'Please don't tell any of our friends.'": <u>BattinVonKarman</u>.

"The main idea in the nonstop trajectory": <u>PreConsiderations</u>.

I reference the following papers largely written by Laning and Battin: MIT Instrumentation Laboratory, Report R-235, "A recoverable interplanetary space probe," 1959; and MIT Instrumentation Laboratory, Report R-273, "Interplanetary navigation system study," 1959.

"The possibility at once suggests itself": <u>PreConsiderations</u>.

"First realistic multiple fly-by mission": <u>BattinTopics</u>.

"America's Program for Orbital and Lunar Landing Operations": <u>BattinBreakwell</u>. According to <u>MurrayBlyCox</u> (p. 54-55) the program was named Apollo in January, 1960 by NASA spaceflight chief Abe Silverstein with Greek gods in mind. The quoted "acronymification" (Paul Fjeld's word in an email of Jan. 14, 2013) probably originated with Dick Battin himself.

"An industry group": <u>BattinVonKarman</u>.

THE SCB, PETE CONRAD (PAGES 125-130)

Kraft's reaction to crew complaints: Steve Copps in an email on March 29, 2012. Copps thought that the crew representative was Dave Scott, the backup CMP. However, Scott had no assignment on that mission and remembers no such incident. John Young was the backup CMP on Apollo 7.

Armstrong's LLTV crash: "The moon had been awaiting us a long time," *Life* magazine (p. 24), Aug. 22, 1969.

Norton's role in failure of Mariner I: Paul E. Ceruzzi, *Beyond the Limits, Flight Enters the Computer Age*, MIT Press, 1989.

"I remember being proud": Steve Copps in an email on March 30, 2012. Norm Sears's recollections of John Norton were in private conversation.

"MIT still has their millions": J.L. Norton to J. Garman, on TRW "AVOID VERBAL ORDERS" form, May 4, 1971.

Norton's later career: James Wallace and Jim Erickson, *Hard Drive: Bill Gates and the Making of the Microsoft Empire*, John Wiley, 1992 (p. 50); Malcolm Gladwell, *Outliers, the Story of Success*, Little Brown, 2008 (p. 54).

APOLLO 7, 8, 9 (PAGES 130-131)

"You better be prepared to discuss": <u>Apollo7Voice</u>.

The system could have navigated to the Moon and back: <u>BattinBreakwell</u>.

Apollo 11 crew assignment: <u>HansenFirstMan</u> (p. 338-340).

"A little pessimistic about our chances": Neil Armstrong, quoted in "The moon had been awaiting us a long time," *Life*, Aug. 22, 1969 (p. 24).

THE LANDING RADAR (PAGES 133-136)

Landing Radar improvements: Bob Covelli, Luminary Memo No. 146, "The New R12," May, 1970.

DUTY CYCLE (PAGES 137-139)

He brought it up with Allan Klumpp in the hallway: <u>MuntzMemoir</u>. In other words, the goal of 15 percent was self-imposed at MIT. The narrative in <u>BlairSmithMemoir</u> (p. 293-294) in which Bill Tindall imposes that goal in knowledge of the potential rendezvous radar interface problem (but does nothing to prevent or work around it) could not have taken place.

TRAINING APOLLO 11 (PAGES 139-142)

Apollo 11 crew training meeting: April, 1969 at MSC. The agenda is on a page titled "G Lunar Landing, How's and Why's," dated April 8, 1969.

A memo we had written together: "LGC-Astronaut Interfaces During Landing", not marked with author or date.

Egress controversy: Deke Slayton, *Deke!*, Tom Doherty Associates, New York, 1994. Also <u>HansenFirstMan</u> (p. 365) quoting Aldrin. NASA's decision on the order of egress was announced on April 14, 1969, as reported in the *New York Times* the next day.

Quotes regarding Aldrin's attitude: Michael Collins, *Carrying the Fire*, Farrar Straus and Giroux, New York, 1974 (p. 347). Also: Gene Cernan and Don Davis, *The Last Man on the Moon*, St. Martins Press, 1999 (p. 231).

Gemini 8 emergency: David Scott at <u>EngineeringApollo</u>, May 10, 2011 and April 22, 2015. Also: Gemini Program Mission Report: Gemini VIII, MSC-G-R-66-4, April, 1966.

APOLLO 11: IGNITION TO HIGH GATE (PAGES 142-152)

General sources: <u>Apollo11Debriefing</u>, <u>Apollo11Downlink</u>, and <u>Apollo11Voice</u>.

"A low altitude pass": Howard W. Tindall Jr., Chief, Apollo Data Priority Coordination, "MIT/MSC review of LUMINARY Descent Programs," 67-FM-T-103, Nov. 9, 1967.

Jack Garman's role: <u>GarmanInterview</u>.

Larson acquiesces with a thumbs up: Personal conversation.

APOLLO 11: HIGH GATE TO TOUCHDOWN (PAGES 152-156)

General sources: <u>Apollo11Debriefing</u>, <u>Apollo11Downlink</u>, and <u>Apollo11Voice</u>.

Armstrong's heart rate: Apollo11Report.

WHAT JUST HAPPENED? (PAGES 156-162)

General sources: I have relied on the recollections of George Silver in describing his actions in the summer of 1968 during the testing of LM-3, his thoughts and actions during the mission, and his analysis of the problem. The voice transcript excerpts are from <u>Apollo11Voice</u> and comments made by the crew after the flight are quoted from <u>Apollo11Debriefing</u>.

Arrival of LM-3 ascent stage at KSC: <u>Apollo9Report</u>, Figure B-4.

It occurred only when the phase mismatch was at its worst: Personal email from George Silver dated February 3, 2004. For the problem to occur, the phase angle between the two 800-hertz signals had to be very near 90 or 270 degrees. In other cases the resolvers were able to settle on an angle that was incorrect, but did not require the CDUs to count continuously at their high rate.

13 percent: The figure usually given (including previously by me) for the amount of processor time "stolen" by the rendezvous radar interface is 15 percent. This number is based on two CDUs counting continually at their maximum rate of 6400 per second, with each count consuming one computer memory cycle of 11.72 microseconds. It is my recollection that Silver's analysis showed that, even in the worst case, the rendezvous radar CDUs would for brief periods *not* count at their maximum rate, and the stolen memory cycles would at most amount to around 13.4 percent. Recently discovered documentation supports this number. After the mission Grumman ran tests in the FMES in an attempt to recreate the flight experience. The maximum rate at which they were able to make the CDUs count was equivalent to 13.36 percent, and landing simulations run at that rate resulted in a pattern of alarms comparable to that which occurred in flight. These results are described in: Clint Tillman, "Simulating the RR-CDU Interface When the RR is in the SLEW or AUTO (not LGC) Mode in the FMES/FCI Laboratory," August 9, 1969.

His 1968 memo: I retain a visual impression of this memo — a few pages with a sine-wave diagram on the first page — but I have not been able to locate a copy of this document.

DEBRIEFING (PAGES 162-165)

For the doomsday case: Susan Mangus and William Larsen, "Lunar Receiving Laboratory Project History," NASA CR-2004-208938, June 2004.

The report I would write: Untitled memo dated Aug. 6, 1969.

WHAT JUST HAPPENED? PART 2 (PAGES 166-169)

The relevant checklist: "Apollo 11, LM Timeline Book," Part No. SKB32100080, S/N 1001.

In their post-flight comments: Apollo11Debriefing.

"675 checklist changes": George M. Low, Manager, Apollo Spacecraft Program, to D.K. Slayton, "Crew Procedures," NASA PA-9-8-24, Aug. 7, 1969, with copies to Gilruth, Kraft, Abbey, Stafford and Conrad.

Interface Control Documents: The relevant ICD is probably one of the following: "LGC-LEM Electrical Interface," LIS-370-10004; "GFE-PGNCS to Rendezvous Radar Angle Electrical Interface," LIS-370-10006; "LM GFE-PGNCS 800 CPS Electrical Interfaces," LIS-370-10007; or "GFE-PGNCS Prime Power Requirements and Characteristics," LIS-390-14001. I have not been able to locate copies of these documents.

Probably in 1964: At a meeting on June 22, 1964, MIT and Grumman "defined" the ICDs in question, as documented in the Grumman document "Minutes of the ICD Meeting between Grumman Aircraft Engineering Corporation and Massachusetts Institute of Technology." The content of the ICDs must have been settled soon after.

Grumman tests run in May, 1968: LM Engineering Memo LMO 541-108. "Detail Data Evaluation Report, LM-3 OCP 61018, Run Between 11 May and 13 May 1968", LM-3 Data Evaluation Team, Grumman, June 18, 1968 (page 13 and enclosure 2).

The software fix: Quoted below is the code designed to prevent the problem that caused the alarms on Apollo 11. Hugh Blair-Smith wrote this code but I inserted the explanatory comments. The effect of this code (which contains a subtlety) was to set bit 1 in channel 12 equal to bit 2 in the flagword RADMODES is set.

```
NORRGMON   CA      RADMODES    IF SELECT SWITCH IS NOT IN LGC, SEND RR
           MASK    AUTOMBIT    CDU ZERO BIT TO PREVENT MEMORY CYCLE
           CCS     A           SNATCHING BY MANIC RR CDUS. BIT2 OF
           NOOP                RADMODES AGREES WITH BIT2 OF CHANNEL
           EXTEND              33. FOR THIS CODING, WHICH ASSUMES
           WOR     CHAN12      AUTOMBIT = BIT2, THANKS TO HUGH B-S.
```

"There were folks who knew about the RR": CherryExegesis.

PINPOINT LANDING (PAGES 170-176)

Promotion to Principal Engineer: My promotion was announced in Richard H. Battin, A-366, "Promotions," July 24, 1969, the day of the Apollo 11 splashdown. Also promoted to Principal Engineer were Peter Adler, Bob Covelli, Don Millard, Larry Berman and Saydean Zeldin. Promoted to Group Leader were Bruce McCoy and Craig Schulenberg.

Pinpoint landing meeting: George Cherry, Luminary Memo No. 102, "Results of the Apollo 12 Pinpoint Landing Data Priority Meeting," Aug. 6, 1969.

"As you know the decision has been made": TindallPinpoint.

"If you would like my guess": TindallPinpoint.

"Absolutely no venting or dumping": TindallPinpoint.

"Analysis based on a typical spacecraft attitude time history": TindallApollo12.

"This basic spacecraft design deficiency": TindallApollo12.

"Pressurization causes the LM to become bloated": Howard W. Tindall Jr., Chief, Apollo Data Priority Coordination, "We don't have to change LUMINARY much for point landing but there's gold in them hills!," 69-PA-T-119A, Sept. 16, 1969.

THE LM SIMULATOR AT THE CAPE (PAGES 176-183)

Noun 69 paperwork: Program Change Request (PCR) 854, "Provide a Flexible Method for Crew to Modify RLS," originated by George Cherry and Don Eyles, Aug. 4, 1969. It had already been approved, on August 1, by Tom Gibson.

Islander Motel: Located on the site of the present Inn at Cocoa Beach.

LMS description: C. H. Woodling et al, "Apollo Experience Report — Simulation of Manned Space Flight for Crew Training," NASA TN D-7112, Manned Spacecraft Center, March, 1973.

Frog story: Related to me by Bob Pearson.

LANDINGS WITH PETE (PAGES 184-187)

No notes.

TRAINING APOLLO 12 (PAGES 187-190, 199-200)

Apollo 12 crew training: Sept. 9-11, 1969 at KSC. The agenda is on a page titled "H1 Mission G&N Briefing," dated Sept. 5, 1969.

DELTA GUIDANCE (PAGES 200-202)

"The pay off could be impressive": TindallDeltaGuid..

"In order to reap one of the greatest benefits": TindallDeltaGuid.

Delta guidance implementation: Don Eyles, Luminary Memo No. 115, "Notes on Implementation of Delta-Guidance," Oct. 9, 1969; Don Eyles, Luminary

Memo No. 123, "More About Delta-Guidance," Nov. 18, 1969; and Don Eyles, Luminary Memo No. 126, "Delta-Guidance," Dec. 2, 1969.

APOLLO 12 (PAGES 202-207)

Spacecraft-ground exchanges: Apollo12Voice. The quoted dialog and Conrad's laughter can be heard on YouTube.

"I would like to take this opportunity": Howard W. Tindall Jr., Chief, Apollo Data Priority Coordination, "Apollo 12 Descent — Final comments," Chief, 69-PA-T-142A, Nov. 4, 1969.

Post flight analysis would show: Apollo12Report (Figure 4-11).

"I didn't LPD for quite a while...": Apollo12Debriefing

"Gosh I went by it...": JonesTranscripts for Apollo 12, section titled "A Visit to the Snowman."

FRANCE AND VENICE (PAGES 207-210)
No notes.

P66 AUTO (PAGES 211-215)

"There is one survivor": Howard W. Tindall Jr., Chairman, Apollo Spacecraft Software Configuration Control Board, "'For whom does the bell toll?', 'Delta Guidance', 'Oh!'," 70-FA-T-16, Feb. 19, 1970. Kriegsman's PCR was: Luminary PCR 1027, "A-Priori Terrain Model," provisionally approved March 4, 1970.

"The thing that was confusing to me": Apollo11Debriefing

"I could see the boulders through the dust": Apollo12Debriefing.

Elimination of P67: Don Eyles, "Landing Changes Put into LUMINARY 1C." Luminary Memo No. 118, Oct. 27, 1969.

"My first knowledge of the P65 guidance equation": KlumppP66Auto.

"The germ of the idea": KlumppP66Auto.

Provisionally approved: K.W. Greene, "Notes on the 34th SCB Meeting, Held at MSC on 18 December 1969", Dec. 19, 1969.

TLOSS (PAGES 215-218)

"A collection of known manifestations": Allan Klumpp, Luminary Memo No. 140, "A Collection of the Known Manifestations of Time Loss in Luminary Revision 131 and LM131 Revision 001 — Suggested Work-Around Procedures," March 4, 1970.

"LM powered flight is approaching a sort of asteroid belt": Don Eyles,

Luminary Memo No. 139, "Description of Variable Servicer," March 3, 1970.

Program change request: Allan Klumpp, Luminary PCR 1013, "Multiple Servicers in P66", approved Feb. 4 and March 4, 1970.

"Even when fatigue was otherwise evident": Dave Hoag, Apollo Project Memorandum No. 3-69, Jan. 10, 1969.

BRIEFING IN CREW QUARTERS (PAGES 218-223)

PCRs dispositioned at meeting: Ken W. Greene, "Notes on the Mainline Apollo SCB Meeting #36, Held at MSC on 4 March 1970", March 6, 1970.

Covelli got rid of the extrapolation: Bob Covelli, Luminary PCR 896, "LR Velocity Read Centered at PIPTIME", approved Oct. 9, 1969.

Terrain model: Bernie Kriegsman, Luminary PCR 1027, "A-Priori Terrain Model." The terrain model as finally implemented is described in: Allan Klumpp, Don Eyles and Bruce McCoy, Luminary Memo No. 147, "Lunar Terrain Model," May 5, 1970.

At the next SCB: Ken W. Greene, "Notes on the Mainline Apollo SCB Meeting #37, Held at MSC on 9 April 1970", April 10, 1970.

Briefing in crew quarters: Probably March 5, 1971.

TRAINING APOLLO 14 (PAGES 223-226)

"You should also know": Don Eyles, untitled memo to Dick Battin and Bob Millard, April 1, 1970.

Margaret Hamilton's role: Hamilton in 2016 received the Medal of Freedom from President Obama with a citation stating that she "led the team that created the on-board flight software for NASA's Apollo command modules and lunar modules." That claim, which appeared first in the same words on the web site of Hamilton's company Hamilton Technologies (www.htius.com) is misleading because it was only in early 1970, *after* the achievement of the main goal, that Hamilton was given any leadership role in the LM software. (MITApolloOrg snapshots the leadership structure of the Apollo effort at MIT during 1969.) Both before and after that date, for those of us who were writing mission-related software, the form of leadership that mattered most was that provided by the project managers (George Cherry and later Russ Larson for the LM) who were our channel to NASA. Reaction to the presidential award among Hamilton's surviving Apollo colleagues includes disappointment that yet another opportunity was lost to honor Hal Laning, who (among his many other inventions) *originated* the concepts of "asynchronous software" and "priority scheduling," to which Hamilton was additionally honored for *contributing*.

Apollo 14 crew training: April 7-9, 1970 at KSC. The agenda and a summary of the meeting are in Jim Nevins and Ed Olsson, DG Memo No. 1569, "Apollo 14 LM How's and Why's Course-Summary," April 15, 1970.

APOLLO 13 (PAGES 227-229)

"A dull but definite bang": Apollo13Debriefing.

"One of the big turning points": Apollo13Debriefing.

BOOKS (PAGES 229-232)

Mailer quotations: Norman Mailer, *Of a Fire on the Moon*, Little, Brown and Company, Boston, 1970 (p. 361-362, 379).

"The computer people": Neil Armstrong, Michael Collins and Edwin E. Aldrin, with Gene Farmer and Dora Jane Hamblin, *First on the Moon*, Little, Brown and Company, Boston, 1970, p. 124-125.

"A small (but interesting) change": Don Eyles, Luminary Memo No. 26, "RTB," May 13, 1968.

TEAR-GASSED (PAGES 232-234)

Passages in italics: From a notebook that I was sporadically writing in at the time.

"I am appalled": Statement by Yale President Kingman Brewster to the Yale University faculty, April 23, 1970.

"Historic triumph": John Hersey, *Letter to the Alumni*, Alfred A. Knopf, 1970.

CASTELLATIONS (PAGES 234-240)

Memos describing each set of changes: DensmoreMemos.

Action Item: Russ Larson, Action Item M-143, authorized by Bruce McCoy, April 22, 1970.

IMU-bob correction: Bruce McCoy, Luminary Memo No. 155, "Luminary 1D re-release," June 1, 1970 (contains short description of IMU-bob correction, probably written by Klumpp).

"Jim Alphin from MSC called": KlumppThrottle. Also: James Alphin, MSC 70-FM22-120, "LM descent engine time constant," July 2, 1970 (with attached memo of the same title from TRW, the engine manufacturer, dated June 18, 1970).

"Months later an outside simulation showed": KlumppThrottle.

Armstrong's heart rate: Apollo11Report (Figure 12-1).

THE SUMMER OF 1970 (PAGES 240-243)

Trouble that they eventually created: Wendell Smith, "Playing King of the Mountain in Harvard Square," *Boston Phoenix*, July 25, 1970.

"My music isn't supposed to make you want to riot": Stu Werbin, "You Know You Got It If It Makes You Feel God," *Boston Phoenix*, Aug. 22, 1970.

Books referred to: Fred Hoyle, *The Black Cloud*, William Heinemann Ltd., London, 1957; and I.S. Shklovskii and Carl Sagan, *Intelligent Life in the Universe*, Dell Publishing Co., New York, 1966.

Program change request: Don Eyles, PCR 1058 for LUMINARY 1E (Apollo 15), "New Landing Analog Displays (R10)," July 6, 1970.

Implementation: Don Eyles, Luminary Memo No. 162, "A New Landing Analog Displays Routine," July 20, 1970; and Don Eyles, Luminary Memo No. 165, "The Return of R10FLAG," July 28, 1970.

THE ERSATZ SCB (PAGES 243-247)

Meeting date: July 22, 1970.

"The approach MIT prefers...": TindallApolll014.

In a memo dated June 10: Howard W. Tindall Jr., Chairman, Apollo Software Configuration Control Board, "DPS throttle oscillations during descent," June 10, 1970.

"The final correction to the program...": TindallApolll014.

"On the other hand": TindallApolll014.

Independent analysis: J. A. Sorensen , "Linear Stability Analysis of LM Rate-of-Descent Guidance Equations," BellComm, Inc., June 25, 1970.

Changing the gains in the control system was the right way: Robert Chilton, Chief, Guidance and Control Division, "Recommendation for LM DPS throttle fix", June 29, 1970; and Kenneth Cox, Chief, Systems Analysis Branch, "P66 Stability Analysis," July 1, 1970.

"Allan and I faced a room at MSC": George Kalan's description of the show-down over the throttle problem in a personal email message, July 30, 2009. Minutes of the meeting are Lynwood C. Dunseith, MSC 70-FS55-132, "Minutes of meeting to discuss the P66 castellation problem," Aug. 19, 1970

JOHN YOUNG'S EXCELLENT IDEA (PAGES 247-255)

Talk with John Young: July 30, 1970.

Variable servicer design review: Aug. 5, 1970 at MSC.

P66 LPD was ready: Don Eyles, Luminary Memo No. 171, "Introduction to ZERLINA 50," Sept. 16, 1970.

APOLLO 14 (PAGES 255-261)

I talked to Allan Klumpp: The issue we discussed is described in: Allan Klumpp, Luminary Memo No. 208, "Apollo 14 Descent Simulation Dispersions: Terrain Model Mismatch Aggravates Drooping Trajectories in P64 and Low Descent Rate in P66," March 16, 1971.

Onboard: Apollo14Debriefing (Sec. 9, p. 9-12).

"'Yep, that's it'": GarmanInterview.

MY FIFTEEN MINUTES (PAGES 261-267)

Memphis Commercial Appeal story: Shirley Downing, "Ex-Memphis Fun Lover Is Apollo Troubleshooter," Memphis Commercial Appeal, Feb. 7, 1971.

"It took some ingenious rewriting": TimesApollo14.

NASA's film: *Apollo 14, Mission to Fra Mauro*, NASA, 1971, available on YouTube.

David Frost show: The David Frost Show, Season 3, Episode 119, March 16, 1971. This show was among those whose tapes were inadvertently recorded over, much to the chagrin of the Frost organization.

Awards ceremony in Houston: Saturday, February 27, 1971.

Grumman bill to North American Rockwell: Grumman Aerospace Corporation, Invoice Number 70-417, April 17, 1970.

MIT bill to Grumman: Massachusetts Institute of Technology, Charles Stark Draper Laboratory, Invoice Number 71-205, March 19, 1971.

Rolling Stone story: Tim Crouse, "Extra! Weird-Looking Freak Saves Apollo 14," *Rolling Stone*, March 18, 1971.

"Triumph of the squares": Remarks by Thomas Paine, NASA Acting Administrator, Dec. 27, 1968.

Bainbridge: William Sims Bainbridge, *The Spaceflight Revolution*, John Wiley & Sons, New York, 1976. A counter to Bainbridge's indulgent portrayal of Wernher von Braun's work before 1945 is in Wayne Biddle, *Dark Side of the Moon*, Norton, 2009.

"A telephone call": Alan Shepard and Deke Slayton, with Jay Barbree and Howard Benedict, *Moon Shot*, Turner Publishing, Atlanta, 1994, p. 298, with no source given. The story is repeated with enhancements in Neal Thompson, *Light this Candle*, Three Rovers Press, 2004, p. 417; and in Ben

Evans, *Foothold in the Heavens: The Seventies,* Springer-Praxis, 2010, p. 422. Another fictional version is in Harry Hurt III, *For All Mankind,* Atlantic Monthly Press, 1988, p. 223.

Apollo 14 episode: *From the Earth to the Moon,* Part 9, HBO, 1998. I was played by Chris Hogan and Bruce McCoy by Dylan Baker. The HBO series was largely based on Andrew Chaikin, *A Man on the Moon,* Viking, 1994, but its depiction of the abort-switch crisis on Apollo 14 went well beyond Chaikin, and is accurate in its technical details.

Landing radar problem: Walter Tanner, Group 23N Memorandum, "Preliminary Report on Apollo 14 Landing Radar Performance," Feb. 16, 1971, not in hand but referenced by Walter Tanner and Ann Hathaway, Group 23N Memorandum, "Apollo 14 Lunar Module Navigation and Guidance System, Landing Radar Performance during Descent and Landing in Fra Mauro Highlands," April 13, 1971. The anomaly is also described in Apollo14Report (starting on page 14-35).

PART THREE • EXPLORING

APOLLO 15 (PAGES 271-276)

Selecting an abort using the DSKY: Craig Schulenberg and Peter Weissman, Luminary Memo No. 216, "Impact of PCR 1107 (Abort Bit Backup) on Apollo 15 Abort Procedures," April 23, 1971; and Craig Schulenberg, Luminary Memo No. 219, "Descent Abort Procedures for Apollo 15," May 26, 1971.

Larry Berman's analysis: Larry Berman, Luminary Memo No. 212, "Effects of Delayed Tipover on Ascent Trajectories," March 29, 1971.

Paper for Dubrovnik: EylesFinalLanding, later published as "Apollo LM Guidance Computer Software for the Final Lunar Descent," in *Automatica, The Journal of the International Federation of Automatic Control,* Volume 9, Number 2, March 1973, Pergammon Press.

Training Apollo 15: May 5-7, 1971 at KSC. The agenda is on a page titled "Agenda for Apollo 15 Crew Training, Rev 2" dated April 29, 1971.

"A program that could be inserted in the computer": TimesApollo14.

Deorbit EMP: Dave Moore, Luminary Memo No. 199, "P99 — Erasable Memory Program for a Guided RCS Burn — Luminary 1E," Feb. 12, 1971.

Erasable memory programs: R-567, "Guidance System Operations Plan for Manned LM earth Orbital and Lunar Missions Using Program LUMINARY 1E," Section 7, Erasable Memory Programs.

EMP 103: Memo to Russ Larson from Don Eyles, Craig Schulenberg and Allan Klumpp, "Backing Up Failed CDUs," July 20, 1971.

"You guys had the best site": Quoted by David Scott at EngineeringApollo, May 10, 2011.

On their own initiative: Conclusion drawn from David Scott and Alexei Leonov, *Two Sides of the Moon*, Simon&Schuster, London, 2004 (p. 271-274).

Scott collecting rock samples: David Scott at <u>EngineeringApollo</u>, April 2, 2013.

"Guess what we just found!": <u>Apollo15Voice</u>.

Howard Hughes's call to Draper: Related by Phil Felleman at lunch on May 19, 1998.

BLOCK ISLAND, DUBROVNIK (PAGES 276-279)

Water main break: *Boston Record-American*, "Line Break Perils Hub, Triggers Near-Riot," June 5, 1971 (p. 1), with photograph by Roland Oxton.

"The justly famous Jimmy the Flea": Lenny Kaye, "Sound Scene," *Cavalier*, Dec. 1971 (p. 12). The article includes a picture of the band (from the same series as the one reproduced in this volume). For an early profile of Lenny Kaye (accompanied by the same photo), see Karen Rose, "Luck and Pluck," *Trouser Press*, June/July 1976, p. 27.

IFAC paper: <u>EylesFinalLanding</u>.

And crashed onto the forecastle: Peter Adler in 2015 did not remember the crane, but he may not have been on deck. I first wrote the version given, in the early 1980s. It is possible that my memory has played a trick and the crane merely wobbled but did not come down. The date was September 13, 1971.

HAYSTACK (PAGES 280-284)

Mars spacecraft: Allan Klumpp, "Preliminary Design Plan for the NERVA Instrumentation and Control System Guidance and Navigation Requirements," memo to J.L. Nevins, Nov. 20, 1970.

Viking spacecraft: Allan Klumpp, "Critique of Viking Lander Guidance Preliminary Design," memo to R.H. Battin and Eldon Hall, March 12, 1971.

Article in the MIT newspaper: Peter Chu, "MIT gains new 'eyes' on the stars," *The Tech*, October 1, 1971, p. 3.

Observatory visits: Feb. 18, 1972. I mention Tim Ferris's subsequent book, *Coming of Age in the Milky Way*, William Morrow and Co., 1988.

Quasars: I refer to and quote from I. S. Shklovskii and Carl Sagan, *Intelligent*

Life in the Universe, Dell Publishing Co., New York, 1966, p. 395.

APOLLO 16 (PAGES 284-289)

No notes.

DINNER WITH DOC (PAGES 289-294)

Edgar Mitchell story: Howard Muson, "Comedown from the Moon — What has happened to the astronauts," *New York Times Magazine*, Dec. 3, 1972.

Two Frenchwomen: Hélène van Gelder and Michelle Piget-Claudin.

APOLLO 17 (PAGES 295-297)

No notes.

DINNER WITH TOM AND ANNIE (PAGES 298-302)

"The space program, you have to understand": Tom Wolfe, "Post-Orbital Remorse, Part Three," *Rolling Stone*, February 15, 1973, p. 27. The other three parts of the story were in the issues of January 4, January 18, and March 1. The handwritten letter from Tom Wolfe to the author is dated March 4, 1973.

LAST LANDINGS AT THE LMS (PAGES 302-304)

No notes.

THE ARTIFACT (PAGES 304-307)

Spacecraft-ground exchanges: Apollo17Voice. Interestingly, in the Apollo 17 JonesTranscripts, section "Geology Station 9," the commentary "(in the TV)" is interpolated after the word "artifact," although it is obvious, from the dialog and the panning movements of the camera, that the word was used in the sense of an object of possibly alien origin, not a glitch in the TV system.

EPILOGUE

(PAGES 309-313)

Edwin Land's testimony: Peter Adler worked for the law firm Fish & Neave, which represented Polaroid. Sullivan & Cromwell represented Kodak. The trial was in US District Court in Boston in 1985. Judge Rya Zobel presided the day I attended. The award, of almost $1 billion, was granted by Judge David Mazzone after Zobel, who had ruled for Polaroid, inherited Kodak stock and stepped down.

Dana Densmore's book: Dana Densmore, *Newton's* Principia, *The Central Argument*, Green Lion Press, Santa Fe, 1995, 1996, 2003.

"The compensation of a very early success": F. Scott Fitzgerald, "Early Success," 1937, published in *The Crack-Up*, New Directions, 1945, p. 89-90.

Computer graphics: Don E. Eyles, "A computer graphics system for visualizing spacecraft in orbit," *Pictorial Communication in Virtual and Real Environments*, Ed. Stephen R. Ellis, Taylor Francis, 1991, p. 196-206. Also see my paper, headlined "Space Station Thrillers Unfold at Draper Lab," *Aerospace America*, vol. 24, Oct. 1986, p. 38-41. While working on the space station simulation I designed a space station configuration that I called "Zig-Zag," a computer-generated image of which appeared in Aviation Week and Space Technology, without credit, on March 19, 1990, p. 93.

Timeliner: The Timeliner sequencing system (known commercially as TLX) is covered by my US Patents 5978786 and 6192356, both entitled "System and method for automatically executing decisional rules." A complete description of the Timeliner language in its Space Station form is the UIL Specification, NASA SSP-30539. I describe the system in my paper, "A Time-Oriented Language for the Writing of Procedures to Sequence the Operation of a Spacecraft and its Systems," Charles Stark Draper Laboratory, 1991 (American Institute of Aeronautics and Astronautics, AIAA-91-3772-CP).

Op-ed column: Don Eyles, "At NASA, Where Was What-If," *New York Times*, March 12, 1986 (op-ed page). In another op-ed column in the same newspaper, titled "Moscow is Gaining an Edge in Space," printed April 21, 1987, I argued against the "Star Wars" program and in favour of civilian manned spaceflight.

Montague: Magnificent Montague, with Bob Baker, *Burn, Baby! BURN!*, University of Illinois Press, 2003.

INDEX

[n : note, p : photo]